Teacher Edition

Eureka Math
Grade 4
Module 1 & 2

Special thanks go to the Gordon A. Cain Center and to the Department of Mathematics at Louisiana State University for their support in the development of *Eureka Math*.

For a free *Eureka Math* Teacher
Resource Pack, Parent Tip
Sheets, and more please
visit www.Eureka.tools

Published by the non-profit Great Minds

Printed in the U.S.A.
This book may be purchased from the publisher at eureka-math.org
10 9
ISBN 978-1-63255-371-3

Eureka Math: A Story of Units Contributors

Katrina Abdussalaam, Curriculum Writer
Tiah Alphonso, Program Manager—Curriculum Production
Kelly Alsup, Lead Writer / Editor, Grade 4
Catriona Anderson, Program Manager—Implementation Support
Debbie Andorka-Aceves, Curriculum Writer
Eric Angel, Curriculum Writer
Leslie Arceneaux, Lead Writer / Editor, Grade 5
Kate McGill Austin, Lead Writer / Editor, Grades PreK–K
Adam Baker, Lead Writer / Editor, Grade 5
Scott Baldridge, Lead Mathematician and Lead Curriculum Writer
Beth Barnes, Curriculum Writer
Bonnie Bergstresser, Math Auditor
Bill Davidson, Fluency Specialist
Jill Diniz, Program Director
Nancy Diorio, Curriculum Writer
Nancy Doorey, Assessment Advisor
Lacy Endo-Peery, Lead Writer / Editor, Grades PreK–K
Ana Estela, Curriculum Writer
Lessa Faltermann, Math Auditor
Janice Fan, Curriculum Writer
Ellen Fort, Math Auditor
Peggy Golden, Curriculum Writer
Maria Gomes, Pre-Kindergarten Practitioner
Pam Goodner, Curriculum Writer
Greg Gorman, Curriculum Writer
Melanie Gutierrez, Curriculum Writer
Bob Hollister, Math Auditor
Kelley Isinger, Curriculum Writer
Nuhad Jamal, Curriculum Writer
Mary Jones, Lead Writer / Editor, Grade 4
Halle Kananak, Curriculum Writer
Susan Lee, Lead Writer / Editor, Grade 3
Jennifer Loftin, Program Manager—Professional Development
Soo Jin Lu, Curriculum Writer
Nell McAnelly, Project Director

Mathematics Curriculum

Table of Contents

GRADE 4 • MODULE 1

Place Value, Rounding, and Algorithms for Addition and Subtraction

Grade 4 • Module 1

Place Value, Rounding, and Algorithms for Addition and Subtraction

OVERVIEW

In this 25-day Grade 4 module, students extend their work with whole numbers. They begin with large numbers using familiar units (hundreds and thousands) and develop their understanding of millions by building knowledge of the pattern of *times ten* in the base ten system on the place value chart (**4.NBT.1**). They recognize that each sequence of three digits is read as hundreds, tens, and ones followed by the naming of the corresponding base thousand unit (thousand, million, billion).[1]

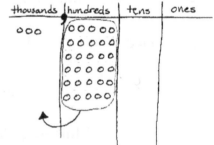

The place value chart is fundamental to Topic A. Building upon their previous knowledge of bundling, students learn that 10 hundreds can be composed into 1 thousand, and therefore, 30 hundreds can be composed into 3 thousands because a digit's value is 10 times what it would be one place to its right (**4.NBT.1**). Students learn to recognize that in a number such as 7,777, each 7 has a value that is 10 times the value of its neighbor to the immediate right. One thousand can be decomposed into 10 hundreds; therefore 7 thousands can be decomposed into 70 hundreds.

Similarly, multiplying by 10 shifts digits one place to the left, and dividing by 10 shifts digits one place to the right.

$$3,000 = 10 \times 300 \qquad 3,000 \div 10 = 300$$

In Topic B, students use place value as a basis for comparing whole numbers. Although this is not a new concept, it becomes more complex as the numbers become larger. For example, it becomes clear that 34,156 is 3 thousands greater than 31,156.

$$34,156 > 31,156$$

Comparison leads directly into rounding, where their skill with isolating units is applied and extended. Rounding to the nearest ten and hundred was mastered with three-digit numbers in Grade 3. Now, Grade 4 students moving into Topic C learn to round to any place value (**4.NBT.3**), initially using the vertical number line though ultimately moving away from the visual model altogether. Topic C also includes word problems where students apply rounding to real life situations.

---

[1] Grade 4 expectations in the NBT standards domain are limited to whole numbers less than or equal to 1,000,000.

In Grade 4, students become fluent with the standard algorithms for addition and subtraction. In Topics D and E, students focus on single like-unit calculations (ones with ones, thousands with thousands, etc.), at times requiring the composition of greater units when adding (10 hundreds are composed into 1 thousand) and decomposition into smaller units when subtracting (1 thousand is decomposed into 10 hundreds) (**4.NBT.4**). Throughout these topics, students apply their algorithmic knowledge to solve word problems. Students also use a variable to represent the unknown quantity.

The module culminates with multi-step word problems in Topic F (**4.OA.3**). Tape diagrams are used throughout the topic to model *additive compare* problems like the one exemplified below. These diagrams facilitate deeper comprehension and serve as a way to support the reasonableness of an answer.

A goat produces 5,212 gallons of milk a year.
A cow produces 17,279 gallons of milk a year.
How much more milk does a goat need to produce to make the
same amount of milk as a cow?

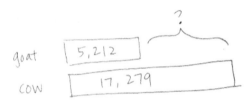

$$17,279 - 5,212 = \underline{\hspace{2cm}}$$

A goat needs to produce _____ more gallons of milk a year.

The Mid-Module Assessment follows Topic C. The End-of-Module Assessment follows Topic F.

Notes on Pacing—Grade 4

Module 1

If pacing is a challenge, consider omitting Lesson 17 since multi-step problems are taught in Lesson 18. Instead, embed problems from Lesson 17 into Module 2 or 3 as extensions. Since multi-step problems are taught in Lesson 18, Lesson 19 could also be omitted.

Module 2

Although composed of just five lessons, Module 2 has great importance in the Grade 4 sequence of modules. Module 2, along with Module 1, is paramount in setting the foundation for developing fluency with the manipulation of place value units, a skill upon which Module 3 greatly depends. Teachers who have taught Module 2 prior to Module 3 have reportedly moved through Module 3 more efficiently than colleagues who have omitted it. Module 2 also sets the foundation for work with fractions and mixed numbers in Module 5. Therefore, it is not recommended to omit any lessons from Module 2.

To help with the pacing of Module 3's Topic A, consider replacing the Convert Units fluencies in Module 2, Lessons 13, with area and perimeter fluencies. Also, consider incorporating Problem 1 from Module 3, Lesson 1, into the fluency component of Module 2, Lessons 4 and 5.

Module 3

Within this module, if pacing is a challenge, consider the following omissions. In Lesson 1, omit Problems 1 and 4 of the Concept Development. Problem 1 could have been embedded into Module 2. Problem 4 can be used for a center activity. In Lesson 8, omit the drawing of models in Problems 2 and 4 of the Concept Development and in Problem 2 of the Problem Set. Instead, have students think about and visualize what they would draw. Omit Lesson 10 because the objective for Lesson 10 is the same as that for Lesson 9. Omit Lesson 19, and instead, embed discussions of interpreting remainders into other division lessons. Omit Lesson 21 because students solve division problems using the area model in Lesson 20. Using the area model to solve division problems with remainders is not specified in the Progressions documents. Omit Lesson 31, and instead, embed analysis of division situations throughout later lessons. Omit Lesson 33, and embed into Lesson 30 the discussion of the connection between division using the area model and division using the algorithm.

Look ahead to the Pacing Suggestions for Module 4. Consider partnering with the art teacher to teach Module 4's Topic A simultaneously with Module 3.

©2015 Great Minds. eureka-math.org
G4-M1M2-TE-BK1-1.3.1-1.2016

Module 4

The placement of Module 4 in *A Story of Units* was determined based on the New York State Education Department Pre-Post Math Standards document, which placed **4.NF.5–7** outside the testing window and **4.MD.5** inside the testing window. This is not in alignment with PARCC's Content Emphases Clusters (http://www.parcconline.org/mcf/mathematics/content-emphases-cluster-0), which reverses those priorities, labeling **4.NF.5–7** as Major Clusters and **4.MD.5** as an Additional Cluster, the status of lowest priority.

Those from outside New York State may want to teach Module 4 after Module 6 and truncate the lessons using the Preparing a Lesson protocol (see the Module Overview, just before the Assessment Overview). This would change the order of the modules to the following: Modules 1, 2, 3, 5, 6, 4, and 7.

Those from New York State might apply the following suggestions and truncate Module 4's lessons using the Preparing a Lesson protocol. Topic A could be taught simultaneously with Module 3 during an art class. Topics B and C could be taught directly following Module 3, prior to Module 5, since they offer excellent scaffolding for the fraction work of Module 5. Topic D could be taught simultaneously with Module 5, 6, or 7 during an art class when students are served well with hands-on, rigorous experiences.

Keep in mind that Topics B and C of this module are foundational to Grade 7's missing angle problems.

Module 5

For Module 5, consider the following modifications and omissions. Study the objectives and the sequence of problems within Lessons 1, 2, and 3, and then consolidate the three lessons. Omit Lesson 4. Instead, in Lesson 5, embed the contrast of the decomposition of a fraction using the tape diagram versus using the area model. Note that the area model's cross hatches are used to transition to multiplying to generate equivalent fractions, add related fractions in Lessons 20 and 21, add decimals in Module 6, add/subtract all fractions in Grade 5's Module 3, and multiply a fraction by a fraction in Grade 5's Module 4. Omit Lesson 29, and embed estimation within many problems throughout the module and curriculum. Omit Lesson 40, and embed line plot problems in social studies or science. Be aware, however, that there is a line plot question on the End-of-Module Assessment.

Module 6

In Module 6, students explore decimal numbers for the first time by means of the decimal numbers' relationship to decimal fractions. Module 6 builds directly from Module 5 and is foundational to students' Grade 5 work with decimal operations. Therefore, it is not recommended to omit any lessons from Module 6.

Module 7

Module 7 affords students the opportunity to use all that they have learned throughout Grade 4 as they first relate multiplication to the conversion of measurement units and then explore multiple strategies for solving measurement problems involving unit conversion. Module 7 ends with practice of the major skills and concepts of the grade as well as the preparation of a take-home summer folder. Therefore, it is not recommended to omit any lessons from Module 7.

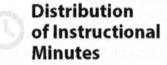

Distribution of Instructional Minutes

This diagram represents a suggested distribution of instructional minutes based on the emphasis of particular lesson components in different lessons throughout the module.

■ Fluency Practice
■ Concept Development
■ Application Problems
■ Student Debrief

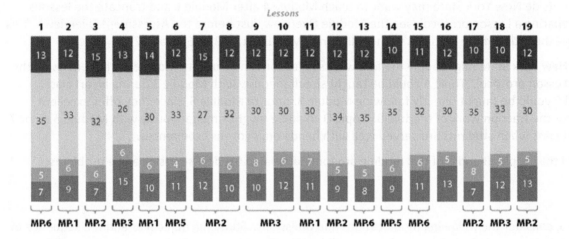

MP = Mathematical Practice

Focus Grade Level Standards

Use the four operations with whole numbers to solve problems.[2]

4.OA.3   Solve multistep word problems posed with whole numbers and having whole-number answers using the four operations, including problems in which remainders must be interpreted. Represent these problems using equations with a letter standing for the unknown quantity. Assess the reasonableness of answers using mental computation and estimation strategies including rounding.

Generalize place value understanding for multi-digit whole numbers. (Grade 4 expectations are limited to whole numbers less than or equal to 1,000,000.)

4.NBT.1   Recognize that in a multi-digit whole number, a digit in one place represents ten times what it represents in the place to its right. *For example, recognize that 700 ÷ 70 = 10 by applying concepts of place value and division.*

---

[2] Only addition and subtraction multi-step word problems are addressed in this module. The balance of this cluster is addressed in Modules 3 and 7.

4.NBT.2   Read and write multi-digit whole numbers using base-ten numerals, number names, and expanded form. Compare two multi-digit numbers based on meanings of the digits in each place, using >, =, and < symbols to record the results of comparisons.

4.NBT.3   Use place value understanding to round multi-digit whole numbers to any place.

Use place value understanding and properties of operations to perform multi-digit arithmetic.[3]

4.NBT.4   Fluently add and subtract multi-digit whole numbers using the standard algorithm.

Foundational Standards

3.OA.8   Solve two-step word problems using the four operations. Represent these problems using equations with a letter standing for the unknown quantity. Assess the reasonableness of answers using mental computation and estimation strategies including rounding.[4]

3.NBT.1   Use place value understanding to round whole numbers to the nearest 10 or 100.

3.NBT.2   Fluently add and subtract within 1000 using strategies and algorithms based on place value, properties of operations, and/or the relationship between addition and subtraction.

Focus Standards for Mathematical Practice

MP.1   **Make sense of problems and persevere in solving them.** Students use the place value chart to draw diagrams of the relationship between a digit's value and what it would be one place to its right, for instance, by representing 3 thousands as 30 hundreds. Students also use the place value chart to compare large numbers.

MP.2   **Reason abstractly and quantitatively.** Students make sense of quantities and their relationships as they use both special strategies and the standard addition algorithm to add and subtract multi-digit numbers. Students decontextualize when they represent problems symbolically and contextualize when they consider the value of the units used and understand the meaning of the quantities as they compute.

MP.3   **Construct viable arguments and critique the reasoning of others.** Students construct arguments as they use the place value chart and model single- and multi-step problems. Students also use the standard algorithm as a general strategy to add and subtract multi-digit numbers when a special strategy is not suitable.

MP.5   **Use appropriate tools strategically.** Students decide on the appropriateness of using special strategies or the standard algorithm when adding and subtracting multi-digit numbers.

MP.6   **Attend to precision.** Students use the place value chart to represent digits and their values as they compose and decompose base ten units.

---

[3] The balance of this cluster is addressed in Modules 3 and 7.

[4] This standard is limited to problems with whole numbers and having whole-number answers; students should know how to perform operations in the conventional order when there are no parentheses to specify a particular order, i.e., the order of operations.

Overview of Module Topics and Lesson Objectives

Standards		Topics and Objectives		Days
4.NBT.1 **4.NBT.2** 4.OA.1	A	**Place Value of Multi-Digit Whole Numbers**		4
		Lesson 1:	Interpret a multiplication equation as a comparison.	
		Lesson 2:	Recognize a digit represents 10 times the value of what it represents in the place to its right.	
		Lesson 3:	Name numbers within 1 million by building understanding of the place value chart and placement of commas for naming base thousand units.	
		Lesson 4:	Read and write multi-digit numbers using base ten numerals, number names, and expanded form.	
4.NBT.2	B	**Comparing Multi-Digit Whole Numbers**		2
		Lesson 5:	Compare numbers based on meanings of the digits using >, <, or = to record the comparison.	
		Lesson 6:	Find 1, 10, and 100 thousand more and less than a given number.	
4.NBT.3	C	**Rounding Multi-Digit Whole Numbers**		4
		Lesson 7:	Round multi-digit numbers to the thousands place using the vertical number line.	
		Lesson 8:	Round multi-digit numbers to any place using the vertical number line.	
		Lesson 9:	Use place value understanding to round multi-digit numbers to any place value.	
		Lesson 10:	Use place value understanding to round multi-digit numbers to any place value using real world applications.	
		Mid-Module Assessment: Topics A–C (review content 1 day, assessment ½ day, return ½ day, remediation or further applications 1 day)		3
4.OA.3 **4.NBT.4** 4.NBT.1 4.NBT.2	D	**Multi-Digit Whole Number Addition**		2
		Lesson 11:	Use place value understanding to fluently add multi-digit whole numbers using the standard addition algorithm, and apply the algorithm to solve word problems using tape diagrams.	
		Lesson 12:	Solve multi-step word problems using the standard addition algorithm modeled with tape diagrams, and assess the reasonableness of answers using rounding.	

EUREKA
MATH™

©2015 Great Minds. eureka-math.org
G4-M1M2-TE-BK1-1.3.1-1.2016

Standards		Topics and Objectives		Days
4.OA.3 **4.NBT.4** 4.NBT.1 4.NBT.2	E	**Multi-Digit Whole Number Subtraction**		4
		Lesson 13:	Use place value understanding to decompose to smaller units once using the standard subtraction algorithm, and apply the algorithm to solve word problems using tape diagrams.	
		Lesson 14:	Use place value understanding to decompose to smaller units up to three times using the standard subtraction algorithm, and apply the algorithm to solve word problems using tape diagrams.	
		Lesson 15:	Use place value understanding to fluently decompose to smaller units multiple times in any place using the standard subtraction algorithm, and apply the algorithm to solve word problems using tape diagrams.	
		Lesson 16:	Solve two-step word problems using the standard subtraction algorithm fluently modeled with tape diagrams, and assess the reasonableness of answers using rounding.	
4.OA.3 4.NBT.1 4.NBT.2 4.NBT.4	F	**Addition and Subtraction Word Problems**		3
		Lesson 17:	Solve *additive compare* word problems modeled with tape diagrams.	
		Lesson 18:	Solve multi-step word problems modeled with tape diagrams, and assess the reasonableness of answers using rounding.	
		Lesson 19:	Create and solve multi-step word problems from given tape diagrams and equations.	
		End-of-Module Assessment: Topics A–F (review content 1 day, assessment ½ day, return ½ day, remediation or further application 1 day)		3
Total Number of Instructional Days				25

Terminology

New or Recently Introduced Terms

- Millions, ten millions, hundred millions (as places on the place value chart)
- Ten thousands, hundred thousands (as places on the place value chart)
- Variables (letters that stand for numbers and can be added, subtracted, multiplied, and divided as numbers are)

©2015 Great Minds. eureka-math.org
G4-M1M2-TE-BK1-1.3.1-1.2016

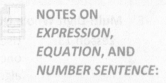

Familiar Terms and Symbols[5]

- =, <, > (equal to, less than, greater than)
- Addend (e.g., in 4 + 5, the numbers 4 and 5 are the addends)
- Algorithm (a step-by-step procedure to solve a particular type of problem)
- Bundling, making, renaming, changing, exchanging, regrouping, trading (e.g., exchanging 10 ones for 1 ten)
- Compose (e.g., to make 1 larger unit from 10 smaller units)
- Decompose (e.g., to break 1 larger unit into 10 smaller units)
- Difference (answer to a subtraction problem)
- Digit (any of the numbers 0 to 9; e.g., What is the value of the digit in the tens place?)
- Endpoint (used with rounding on the number line; the numbers that mark the beginning and end of a given interval)
- Equation (e.g., 2,389 + 80,601 = _____)
- Estimate (an approximation of a quantity or number)
- Expanded form (e.g., 100 + 30 + 5 = 135)
- Expression (e.g., 2 thousands × 10)
- Halfway (with reference to a number line, the midpoint between two numbers; e.g., 5 is halfway between 0 and 10)
- Number line (a line marked with numbers at evenly spaced intervals)
- Number sentence (e.g., 4 + 3 = 7)
- Place value (the numerical value that a digit has by virtue of its position in a number)
- Rounding (approximating the value of a given number)
- Standard form (a number written in the format 135)
- Sum (answer to an addition problem)
- Tape diagram (bar diagram)
- Unbundling, breaking, renaming, changing, regrouping, trading (e.g., exchanging 1 ten for 10 ones)
- Word form (e.g., one hundred thirty-five)

NOTES ON EXPRESSION, EQUATION, AND NUMBER SENTENCE:

Please note the descriptions for the following terms, which are frequently misused:

- **Expression:** A number, or any combination of sums, differences, products, or divisions of numbers that evaluates to a number (e.g., 3 + 4, 8 × 3, 15 ÷ 3 as distinct from an equation or number sentence).
- **Equation:** A statement that two expressions are equal (e.g., 3 × ___ = 12, 5 × b =20, 3 + 2 = 5).
- **Number sentence** (also addition, subtraction, multiplication, or division sentence): An equation or inequality for which both expressions are numerical and can be evaluated to a single number (e.g., 4 + 3 = 6 + 1, 2 = 2, 21 > 7 × 2, 5 ÷ 5 = 1). Number sentences are either true or false (e.g., 4 + 4 < 6 × 2 and 21 ÷ 7 = 4) and contain no unknowns.

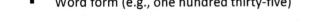

[5] These are terms and symbols students have used or seen previously.

©2015 Great Minds. eureka-math.org
G4-M1M2-TE-BK1-1.3.1-1.2016

Suggested Tools and Representations

- Number lines (vertical to represent rounding *up* and rounding *down*)
- Personal white boards (one per student; see explanation on the following pages)
- Place value cards (one large set per classroom including 7 units to model place value)
- Place value chart (templates provided in lessons to insert into personal white boards)
- Place value disks (can be concrete manipulatives or pictorial drawings, such as the chip model, to represent numbers)
- Tape diagrams (drawn to model a word problem)

millions	hundred thousands	ten thousands	thousands	hundreds	tens	ones

Place Value Chart with Headings
(used for numbers or the chip model)

Place Value Chart Without Headings
(used for place value disk manipulatives or drawings)

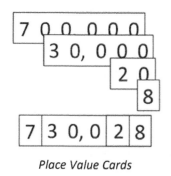

Place Value Cards

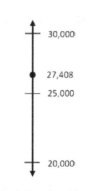

Vertical Number Line

Place Value Disks

Suggested Methods of Instructional Delivery

Directions for Administration of Sprints

Sprints are designed to develop fluency. They should be fun, adrenaline-rich activities that intentionally build energy and excitement. A fast pace is essential. During Sprint administration, teachers assume the role of athletic coaches. A rousing routine fuels students' motivation to do their personal best. Student recognition of increasing success is critical, and so every improvement is celebrated.

One Sprint has two parts with closely related problems on each. Students complete the two parts of the Sprint in quick succession with the goal of improving on the second part, even if only by one more.

With practice, the following routine takes about nine minutes.

Sprint A

Pass Sprint A out quickly, facedown on student desks with instructions to not look at the problems until the signal is given. (Some Sprints include words. If necessary, prior to starting the Sprint, quickly review the words so that reading difficulty does not slow students down.)

- T: You will have 60 seconds to do as many problems as you can. I do not expect you to finish all of them. Just do as many as you can, your personal best. (If some students are likely to finish before time is up, assign a number to count by on the back.)
- T: Take your mark! Get set! THINK!

Students immediately turn papers over and work furiously to finish as many problems as they can in 60 seconds. Time precisely.

- T: Stop! Circle the last problem you did. I will read just the answers. If you got it right, call out "Yes!" If you made a mistake, circle it. Ready?
- T: (Energetically, rapid-fire call the first answer.)
- S: Yes!
- T: (Energetically, rapid-fire call the second answer.)
- S: Yes!

Repeat to the end of Sprint A or until no student has a correct answer. If needed, read the count-by answers in the same way as Sprint answers. Each number counted-by on the back is considered a correct answer.

- T: Fantastic! Now, write the number you got correct at the top of your page. This is your personal goal for Sprint B.
- T: How many of you got one right? (All hands should go up.)
- T: Keep your hand up until I say the number that is one more than the number you got correct. So, if you got 14 correct, when I say 15, your hand goes down. Ready?
- T: (Continue quickly.) How many got two correct? Three? Four? Five? (Continue until all hands are down.)

If the class needs more practice with Sprint A, continue with the optional routine presented below.

- T: I'll give you one minute to do more problems on this half of the Sprint. If you finish, stand behind your chair.

As students work, the student who scored highest on Sprint A might pass out Sprint B.

- T: Stop! I will read just the answers. If you got it right, call out "Yes!" If you made a mistake, circle it. Ready? (Read the answers to the first half again as students stand.)

Movement

To keep the energy and fun going, always do a stretch or a movement game in between Sprints A and B. For example, the class might do jumping jacks while skip-counting by 5 for about one minute. Feeling invigorated, students take their seats for Sprint B, ready to make every effort to complete more problems this time.

Sprint B

Pass Sprint B out quickly, facedown on student desks with instructions to not look at the problems until the signal is given. (Repeat the procedure for Sprint A up through the show of hands for how many right.)

- T: Stand up if you got more correct on the second Sprint than on the first.
- S: (Stand.)
- T: Keep standing until I say the number that tells how many more you got right on Sprint B. If you got three more right on Sprint B than you did on Sprint A, when I say "three," you sit down. Ready? (Call out numbers starting with one. Students sit as the number by which they improved is called. Celebrate students who improved most with a cheer.)
- T: Well done! Now, take a moment to go back and correct your mistakes. Think about what patterns you noticed in today's Sprint.
- T: How did the patterns help you get better at solving the problems?
- T: Rally Robin your thinking with your partner for one minute. Go!

Rally Robin is a style of sharing in which partners trade information back and forth, one statement at a time per person, for about one minute. This is an especially valuable part of the routine for students who benefit from their friends' support to identify patterns and try new strategies.

Students may take Sprints home.

RDW or Read, Draw, Write (an Equation and a Statement)

Mathematicians and teachers suggest a simple process applicable to all grades:

1. Read.
2. Draw and label.
3. Write an equation.
4. Write a word sentence (statement).

The more students participate in reasoning through problems with a systematic approach, the more they internalize those behaviors and thought processes.

- What do I see?
- Can I draw something?
- What conclusions can I make from my drawing?

Modeling with Interactive Questioning	Guided Practice	Independent Practice
The teacher models the whole process with interactive questioning, some choral response, and talk moves, such as "What did Monique say, everyone?" After completing the problem, students might reflect with a partner on the steps they used to solve the problem. "Students, think back on what we did to solve this problem. What did we do first?" Students might then be given the same or similar problem to solve for homework.	Each student has a copy of the question. Though guided by the teacher, they work independently at times and then come together again. Timing is important. Students might hear, "You have two minutes to do your drawing." Or, "Put your pencils down. Time to work together again." The Student Debrief might include selecting different student work to share.	Students are given a problem to solve and possibly a designated amount of time to solve it. The teacher circulates, supports, and is thinking about which student work to show to support the mathematical objectives of the lesson. When sharing student work, students are encouraged to think about the work with questions, such as "What do you see Jeremy did?" "What is the same about Jeremy's work and Sara's work?" "How did Jeremy show the $\frac{3}{7}$ of the students?" "How did Sara show the $\frac{3}{7}$ of the students?"

Personal White Boards

Materials Needed for Personal White Boards

    1 heavy-duty clear sheet protector
    1 piece of stiff red tag board 11" × 8¼"
    1 piece of stiff white tag board 11" × 8 ¼"
    1 3" × 3" piece of dark synthetic cloth for an eraser (e.g., felt)
    1 low-odor blue dry-erase marker, fine point

Directions for Creating Personal White Boards

Cut the white and red tag to specifications. Slide into the sheet protector. Store the eraser on the red side. Store markers in a separate container to avoid stretching the sheet protector.

Frequently Asked Questions About Personal White Boards

Why is one side red and one white?

- The white side of the board is the "paper." Students generally write on it, and if working individually, turn the board over to signal to the teacher that they have completed their work. The teacher then says, "Show me your boards," when most of the class is ready.

What are some of the benefits of a personal white board?

- The teacher can respond quickly to a gap in student understandings and skills. "Let's do some of these on our personal white boards until we have more mastery."

- Students can erase quickly so that they do not have to suffer the evidence of their mistake.
- They are motivating. Students love both the drill and thrill capability and the chance to do story problems with an engaging medium.
- Checking work gives the teacher instant feedback about student understanding.

What is the benefit of this personal white board over a commercially purchased dry-erase board?

- It is much less expensive.
- Templates such as place value charts, number bond mats, hundreds boards, and number lines can be stored between the two pieces of tag board for easy access and reuse.
- Worksheets, story problems, and other problem sets can be done without marking the paper so that students can work on the problems independently at another time.
- Strips with story problems, number lines, and arrays can be inserted and still have a full piece of paper on which to write.
- The red versus white side distinction clarifies expectations. When working collaboratively, there is no need to use the red side. When working independently, students know how to keep their work private.
- The tag board can be removed so that student work can be projected on an overhead.

Scaffolds[6]

The scaffolds integrated into *A Story of Units* give alternatives for how students access information as well as express and demonstrate their learning. Strategically placed margin notes are provided within each lesson elaborating on the use of specific scaffolds at applicable times. They address many needs presented by English language learners, students with disabilities, students performing above grade level, and students performing below grade level. Many of the suggestions are organized by Universal Design for Learning (UDL) principles and are applicable to more than one population. To read more about the approach to differentiated instruction in *A Story of Units,* please refer to "How to Implement *A Story of Units.*"

---

[6] Students with disabilities may require Braille, large print, audio, or special digital files. Please visit the website www.p12.nysed.gov/specialed/aim for specific information on how to obtain student materials that satisfy the National Instructional Materials Accessibility Standard (NIMAS) format.

Preparing to Teach a Module

Preparation of lessons will be more effective and efficient if there has been an adequate analysis of the module first. Each module in *A Story of Units* can be compared to a chapter in a book. How is the module moving the plot, the mathematics, forward? What new learning is taking place? How are the topics and objectives building on one another? The following is a suggested process for preparing to teach a module.

Step 1: Get a preview of the plot.

    A: Read the Table of Contents. At a high level, what is the plot of the module? How does the story develop across the topics?

    B: Preview the module's Exit Tickets[7] to see the trajectory of the module's mathematics and the nature of the work students are expected to be able to do.

Note: When studying a PDF file, enter "Exit Ticket" into the search feature to navigate from one Exit Ticket to the next.

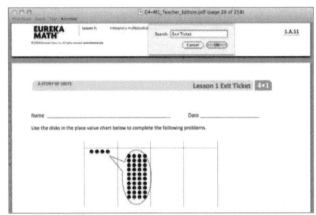

Step 2: Dig into the details.

    A: Dig into a careful reading of the Module Overview. While reading the narrative, *liberally* reference the lessons and Topic Overviews to clarify the meaning of the text—the lessons demonstrate the strategies, show how to use the models, clarify vocabulary, and build understanding of concepts. Consider searching the video gallery on *Eureka Math*'s website to watch demonstrations of the use of models and other teaching techniques.

    B: Having thoroughly investigated the Module Overview, read through the chart entitled Overview of Module Topics and Lesson Objectives to further discern the plot of the module. How do the topics flow and tell a coherent story? How do the objectives move from simple to complex?

Step 3: Summarize the story.

    Complete the Mid- and End-of-Module Assessments. Use the strategies and models presented in the module to explain the thinking involved. Again, liberally reference the work done in the lessons to see how students who are learning with the curriculum might respond.

---

[7] A more in-depth preview can be done by searching the Problem Sets rather than the Exit Tickets. Furthermore, this same process can be used to preview the coherence or flow of any component of the curriculum, such as Fluency Practice or Application Problems.

Preparing to Teach a Lesson

A three-step process is suggested to prepare a lesson. It is understood that at times teachers may need to make adjustments (customizations) to lessons to fit the time constraints and unique needs of their students. The recommended planning process is outlined below. Note: The ladder of Step 2 is a metaphor for the teaching sequence. The sequence can be seen not only at the macro level in the role that this lesson plays in the overall story, but also at the lesson level, where each rung in the ladder represents the next step in understanding or the next skill needed to reach the objective. To reach the objective, or the top of the ladder, all students must be able to access the first rung and each successive rung.

Step 1: Discern the plot.

A: Briefly review the Table of Contents for the module, recalling the overall story of the module and analyzing the role of this lesson in the module.

B: Read the Topic Overview of the lesson, and then review the Problem Set and Exit Ticket of each lesson of the topic.

C: Review the assessment following the topic, keeping in mind that assessments can be found midway through the module and at the end of the module.

Step 2: Find the ladder.

A: Complete the lesson's Problem Set.

B: Analyze and write notes on the new complexities of each problem as well as the sequences and progressions throughout problems (e.g., pictorial to abstract, smaller to larger numbers, single- to multi-step problems). The new complexities are the rungs of the ladder.

C: Anticipate where students might struggle, and write a note about the potential cause of the struggle.

D: Answer the Student Debrief questions, always anticipating how students will respond.

Step 3: Hone the lesson.

At times, the lesson and Problem Set are appropriate for all students and the day's schedule. At others, they may need customizing. If the decision is to customize based on either the needs of students or scheduling constraints, a suggestion is to decide upon and designate "Must Do" and "Could Do" problems.

A: Select "Must Do" problems from the Problem Set that meet the objective and provide a coherent experience for students; reference the ladder. The expectation is that the majority of the class will complete the "Must Do" problems within the allocated time. While choosing the "Must Do" problems, keep in mind the need for a balance of calculations, various word problem types[8], and work at both the pictorial and abstract levels.

---

[8] See the Progression Documents "K, Counting and Cardinality" and "K–5, Operations and Algebraic Thinking" pp. 9 and 23, respectively.

B: "Must Do" problems might also include remedial work as necessary for the whole class, a small group, or individual students. Depending on anticipated difficulties, those problems might take different forms as shown in the chart below.

Anticipated Difficulty	"Must Do" Remedial Problem Suggestion
The first problem of the Problem Set is too challenging.	Write a short sequence of problems on the board that provides a ladder to Problem 1. Direct the class or small group to complete those first problems to empower them to begin the Problem Set. Consider labeling these problems "Zero Problems" since they are done prior to Problem 1.
There is too big of a jump in complexity between two problems.	Provide a problem or set of problems that creates a bridge between the two problems. Label them with the number of the problem they follow. For example, if the challenging jump is between Problems 2 and 3, consider labeling these problems "Extra 2s."
Students lack fluency or foundational skills necessary for the lesson.	Before beginning the Problem Set, do a quick, engaging fluency exercise, such as a Rapid White Board Exchange, "Thrilling Drill," or Sprint. Before beginning any fluency activity for the first time, assess that students are poised for success with the easiest problem in the set.
More work is needed at the concrete or pictorial level.	Provide manipulatives or the opportunity to draw solution strategies. Especially in Kindergarten, at times the Problem Set or pencil and paper aspect might be completely excluded, allowing students to simply work with materials.
More work is needed at the abstract level.	Hone the Problem Set to reduce the amount of drawing as appropriate for certain students or the whole class.

C: "Could Do" problems are for students who work with greater fluency and understanding and can, therefore, complete more work within a given time frame. Adjust the Exit Ticket and Homework to reflect the "Must Do" problems or to address scheduling constraints.

D: At times, a particularly tricky problem might be designated as a "Challenge!" problem. This can be motivating, especially for advanced students. Consider creating the opportunity for students to share their "Challenge!" solutions with the class at a weekly session or on video.

E: Consider how to best use the vignettes of the Concept Development section of the lesson. Read through the vignettes, and highlight selected parts to be included in the delivery of instruction so that students can be independently successful on the assigned task.

F: Pay close attention to the questions chosen for the Student Debrief. Regularly ask students, "What was the lesson's learning goal today?" Hone the goal with them.

Assessment Summary

Type	Administered	Format	Standards Addressed
Mid-Module Assessment Task	After Topic C	Constructed response with rubric	4.NBT.1 4.NBT.2 4.NBT.3
End-of-Module Assessment Task	After Topic F	Constructed response with rubric	4.NBT.1 4.NBT.2 4.NBT.3 4.NBT.4 4.OA.3

4
GRADE

Mathematics Curriculum

Topic A

Place Value of Multi-Digit Whole Numbers

4.NBT.1, **4.NBT.2**, 4.OA.1

Focus Standard:	4.NBT.1	Recognize that in a multi-digit whole number, a digit in one place represents ten times what it represents in the place to its right. *For example, recognize that 700 ÷ 70 = 10 by applying concepts of place value and division.*
	4.NBT.2	Read and write multi-digit whole numbers using base-ten numerals, number names, and expanded form. Compare two multi-digit numbers based on meanings of the digits in each place, using >, =, and < symbols to record the results of comparisons.
Instructional Days:	4	
Coherence -Links from:	G3–M2	Place Value and Problem Solving with Units of Measure
-Links to:	G5–M1	Place Value and Decimal Fractions

In Topic A, students build the place value chart to 1 million and learn the relationship between each place value as *10 times* the value of the place to the right. Students manipulate numbers to see this relationship, such as 30 hundreds composed as 3 thousands. They decompose numbers to see that 7 thousands is the same as 70 hundreds. As students build the place value chart into thousands and up to 1 million, the sequence of three digits is emphasized. They become familiar with the base thousand unit names up to 1 billion. Students fluently write numbers in multiple formats: as digits, in unit form, as words, and in expanded form up to 1 million.

A Teaching Sequence Toward Mastery of Place Value of Multi-Digit Whole Numbers
Objective 1: Interpret a multiplication equation as a comparison. (Lesson 1)
Objective 2: Recognize a digit represents 10 times the value of what it represents in the place to its right. (Lesson 2)
Objective 3: Name numbers within 1 million by building understanding of the place value chart and placement of commas for naming base thousand units. (Lesson 3)
Objective 4: Read and write multi-digit numbers using base ten numerals, number names, and expanded form. (Lesson 4)

©2015 Great Minds. eureka-math.org
G4-M1M2-TE-BK1-1.3.1-1.2016

Lesson 1

Objective: Interpret a multiplication equation as a comparison.

Suggested Lesson Structure

■ Fluency Practice   (13 minutes)
■ Application Problem   (5 minutes)
☐ Concept Development   (35 minutes)
■ Student Debrief   (7 minutes)
   Total Time   **(60 minutes)**

Fluency Practice (13 minutes)

- Sprint: Multiply and Divide by 10 **4.NBT.1**   (10 minutes)
- Place Value **4.NBT.2**   (3 minutes)

Sprint: Multiply and Divide by 10 (10 minutes)

Materials: (S) Multiply and Divide by 10 Sprint

Note: Reviewing this fluency activity acclimates students to the Sprint routine, a vital component of the fluency program.

Place Value (3 minutes)

Materials: (S) Personal white board, unlabeled thousands place value chart (Template)

Note: Reviewing and practicing place value skills in isolation prepares students for success in multiplying different place value units during the lesson.

T: (Project place value chart to the thousands.) Show 4 ones as place value disks. Write the number below it.

S: (Draw 4 ones disks and write 4 below it.)

T: Show 4 tens disks, and write the number below it.

S: (Draw 4 tens disks and write 4 at the bottom of the tens column.)

T: Say the number in unit form.

S: 4 tens 4 ones.

> **NOTES ON FLUENCY PRACTICE:**
>
> Think of fluency as having three goals:
>
> 1. Maintenance (staying sharp on previously learned skills).
> 2. Preparation (targeted practice for the current lesson).
> 3. Anticipation (skills that ensure that students are ready for the in-depth work of upcoming lessons).

> **NOTES ON MULTIPLE MEANS OF ACTION AND EXPRESSION:**
>
> For the Place Value fluency activity, students may represent ones, etc., using counters rather than drawing.
>
> Others may benefit from the opportunity to practice simultaneously speaking and showing units (e.g., tens).
>
> Provide sentence frames to support oral response, such as "_____ tens _____ ones is _____ (standard form) _____."

place value chart

EUREKA MATH

T: Say the number in standard form.

S: 44.

Continue for the following possible sequence: 2 tens 3 ones, 2 hundreds 3 ones, 2 thousands 3 hundreds, 2 thousands 3 tens, and 2 thousands 3 hundreds 5 tens and 4 ones.

Application Problem (5 minutes)

Ben has a rectangular area 9 meters long and 6 meters wide. He wants a fence that will go around it as well as grass sod to cover it. How many meters of fence will he need? How many square meters of grass sod will he need to cover the entire area?

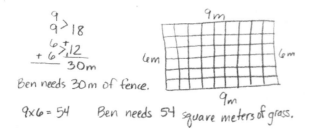

> **NOTES ON MULTIPLE MEANS OF ENGAGEMENT:**
>
> Enhance the relevancy of the Application Problem by substituting names, settings, and tasks to reflect students and their experiences.
>
> Set individual student goals and expectations. Some students may successfully solve for area and perimeter in five minutes, others may solve for one, and others may solve for both and compose their own application problems.

Note: As the first lesson of the year, this Application Problem reviews area, perimeter, multiplication, and addition—all important concepts from Grade 3. This problem can be extended after the Concept Development by asking students to find an area 10 times as much as the grass sod or to find a perimeter 10 times as wide and 10 times as long.

Concept Development (35 minutes)

Materials: (T) Place value disks: ones, tens, hundreds, and thousands; unlabeled thousands place value chart (Template) (S) Personal white board, unlabeled thousands place value chart (Template)

Problem 1: 1 ten is 10 times as much as 1 one.

T: (Have a place value chart ready. Draw or place 1 unit into the ones place.)

T: How many units do I have?

S: 1.

MP.6

T: What is the name of this unit?

S: A one.

T: Count the ones with me. (Draw ones as they do so.)

S: 1 one, 2 ones, 3 ones, 4 ones, 5 ones…,10 ones.

T: 10 ones. What larger unit can I make?

S: 1 ten.

T: I change 10 ones for 1 ten. We say, "1 ten is 10 times as much as 1 one." Tell your partner what we say and what that means. Use the model to help you.

MP.6

S: 10 ones make 1 ten. → 10 times 1 one is 1 ten or 10 ones. → We say 1 ten is 10 times as many as 1 one.

Problem 2: One hundred is 10 times as much as 1 ten.

Quickly repeat the process from Problem 1 with 10 copies of 1 ten.

Problem 3: One thousand is 10 times as much as 1 hundred.

Quickly repeat the process from Problem 1 with 10 copies of 1 hundred.

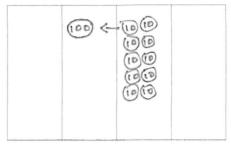

T: Discuss the patterns you have noticed with your partner.

S: 10 ones make 1 ten. 10 tens make 1 hundred. 10 hundreds make 1 thousand. → Every time we get 10, we bundle and make a bigger unit. → We copy a unit 10 times to make the next larger unit. → If we take any of the place value units, the next unit on the left is ten times as many.

T: Let's review, in words, the multiplication pattern that matches our models and 10 times as many.

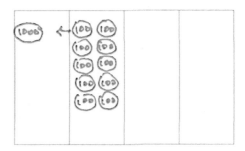

Display the following information for student reference:

1 ten = 10 × 1 one	(Say, "1 ten is 10 times as much as 1 one.")
1 hundred = 10 × 1 ten	(Say, "1 hundred is 10 times as much as 1 ten.")
1 thousand = 10 × 1 hundred	(Say, "1 thousand is 10 times as much as 1 hundred.")

Problem 4: Model *10 times as much as* on the place value chart with an accompanying equation.

Note: Place value disks are used as models throughout the curriculum and can be represented in two different ways. A disk with a value labeled inside of it, such as in Problem 1, should be drawn or placed on a place value chart with no headings. The value of the disk in its appropriate column indicates the column heading. A place value disk drawn as a dot should be used on place value charts with headings, as in Problem 4. This type of representation is called the *chip model*. The chip model is a faster way to represent place value disks and is used as students move away from a concrete stage of learning.

(Model 2 tens is 10 times as much as 2 ones on the place value chart and as an equation.)

T: Draw place value disks as dots. Because you are using dots, label your columns with the unit value.

T: Represent 2 ones. Solve to find 10 times as many as 2 ones. Work together.

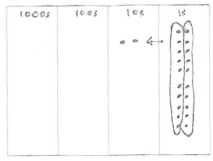

EUREKA MATH

S: (Work together.)

T: 10 times as many as 2 ones is…?

S: 20 ones. → 2 tens.

T: Explain this equation to your partner using your model.

S: 10 × 2 ones = 20 ones = 2 tens.

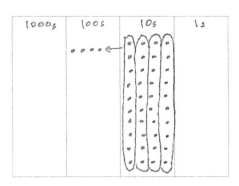

Repeat the process with 10 times as many as 4 tens is 40 tens is 4 hundreds and 10 times as many as 7 hundreds is 70 hundreds is 7 thousands.

> 10 × 4 tens = 40 tens = 4 hundreds
>
> 10 × 7 hundreds = 70 hundreds = 7 thousands

Problem 5: Model as an equation 10 times as much as 9 hundreds is 9 thousands.

T: Write an equation to find the value of 10 times as many as 9 hundreds. (Circulate and assist students as necessary.)

T: Show me your board. Read your equation.

S: 10 × 9 hundreds = 90 hundreds = 9 thousands.

T: Yes. Discuss whether this is true with your partner. (Write 10 × 9 hundreds = 9 thousands.)

S: Yes, it is true because 90 hundreds equals 9 thousands, so this equation just eliminates that extra step. → Yes. We know 10 of a smaller unit equals 1 of the next larger unit, so we just avoided writing that step.

Problem Set (10 minutes)

Students should do their personal best to complete the Problem Set within the allotted 10 minutes. Some problems do not specify a method for solving. This is an intentional reduction of scaffolding that invokes MP.5, Use Appropriate Tools Strategically. Students should solve these problems using the RDW approach used for Application Problems.

For some classes, it may be appropriate to modify the assignment by specifying which problems students should work on first. With this option, let the purposeful sequencing of the Problem Set guide the selections so that problems continue to be scaffolded. Balance word problems with other problem types to ensure a range of practice. Consider assigning incomplete problems for homework or at another time during the day.

Challenge quick finishers to write their own 10 times as many statements similar to Problems 2 and 5.

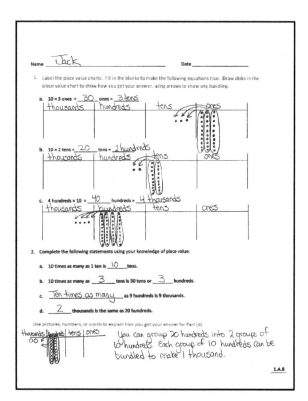

Student Debrief (7 minutes)

Lesson Objective: Interpret a multiplication equation as a comparison.

Invite students to review their solutions for the Problem Set and the totality of the lesson experience. They should check work by comparing answers with a partner before going over answers as a class. Look for misconceptions or misunderstandings that can be addressed in the Student Debrief. Guide students in a conversation to debrief the Problem Set.

Any combination of the questions below may be used to lead the discussion.

- What relationship do you notice between the problem of Matthew's stamps and Problems 1(a) and 1(b)?

- How did Problem 1(c) help you to solve Problem 4?

- In Problem 5, which solution proved most difficult to find? Why?

- How does the answer about Sarah's age and her grandfather's age relate to our lesson's objective?

- What are some ways you could model 10 times as many? What are the benefits and drawbacks of each way of modeling? (Money, base ten materials, disks, labeled drawings of disks, dots on a labeled place value chart, tape diagram.)

- Take two minutes to explain to your partner what we learned about the value of each unit as it moves from right to left on the place value chart.

- Write and complete the following statements:

    _____ ten is _____ times as many as _____ one.

    _____ hundred is _____ times as many as _____ ten.

    _____ thousand is _____ times as many as _____ hundred.

Exit Ticket (3 minutes)

After the Student Debrief, instruct students to complete the Exit Ticket. A review of their work will help with assessing students' understanding of the concepts that were presented in today's lesson and planning more effectively for future lessons. The questions may be read aloud to the students.

Lesson 1:   Interpret a multiplication equation as a comparison.

Number Correct: _____

A

Multiply and Divide by 10

1.	2 × 10 =	
2.	3 × 10 =	
3.	4 × 10 =	
4.	5 × 10 =	
5.	1 × 10 =	
6.	20 ÷ 10 =	
7.	30 ÷ 10 =	
8.	50 ÷ 10 =	
9.	10 ÷ 10 =	
10.	40 ÷ 10 =	
11.	6 × 10 =	
12.	7 × 10 =	
13.	8 × 10 =	
14.	9 × 10 =	
15.	10 × 10 =	
16.	80 ÷ 10 =	
17.	70 ÷ 10 =	
18.	90 ÷ 10 =	
19.	60 ÷ 10 =	
20.	100 ÷ 10 =	
21.	__ × 10 = 50	
22.	__ × 10 = 10	

23.	__ × 10 = 100	
24.	__ × 10 = 20	
25.	__ × 10 = 30	
26.	100 ÷ 10 =	
27.	50 ÷ 10 =	
28.	10 ÷ 10 =	
29.	20 ÷ 10 =	
30.	30 ÷ 10 =	
31.	__ × 10 = 60	
32.	__ × 10 = 70	
33.	__ × 10 = 90	
34.	__ × 10 = 80	
35.	70 ÷ 10 =	
36.	90 ÷ 10 =	
37.	60 ÷ 10 =	
38.	80 ÷ 10 =	
39.	11 × 10 =	
40.	110 ÷ 10 =	
41.	30 ÷ 10 =	
42.	120 ÷ 10 =	
43.	14 × 10 =	
44.	140 ÷ 10 =	

©2015 Great Minds. eureka-math.org
G4-M1M2-TE-BK1-1.3.1-1.2016

B

Number Correct: _____

Improvement: _____

Multiply and Divide by 10

1.	$1 \times 10 =$	
2.	$2 \times 10 =$	
3.	$3 \times 10 =$	
4.	$4 \times 10 =$	
5.	$5 \times 10 =$	
6.	$30 \div 10 =$	
7.	$20 \div 10 =$	
8.	$40 \div 10 =$	
9.	$10 \div 10 =$	
10.	$50 \div 10 =$	
11.	$10 \times 10 =$	
12.	$6 \times 10 =$	
13.	$7 \times 10 =$	
14.	$8 \times 10 =$	
15.	$9 \times 10 =$	
16.	$70 \div 10 =$	
17.	$60 \div 10 =$	
18.	$80 \div 10 =$	
19.	$100 \div 10 =$	
20.	$90 \div 10 =$	
21.	$\_\_ \times 10 = 10$	
22.	$\_\_ \times 10 = 50$	

23.	$\_\_ \times 10 = 20$	
24.	$\_\_ \times 10 = 100$	
25.	$\_\_ \times 10 = 30$	
26.	$20 \div 10 =$	
27.	$10 \div 10 =$	
28.	$100 \div 10 =$	
29.	$50 \div 10 =$	
30.	$30 \div 10 =$	
31.	$\_\_ \times 10 = 30$	
32.	$\_\_ \times 10 = 40$	
33.	$\_\_ \times 10 = 90$	
34.	$\_\_ \times 10 = 70$	
35.	$80 \div 10 =$	
36.	$90 \div 10 =$	
37.	$60 \div 10 =$	
38.	$70 \div 10 =$	
39.	$11 \times 10 =$	
40.	$110 \div 10 =$	
41.	$12 \times 10 =$	
42.	$120 \div 10 =$	
43.	$13 \times 10 =$	
44.	$130 \div 10 =$	

EUREKA MATH™

Name _____   Date _____

1. Label the place value charts. Fill in the blanks to make the following equations true. Draw disks in the place value chart to show how you got your answer, using arrows to show any bundling.

   a.   10 × 3 ones = _____ ones = _____

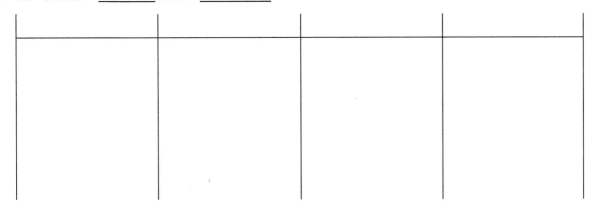

   b.   10 × 2 tens = _____ tens = _____

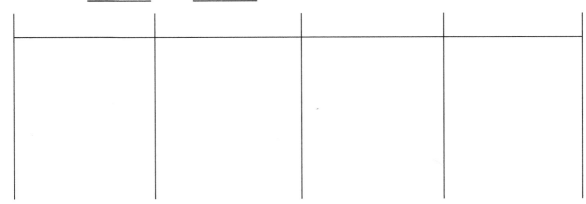

   c.   4 hundreds × 10 = _____ hundreds = _____

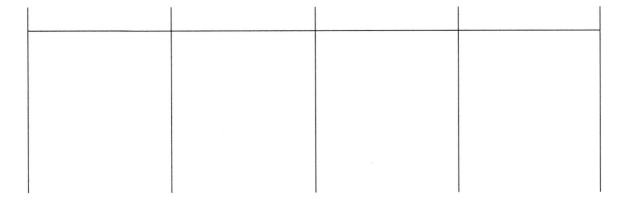

2. Complete the following statements using your knowledge of place value:

a. 10 times as many as 1 ten is _____ tens.

b. 10 times as many as _____ tens is 30 tens or _____ hundreds.

c. _____ as 9 hundreds is 9 thousands.

d. _____ thousands is the same as 20 hundreds.

Use pictures, numbers, or words to explain how you got your answer for Part (d).

3. Matthew has 30 stamps in his collection. Matthew's father has 10 times as many stamps as Matthew. How many stamps does Matthew's father have? Use numbers or words to explain how you got your answer.

Lesson 1:   Interpret a multiplication equation as a comparison.

©2015 Great Minds. eureka-math.org
G4-M1M2-TE-BK1-1.3.1-1.2016

4. Jane saved $800. Her sister has 10 times as much money. How much money does Jane's sister have? Use numbers or words to explain how you got your answer.

5. Fill in the blanks to make the statements true.

   a. 2 times as much as 4 is _____.

   b. 10 times as much as 4 is _____.

   c. 500 is 10 times as much as _____.

   d. 6,000 is _____ as 600.

6. Sarah is 9 years old. Sarah's grandfather is 90 years old. Sarah's grandfather is how many times as old as Sarah?

   Sarah's grandfather is _____ times as old as Sarah.

Name _____   Date _____

Use the disks in the place value chart below to complete the following problems:

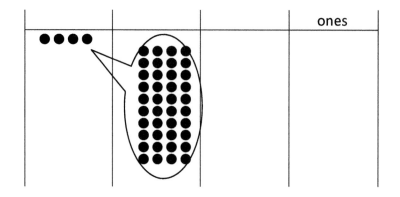

				ones

1. Label the place value chart.

2. Tell about the movement of the disks in the place value chart by filling in the blanks to make the following equation match the drawing in the place value chart:

_____ × 10 = _____ = _____

3. Write a statement about this place value chart using the words *10 times as many*.

Lesson 1:   Interpret a multiplication equation as a comparison.

Name _____ Date _____

1. Label the place value charts. Fill in the blanks to make the following equations true. Draw disks in the place value chart to show how you got your answer, using arrows to show any regrouping.

   a.   10 × 4 ones = _____ ones = _____

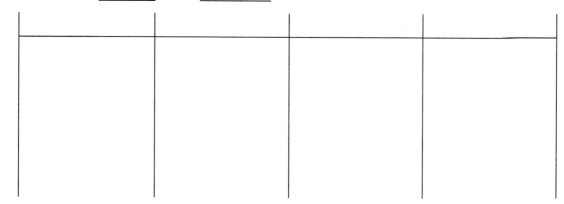

   b.   10 × 2 tens = _____ tens = _____

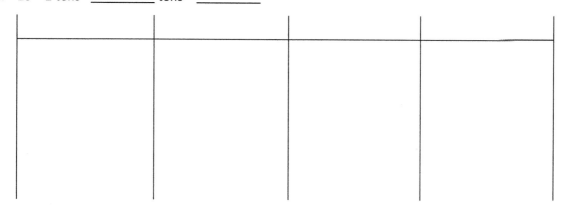

   c.   5 hundreds × 10 = _____ hundreds = _____

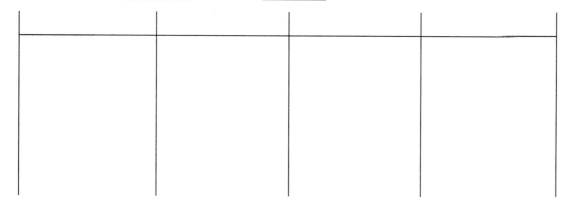

2. Complete the following statements using your knowledge of place value:

    a. 10 times as many as 1 hundred is _____ hundreds or _____ thousand.

    b. 10 times as many as _____ hundreds is 60 hundreds or _____ thousands.

    c. _____ as 8 hundreds is 8 thousands.

    d. _____ hundreds is the same as 4 thousands.

    Use pictures, numbers, or words to explain how you got your answer for Part (d).

3. Katrina has 60 GB of storage on her tablet. Katrina's father has 10 times as much storage on his computer. How much storage does Katrina's father have? Use numbers or words to explain how you got your answer.

EUREKA
MATH

©2015 Great Minds. eureka-math.org
G4-M1M2-TE-BK1-1.3.1-1.2016

4. Katrina saved $200 to purchase her tablet. Her father spent 10 times as much money to buy his new computer. How much did her father's computer cost? Use numbers or words to explain how you got your answer.

5. Fill in the blanks to make the statements true.

a. 4 times as much as 3 is _____.

b. 10 times as much as 9 is _____.

c. 700 is 10 times as much as _____.

d. 8,000 is _____ as 800.

6. Tomas's grandfather is 100 years old. Tomas's grandfather is 10 times as old as Tomas. How old is Tomas?

unlabeled thousands place value chart

Lesson 1: Interpret a multiplication equation as a comparison.

Lesson 2

Objective: Recognize a digit represents 10 times the value of what it represents in the place to its right.

Suggested Lesson Structure

■ Fluency Practice	(12 minutes)
■ Application Problem	(6 minutes)
■ Concept Development	(33 minutes)
■ Student Debrief	(9 minutes)
Total Time	**(60 minutes)**

Fluency Practice (12 minutes)

- Skip-Counting **3.OA.7**   (4 minutes)
- Place Value **4.NBT.2**   (4 minutes)
- Multiply by 10 **4.NB5.1**   (4 minutes)

Skip-Counting (4 minutes)

Note: Practicing skip-counting on the number line builds a foundation for accessing higher-order concepts throughout the year.

Direct students to count by threes forward and backward to 36, focusing on the crossing-ten transitions.

Example: (3, 6, 9, 12, 9, 12, 9, 12, 15, 18, 21, 18, 21, 24, 27, 30, 27, 30, 33, 30, 33, 30, 33, 36…). The purpose of focusing on crossing the ten transitions is to help students make the connection that, for example, when adding 3 to 9, 9 + 1 is 10, and then 2 more is 12.

There is a similar purpose in counting down by threes; 12 − 2 is 10, and subtracting 1 more is 9. This work builds on the fluency work of previous grade levels. Students should understand that when crossing the ten, they are regrouping.

Direct students to count by fours forward and backward to 48, focusing on the crossing-ten transitions.

Place Value (4 minutes)

Materials: (S) Personal white board, unlabeled thousands place value chart (Lesson 1 Template)

Note: Reviewing and practicing place value skills in isolation prepares students for success in multiplying different place value units during the lesson.

EUREKA MATH   Lesson 2:   Recognize a digit represents 10 times the value of what it represents in the place to its right.   37

©2015 Great Minds. eureka-math.org
G4-M1M2-TE-BK1-1.3.1-1.2016

T: (Project the place value chart to the thousands place.) Show 5 tens as place value disks, and write the number below it.

S: (Draw 5 tens. Write 5 below the tens column and 0 below the ones column.)

T: (Draw to correct student misunderstanding.) Say the number in unit form.

S: 5 tens.

T: Say the number in standard form.

S: 50.

Continue for the following possible sequence: 3 tens 2 ones, 4 hundreds 3 ones, 1 thousand 2 hundreds, 4 thousands 2 tens, and 4 thousands 2 hundreds 3 tens 5 ones.

Multiply by 10 (4 minutes)

Materials: (S) Personal white board

Note: This fluency activity reviews concepts learned in Lesson 1.

T: (Project 10 ones × 10 = 1 _____.) Fill in the blank.

S: (Write 10 ones × 10 = 1 hundred.)

T: Say the multiplication sentence in standard form.

S: $10 \times 10 = 100$.

Repeat for the following possible sequence: 10 × _____ = 2 hundreds; 10 × _____ = 3 hundreds; 10 × _____ = 7 hundreds; 10 × 1 hundred = 1 _____; 10 × ____ = 2 thousands; 10 × _____ = 8 thousands; 10 × 10 thousands = _____.

Application Problem (6 minutes)

Amy is baking muffins. Each baking tray can hold 6 muffins.

  a. If Amy bakes 4 trays of muffins, how many muffins will she have in all?

  b. The corner bakery produced 10 times as many muffins as Amy baked. How many muffins did the bakery produce?

Extension: If the corner bakery packages the muffins in boxes of 100, how many boxes of 100 could they make?

a) $4 \times 6 = 24$
Amy will have 24 muffins in all.

b) $10 \times 24 = 240$
The bakery produced 240 muffins.

Extension: They could make 2 boxes of 100 muffins.

Note: This Application Problem builds on the concept from the previous lesson of *10 times as many*.

         Lesson 2:   Recognize a digit represents 10 times the value of what it represents in the place to its right.

Concept Development (33 minutes)

Materials: (S) Personal white board, unlabeled millions place value chart (Template)

Problem 1: Multiply single units by 10 to build the place value chart to 1 million. Divide to reverse the process.

T: Label ones, tens, hundreds, and thousands on your place value chart.

T: On your personal white board, write the multiplication sentence that shows the relationship between 1 hundred and 1 thousand.

S: (Write 10 × 1 hundred = 10 hundreds = 1 thousand.)

T: Draw place value disks on your place value chart to find the value of 10 times 1 thousand.

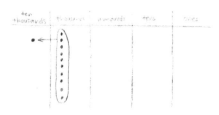

T: (Circulate.) I saw that Tessa drew 10 disks in the thousands column. What does that represent?

S: 10 times 1 thousand equals 10 thousands. (10 × 1 thousand = 10 thousands.)

T: How else can 10 thousands be represented?

S: 10 thousands can be bundled because, when you have 10 of one unit, you can bundle them and move the bundle to the next column.

T: (Point to the place value chart.) Can anyone think of what the name of our next column after the thousands might be? (Students share. Label the **ten thousands** column.)

T: Now, write a complete multiplication sentence to show 10 times the value of 1 thousand. Show how you regroup.

S: (Write 10 × 1 thousand = 10 thousands = 1 ten thousand.)

T: On your place value chart, show what 10 times the value of 1 ten thousand equals. (Circulate and assist students as necessary.)

T: What is 10 times 1 ten thousand?

S: 10 ten thousands. → **1 hundred thousand.**

T: That is our next larger unit. (Write 10 × 1 ten thousand = 10 ten thousands = 1 hundred thousand.)

T: To move another column to the left, what would be my next 10 times statement?

S: 10 times 1 hundred thousand.

T: Solve to find 10 times 1 hundred thousand. (Circulate and assist students as necessary.)

T: 10 hundred thousands can be bundled and represented as **1 million**. Title your column, and write the multiplication sentence.

S: (Write 10 × 1 hundred thousand = 10 hundred thousands = 1 million.)

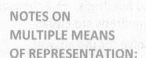

NOTES ON MULTIPLE MEANS OF REPRESENTATION:

Scaffold student understanding of the place value pattern by recording the following sentence frames:

- 10 × 1 one is 1 ten
- 10 × 1 ten is 1 hundred
- 10 × 1 hundred is 1 thousand
- 10 × 1 thousand is 1 ten thousand
- 10 × 1 ten thousand is 1 hundred thousand

Students may benefit from speaking this pattern chorally. Deepen understanding with prepared visuals (perhaps using an interactive whiteboard).

Lesson 2:   Recognize a digit represents 10 times the value of what it represents in the place to its right.

After having built the place value chart by multiplying by ten, quickly review the process simply moving from right to left on the place value chart and then reversing and moving left to right (e.g., 2 tens times 10 equals 2 hundreds; 2 hundreds times 10 equals 2 thousands; 2 thousands divided by 10 equals 2 hundreds; 2 hundreds divided by 10 equals 2 tens).

Problem 2: Multiply multiple copies of one unit by 10.

T: Draw place value disks, and write a multiplication sentence to show the value of 10 times 4 ten thousands.

T: 10 times 4 ten thousands is…?

S: 40 ten thousands. → 4 hundred thousands.

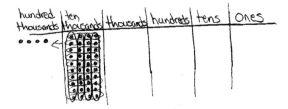

T: (Write 10 × 4 ten thousands = 40 ten thousands = 4 hundred thousands.) Explain to your partner how you know this equation is true.

Repeat with 10 × 3 hundred thousands.

Problem 3: Divide multiple copies of one unit by 10.

T: (Write 2 thousands ÷ 10.) What is the process for solving this division expression?

S: Use a place value chart. → Represent 2 thousands on a place value chart. Then, change them for smaller units so we can divide.

T: What would our place value chart look like if we changed each thousand for 10 smaller units?

S: 20 hundreds. → 2 thousands can be changed to be 20 hundreds because 2 thousands and 20 hundreds are equal.

T: Solve for the answer.

S: 2 hundreds. → 2 thousands ÷ 10 is 2 hundreds because 2 thousands unbundled becomes 20 hundreds. → 20 hundreds divided by 10 is 2 hundreds. → 2 thousands ÷ 10 = 20 hundreds ÷ 10 = 2 hundreds.

MP.1

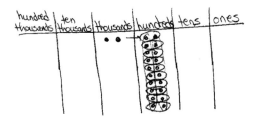

Repeat with 3 hundred thousands ÷ 10.

Lesson 2:   Recognize a digit represents 10 times the value of what it represents in the place to its right.

©2015 Great Minds. eureka-math.org
G4-M1M2-TE-BK1-1.3.1-1.2016

EUREKA
MATH

Problem 4: Multiply and divide multiple copies of two different units by 10.

T: Draw place value disks to show 3 hundreds and 2 tens.

T: (Write 10 × (3 hundreds 2 tens).) Work in pairs to solve this expression. I wrote 3 hundreds 2 tens in parentheses to show it is one number. (Circulate as students work. Clarify that both hundreds and tens must be multiplied by 10.)

T: What is your product?

S: 3 thousands 2 hundreds.

T: (Write 10 × (3 hundreds 2 tens) = 3 thousands 2 hundreds.) How do we write this in standard form?

S: 3,200.

T: (Write 10 × (3 hundreds 2 tens) = 3 thousands 2 hundreds = 3,200.)

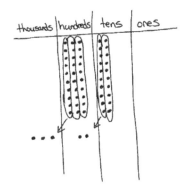
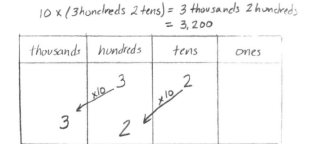

T: (Write (4 ten thousands 2 tens) ÷ 10.) In this expression, we have two units. Explain how you will find your answer.

S: We can use the place value chart again and represent the unbundled units and then divide. (Represent in the place value chart, and record the number sentence (4 ten thousands 2 tens) ÷ 10 = 4 thousands 2 ones = 4,002.)

T: Watch as I represent numbers in the place value chart to multiply or divide by ten instead of drawing disks.

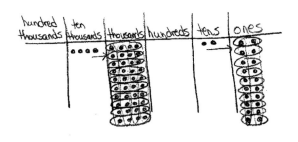
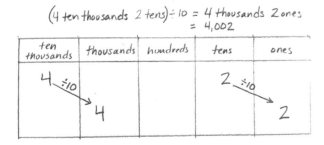

Repeat with 10 × (4 thousands 5 hundreds) and (7 hundreds 9 tens) ÷ 10.

Problem Set (10 minutes)

Students should do their personal best to complete the Problem Set within the allotted 10 minutes. For some classes, it may be appropriate to modify the assignment by specifying which problems they work on first. Some problems do not specify a method for solving. Students should solve these problems using the RDW approach used for Application Problems.

Student Debrief (9 minutes)

Lesson Objective: Recognize a digit represents 10 times the value of what it represents in the place to its right.

Invite students to review their solutions for the Problem Set and the totality of the lesson experience. They should check work by comparing answers with a partner before going over answers as a class. Look for misconceptions or misunderstandings that can be addressed in the Student Debrief. Guide students in a conversation to debrief the Problem Set.

Any combination of the questions below may be used to lead the discussion.

- How did we use patterns to predict the increasing units on the place value chart up to **1 million**? Can you predict the unit that is 10 times 1 million? 100 times 1 million?

- What happens when you multiply a number by 10? 1 **ten thousand** is what times 10? 1 **hundred thousand** is what times 10?

- Gail said she noticed that when you multiply a number by 10, you shift the digits one place to the left and put a zero in the ones place. Is she correct?

- How can you use multiplication and division to describe the relationship between units on the place value chart? Use Problem 1 (a) and (c) to help explain.

- Practice reading your answers in Problem 2 out loud. What similarities did you find in saying the numbers in unit form and standard form? Differences?

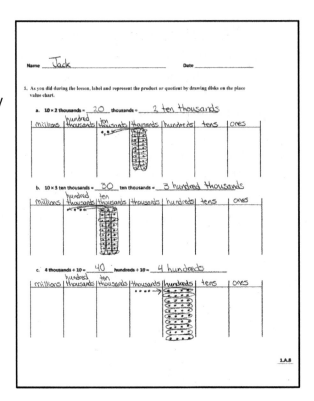

Lesson 2:   Recognize a digit represents 10 times the value of what it represents in the place to its right.

©2015 Great Minds. eureka-math.org
G4-M1M2-TE-BK1-1.3.1-1.2016

- In Problem 7, did you write your equation as a multiplication or division sentence? Which way is correct?

- Which part in Problem 3 was hardest to solve?

- When we multiply 6 tens times 10, as in Problem 2, are we multiplying the 6, the tens, or both? Does the digit or the unit change?

- Is 10 times 6 tens the same as 6 times 10 tens? (Use a place value chart to model.)

- Is 10 times 10 times 6 the same as 10 tens times 6? (Use a place value chart to model 10 times 10 is the same as 1 ten times 1 ten.)

- When we multiply or divide by 10, do we change the digits or the unit? Make a few examples.

Exit Ticket (3 minutes)

After the Student Debrief, instruct students to complete the Exit Ticket. A review of their work will help with assessing students' understanding of the concepts that were presented in today's lesson and planning more effectively for future lessons. The questions may be read aloud to the students.

EUREKA
MATH™

Lesson 2:   Recognize a digit represents 10 times the value of what it represents in the place to its right.

43

©2015 Great Minds. eureka-math.org
G4-M1M2-TE-BK1-1.3.1-1.2016

Name _____　　Date _____

1. As you did during the lesson, label and represent the product or quotient by drawing disks on the place value chart.

   a.　10 × 2 thousands = _____ thousands = _____

   b.　10 × 3 ten thousands = _____ ten thousands = _____

   c.　4 thousands ÷ 10 = _____ hundreds ÷ 10 = _____

　　Lesson 2:　Recognize a digit represents 10 times the value of what it represents in the place to its right.

©2015 Great Minds. eureka-math.org
G4-M1M2-TE-BK1-1.3.1-1.2016

EUREKA
MATH™

2. Solve for each expression by writing the solution in unit form and in standard form.

Expression	Unit form	Standard Form
10 × 6 tens		
7 hundreds × 10		
3 thousands ÷ 10		
6 ten thousands ÷ 10		
10 × 4 thousands		

3. Solve for each expression by writing the solution in unit form and in standard form.

Expression	Unit form	Standard Form
(4 tens 3 ones) × 10		
(2 hundreds 3 tens) × 10		
(7 thousands 8 hundreds) × 10		
(6 thousands 4 tens) ÷ 10		
(4 ten thousands 3 tens) ÷ 10		

4. Explain how you solved 10 × 4 thousands. Use a place value chart to support your explanation.

5. Explain how you solved (4 ten thousands 3 tens) ÷ 10. Use a place value chart to support your explanation.

6. Jacob saved 2 thousand dollar bills, 4 hundred dollar bills, and 6 ten dollar bills to buy a car. The car costs 10 times as much as he has saved. How much does the car cost?

7. Last year the apple orchard experienced a drought and did not produce many apples. But this year, the apple orchard produced 45 thousand Granny Smith apples and 9 hundred Red Delicious apples, which is 10 times as many apples as last year. How many apples did the orchard produce last year?

Lesson 2:   Recognize a digit represents 10 times the value of what it represents in the place to its right.

©2015 Great Minds. eureka-math.org
G4-M1M2-TE-BK1-1.3.1-1.2016

8. Planet Ruba has a population of 1 million aliens. Planet Zamba has 1 hundred thousand aliens.

   a. How many more aliens does Planet Ruba have than Planet Zamba?

   b. Write a sentence to compare the populations for each planet using the words *10 times as many*.

Lesson 2:   Recognize a digit represents 10 times the value of what it represents in
             the place to its right.

©2015 Great Minds. eureka-math.org
G4-M1M2-TE-BK1-1.3.1-1.2016

47

Name _____ Date _____

1. Fill in the blank to make a true number sentence. Use standard form.

    a. (4 ten thousands 6 hundreds) × 10 = _____

    b. (8 thousands 2 tens) ÷ 10 = _____

2. The Carson family saved up $39,580 for a new home. The cost of their dream home is 10 times as much as they have saved. How much does their dream home cost?

Lesson 2: Recognize a digit represents 10 times the value of what it represents in the place to its right.

©2015 Great Minds. eureka-math.org
G4-M1M2-TE-BK1-1.3.1-1.2016

EUREKA
MATH™

Name _____   Date _____

1. As you did during the lesson, label and represent the product or quotient by drawing disks on the place value chart.

a.   10 × 4 thousands = _____ thousands = _____

b.   4 thousands ÷ 10 = _____ hundreds ÷ 10 = _____

2. Solve for each expression by writing the solution in unit form and in standard form.

Expression	Unit Form	Standard Form
10 × 3 tens		
5 hundreds × 10		
9 ten thousands ÷ 10		
10 × 7 thousands		

3. Solve for each expression by writing the solution in unit form and in standard form.

Expression	Unit Form	Standard Form
(2 tens 1 one) × 10		
(5 hundreds 5 tens) × 10		
(2 thousands 7 tens) ÷ 10		
(4 ten thousands 8 hundreds) ÷ 10		

4. a. Emily collected $950 selling Girl Scout cookies all day Saturday. Emily's troop collected 10 times as much as she did. How much money did Emily's troop raise?

   b. On Saturday, Emily made 10 times as much as on Monday. How much money did Emily collect on Monday?

Lesson 2:   Recognize a digit represents 10 times the value of what it represents in the place to its right.

©2015 Great Minds. eureka-math.org
G4-M1M2-TE-BK1-1.3.1-1.2016

EUREKA MATH

unlabeled millions place value chart

Lesson 3

Objective: Name numbers within 1 million by building understanding of the place value chart and placement of commas for naming base thousand units.

Suggested Lesson Structure

■ Fluency Practice   (15 minutes)
■ Application Problem   (6 minutes)
☐ Concept Development   (32 minutes)
■ Student Debrief   (7 minutes)
   Total Time   **(60 minutes)**

Fluency Practice (15 minutes)

- Sprint: Multiply by 3 **3.OA.7**   (10 minutes)
- Place Value and Value **4.NBT.2**   (3 minutes)
- Base Ten Units **4.NBT.1**   (2 minutes)

Sprint: Multiply by 3 (10 minutes)

Materials: (S) Multiply by 3 Sprint

Note: This fluency activity reviews a foundational Grade 3 standard that helps students learn standard **4.NBT.5**.

Place Value and Value (3 minutes)

Materials: (T) Unlabeled millions place value chart (Lesson 2 Template)

> **A NOTE ON STANDARDS ALIGNMENT:**
>
> In this lesson, students extend past 1 million (4.NBT standards limit to whole numbers less than or equal to 1 million) to establish a pattern of ones, tens, and hundreds within each base ten unit (thousands, millions, billions, trillions).
>
> Calculations in following lessons are limited to less than or equal to 1 million. If students are not ready for this step, omit establishing the pattern and internalize the units of the thousands period.

Note: Reviewing and practicing place value skills in isolation prepares students for success in multiplying different place value units during the lesson.

   T: (Project the number 1,468,357 on a place value chart. Underline the 5.) Say the digit.
   S: 5.
   T: Say the place value of the 5.
   S: Tens.

EUREKA MATH™

T: Say the value of 5 tens.

S: 50.

Repeat the process, underlining 8, 4, 1, and 6.

Base Ten Units (2 minutes)

Note: This fluency activity bolsters students' place value proficiency while reviewing multiplication concepts learned in Lessons 1 and 2.

T: (Project 2 tens =____.) Say the number in standard form.

S: 2 tens = 20.

Repeat for the following possible sequence: 3 tens, 9 tens, 10 tens, 11 tens, 12 tens, 19 tens, 20 tens, 30 tens, 40 tens, 80 tens, 84 tens, and 65 tens.

Application Problem (6 minutes)

The school library has 10,600 books.
The town library has 10 times as many books.
How many books does the town library have?

Note: This Application Problem builds on the concept from the previous lesson of determining 10 times as much as a number.

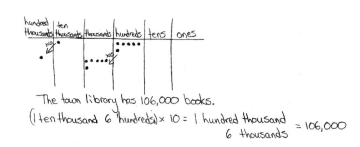

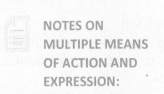

Concept Development (32 minutes)

Materials: (S) Personal white board, unlabeled millions place value chart (Lesson 2 Template)

Note: Students will go beyond the **4.NBT** standard of using numbers less than or equal to 1 million to establish a pattern within the base ten units.

Introduction: Patterns of the base ten system.

T: In the last lesson, we extended the place value chart to 1 million. Take a minute to label the place value headings on your place value chart. (Circulate and check all headings.)

T: Excellent. Now, talk with your partner about similarities and differences you see in those heading names.

S: I notice some words repeat, like *ten, hundred,* and *thousand,* but *ones* appears once. → I notice the thousand unit repeats 3 times—thousands, ten thousands, hundred thousands.

EUREKA MATH   Lesson 3:   Name numbers within 1 million by building understanding of the place   53
value chart and placement of commas for naming base thousand units.

©2015 Great Minds. eureka-math.org
G4-M1M2-TE-BK1-1.3.1-1.2016

T: That's right! Beginning with thousands, we start naming new place value units by how many one thousands, ten thousands, and hundred thousands we have. What do you think the next unit might be called after 1 million?

S: **Ten millions**.

T: (Extend chart to the ten millions.) And the next?

S: **Hundred millions**.

T: (Extend chart again.) That's right! Just like with thousands, we name new units here in terms of how many one millions, ten millions, and hundred millions we have. 10 hundred millions gets renamed as 1 billion. Talk with your partner about what the next two place value units should be.

S: Ten billions and hundred billions. → It works just like it does for thousands and millions.

Problem 1: Placing commas in and naming numbers.

T: You've noticed a pattern: ones, tens, and hundreds; one thousands, ten thousands, and hundred thousands; one millions, ten millions, and hundred millions; and so on. We use commas to indicate this grouping of units, taken 3 at a time. For example, ten billion would be written: 10,000,000,000.

T: (Write 608430325.) Record this number, and place the commas to show our groupings of units.

S: (Record the number and place the commas.)

T: (Show 430,325 on a place value chart.) How many thousands are in this number?

S: 430.

T: 430 what?

S: 430 thousands.

T: Correct. We read this number as "four hundred thirty thousand, three hundred twenty-five."

T: (Extend chart, and show 608,430,325.) How many millions are there in this number?

S: 608 millions.

T: Using what you know about our pattern in naming units, talk with your partner about how to name this number.

S: Six hundred eight million, four hundred thirty thousand, three hundred twenty-five.

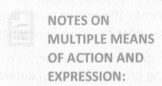

NOTES ON
MULTIPLE MEANS
OF ACTION AND
EXPRESSION:

Scaffold reading numbers into the hundred thousands with questioning such as:

T: What's the value of the 3?

S: 30 thousand.

T: How many thousands altogether?

S: 36 thousands.

T: What's the value of the 8?

S: 80.

T: Add the remaining ones.

S: 89.

T: Read the whole number.

S: Thirty-six thousand, eighty-nine.

Continue with similar numbers until students reach fluency. Alternate the student recording numbers, modeling, and reading.

Problem 2: Add to make 10 of a unit and bundling up to 1 million.

T: What would happen if we combined 2 groups of 5 hundreds? With your partner, draw place value disks to solve. Use the largest unit possible to express your answer.

S: 2 groups of 5 hundreds equals 10 hundreds.
→ It would make 10 hundreds, which can be bundled to make 1 thousand.

T: Now, solve for 5 thousands plus 5 thousands. Bundle in order to express your answer using the largest unit possible.

MP.2

S: 5 thousands plus 5 thousands equals 10 thousands. We can bundle 10 thousands to make 1 ten thousand.

T: Solve for 4 ten thousands plus 6 ten thousands. Express your answer using the largest unit possible.

S: 4 ten thousands plus 6 ten thousands equals 10 ten thousands. We can bundle 10 ten thousands to make 1 hundred thousand.

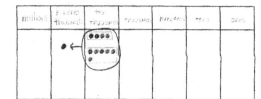

Continue renaming problems, showing regrouping as necessary.

- 3 hundred thousands + 7 hundred thousands
- 23 thousands + 4 ten thousands
- 43 ten thousands + 11 thousands

Problem 3: 10 times as many with multiple units.

T: On your place value chart, model 5 hundreds and 3 tens with place value disks. What is 10 times 5 hundreds 3 tens?

S: (Show charts.) 5 thousands 3 hundreds.

T: Model 10 times 5 hundreds 3 tens with digits on the place value chart. Record your answer in standard form.

S: (Show 10 times 5 hundreds is 5 thousands and 10 times 3 tens is 3 hundreds as digits.) 5,300.

T: Check your partner's work, and remind him of the comma's role in this number.

T: (Write 10 × 1 ten thousand 5 thousands 3 hundreds 9 ones = _____.) With your partner, solve this problem, and write your answer in standard form.

S: 10 × 15,309 = 153,090.

Lesson 3:   Name numbers within 1 million by building understanding of the place value chart and placement of commas for naming base thousand units.   55

©2015 Great Minds. eureka-math.org
G4-M1M2-TE-BK1-1.3.1-1.2016

Problem Set (10 minutes)

Students should do their personal best to complete the Problem
Set within the allotted 10 minutes. For some classes, it may be
appropriate to modify the assignment by specifying which
problems they work on first. Some problems do not specify a
method for solving. Students should solve these problems using
the RDW approach used for Application Problems.

Student Debrief (7 minutes)

Lesson Objective: Name numbers within 1 million by
building understanding of the place value chart and
placement of commas for naming base thousand units.

Invite students to review their solutions for the Problem Set
and the totality of the lesson experience. They should check
work by comparing answers with a partner before going over
answers as a class. Look for misconceptions or
misunderstandings that can be addressed in the Student
Debrief. Guide students in a conversation to debrief the
Problem Set.

Any combination of the questions below may be used to
lead the discussion.

- In Problem 1, how did you know where to place
  commas within a number?

- Read aloud the numbers in Problem 1 (d) and (e)
  with your partner. What role do the commas
  have as you read the numbers?

- How does place value understanding and the role
  of commas help you to read the value in the
  millions period that is represented by the number
  of millions, **ten millions**, and **hundred millions**?

- What did you discover as you solved Problem 3?
  How did 3(a) help you to solve 3(b)?

- How did you use the place value chart to help you
  compare unlike units in Problem 5?

- When might it be useful to omit commas?
  (Please refer to the UDL box for commas to guide
  your discussion.)

NOTES ON COMMAS:

Commas are optional for 4-digit
numbers, as omitting them supports
visualization of the total amount of
each unit. For example, in the number
3247, 32 hundreds or 324 tens is easier
to visualize when 3247 is written
without a comma. In Grade 3, students
understand 324 as 324 ones, 32 tens 4
ones, or 3 hundreds 2 tens 4 ones. This
flexible thinking allows for seeing
simplifying strategies (e.g., to solve
3247 – 623, rather than decompose 3
thousands, students might subtract 6
hundreds from 32 hundreds: 32
hundreds – 6 hundreds + 47 ones – 23
ones is 26 hundreds and 24 ones or
2624).

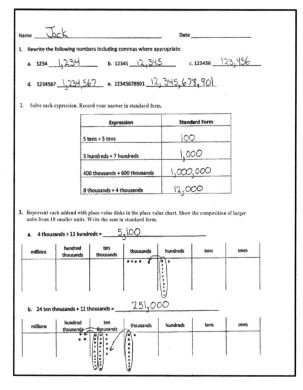

Lesson 3:   Name numbers within 1 million by building understanding of the place
value chart and placement of commas for naming base thousand units.

©2015 Great Minds. eureka-math.org
G4-M1M2-TE-BK1-1.3.1-1.2016

**EUREKA
MATH**

Exit Ticket (3 minutes)

After the Student Debrief, instruct students to complete the Exit Ticket. A review of their work will help with assessing students' understanding of the concepts that were presented in today's lesson and planning more effectively for future lessons. The questions may be read aloud to the students.

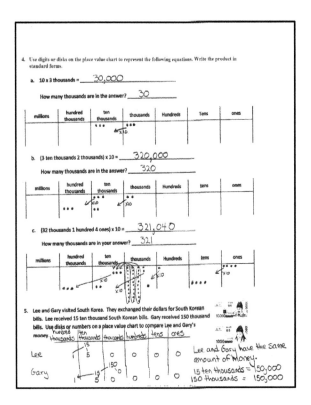

Lesson 3:   Name numbers within 1 million by building understanding of the place value chart and placement of commas for naming base thousand units.

57

A

Number Correct: _____

Multiply by 3

1.	1 × 3 =	
2.	3 × 1 =	
3.	2 × 3 =	
4.	3 × 2 =	
5.	3 × 3 =	
6.	4 × 3 =	
7.	3 × 4 =	
8.	5 × 3 =	
9.	3 × 5 =	
10.	6 × 3 =	
11.	3 × 6 =	
12.	7 × 3 =	
13.	3 × 7 =	
14.	8 × 3 =	
15.	3 × 8 =	
16.	9 × 3 =	
17.	3 × 9 =	
18.	10 × 3 =	
19.	3 × 10 =	
20.	3 × 3 =	
21.	1 × 3 =	
22.	2 × 3 =	

23.	10 × 3 =	
24.	9 × 3 =	
25.	4 × 3 =	
26.	8 × 3 =	
27.	5 × 3 =	
28.	7 × 3 =	
29.	6 × 3 =	
30.	3 × 10 =	
31.	3 × 5 =	
32.	3 × 6 =	
33.	3 × 1 =	
34.	3 × 9 =	
35.	3 × 4 =	
36.	3 × 3 =	
37.	3 × 2 =	
38.	3 × 7 =	
39.	3 × 8 =	
40.	11 × 3 =	
41.	3 × 11 =	
42.	12 × 3 =	
43.	3 × 13 =	
44.	13 × 3 =	

Lesson 3: Name numbers within 1 million by building understanding of the place value chart and placement of commas for naming base thousand units.

EUREKA MATH™

B

Number Correct: _____

Improvement: _____

Multiply by 3

1.	3 × 1 =	
2.	1 × 3 =	
3.	3 × 2 =	
4.	2 × 3 =	
5.	3 × 3 =	
6.	3 × 4 =	
7.	4 × 3 =	
8.	3 × 5 =	
9.	5 × 3 =	
10.	3 × 6 =	
11.	6 × 3 =	
12.	3 × 7 =	
13.	7 × 3 =	
14.	3 × 8 =	
15.	8 × 3 =	
16.	3 × 9 =	
17.	9 × 3 =	
18.	3 × 10 =	
19.	10 × 3 =	
20.	1 × 3 =	
21.	10 × 3 =	
22.	2 × 3 =	

23.	9 × 3 =	
24.	3 × 3 =	
25.	8 × 3 =	
26.	4 × 3 =	
27.	7 × 3 =	
28.	5 × 3 =	
29.	6 × 3 =	
30.	3 × 5 =	
31.	3 × 10 =	
32.	3 × 1 =	
33.	3 × 6 =	
34.	3 × 4 =	
35.	3 × 9 =	
36.	3 × 2 =	
37.	3 × 7 =	
38.	3 × 3 =	
39.	3 × 8 =	
40.	11 × 3 =	
41.	3 × 11 =	
42.	13 × 3 =	
43.	3 × 13 =	
44.	12 × 3 =	

EUREKA
MATH™

Lesson 3: Name numbers within 1 million by building understanding of the place value chart and placement of commas for naming base thousand units.

59

Name _____ Date _____

1. Rewrite the following numbers including commas where appropriate:

   a. 1234 _____   b. 12345 _____   c. 123456 _____

   d. 1234567 _____   e. 12345678901 _____

2. Solve each expression. Record your answer in standard form.

Expression	Standard Form
5 tens + 5 tens	
3 hundreds + 7 hundreds	
400 thousands + 600 thousands	
8 thousands + 4 thousands	

3. Represent each addend with place value disks in the place value chart. Show the composition of larger units from 10 smaller units. Write the sum in standard form.

   a.   4 thousands + 11 hundreds = _____

millions	hundred thousands	ten thousands	thousands	hundreds	tens	ones

Lesson 3:   Name numbers within 1 million by building understanding of the place value chart and placement of commas for naming base thousand units.

EUREKA MATH

b.   24 ten thousands + 11 thousands = _____

millions	hundred thousands	ten thousands	thousands	hundreds	tens	ones

4.   Use digits or disks on the place value chart to represent the following equations. Write the product in standard form.

a.   10 × 3 thousands = _____

How many thousands are in the answer? _____

millions	hundred thousands	ten thousands	thousands	hundreds	tens	ones

b.   (3 ten thousands 2 thousands) × 10 = _____

How many thousands are in the answer? _____

millions	hundred thousands	ten thousands	thousands	hundreds	tens	ones

Lesson 3:   Name numbers within 1 million by building understanding of the place value chart and placement of commas for naming base thousand units.

61

©2015 Great Minds. eureka-math.org
G4-M1M2-TE-BK1-1.3.1-1.2016

c. (32 thousands 1 hundred 4 ones) × 10 = _____

How many thousands are in your answer? _____

millions	hundred thousands	ten thousands	thousands	hundreds	tens	ones

5. Lee and Gary visited South Korea. They exchanged their dollars for South Korean bills. Lee received 15 ten thousand South Korean bills. Gary received 150 thousand bills. Use disks or numbers on a place value chart to compare Lee's and Gary's money.

Lesson 3:   Name numbers within 1 million by building understanding of the place value chart and placement of commas for naming base thousand units.

©2015 Great Minds. eureka-math.org
G4-M1M2-TE-BK1-1.3.1-1.2016

EUREKA MATH™

Name _____   Date _____

1. In the spaces provided, write the following units in standard form. Be sure to place commas where appropriate.

    a. 9 thousands 3 hundreds 4 ones _____

    b. 6 ten thousands 2 thousands 7 hundreds 8 tens 9 ones _____

    c. 1 hundred thousand 8 thousands 9 hundreds 5 tens 3 ones _____

2. Use digits or disks on the place value chart to write 26 thousands 13 hundreds.

millions	hundred thousands	ten thousands	thousands	hundreds	tens	ones

    How many thousands are in the number you have written? _____

EUREKA
MATH™

Lesson 3:   Name numbers within 1 million by building understanding of the place
value chart and placement of commas for naming base thousand units.

©2015 Great Minds. eureka-math.org
G4-M1M2-TE-BK1-1.3.1-1.2016

63

Name _____ Date _____

1. Rewrite the following numbers including commas where appropriate:

   a. 4321 _____   b. 54321 _____

   c. 224466 _____   d. 2224466 _____

   e. 10010011001 _____

2. Solve each expression. Record your answer in standard form.

Expression	Standard Form
4 tens + 6 tens	
8 hundreds + 2 hundreds	
5 thousands + 7 thousands	

3. Represent each addend with place value disks in the place value chart. Show the composition of larger units from 10 smaller units. Write the sum in standard form.

   a.   2 thousands + 12 hundreds = _____

millions	hundred thousands	ten thousands	thousands	hundreds	tens	ones

Name numbers within 1 million by building understanding of the place value chart and placement of commas for naming base thousand units.

EUREKA MATH

b.   14 ten thousands + 12 thousands = _____

millions	hundred thousands	ten thousands	thousands	hundreds	tens	ones

4.   Use digits or disks on the place value chart to represent the following equations. Write the product in standard form.

a.   10 × 5 thousands = _____

How many thousands are in the answer? _____

millions	hundred thousands	ten thousands	thousands	hundreds	tens	ones

b.   (4 ten thousands 4 thousands) × 10 = _____

How many thousands are in the answer? _____

millions	hundred thousands	ten thousands	thousands	hundreds	tens	ones

Lesson 3:   Name numbers within 1 million by building understanding of the place   65
              value chart and placement of commas for naming base thousand units.

©2015 Great Minds. eureka-math.org
G4-M1M2-TE-BK1-1.3.1-1.2016

c.   (27 thousands 3 hundreds 5 ones) × 10 = _____

How many thousands are in your answer? _____

millions	hundred thousands	ten thousands	thousands	hundreds	tens	ones

5. A large grocery store received an order of 2 thousand apples. A neighboring school received an order of 20 boxes of apples with 100 apples in each. Use disks or disks on a place value chart to compare the number of apples received by the school and the number of apples received by the grocery store.

Lesson 3:   Name numbers within 1 million by building understanding of the place value chart and placement of commas for naming base thousand units.

©2015 Great Minds. eureka-math.org
G4-M1M2-TE-BK1-1.3.1-1.2016

EUREKA MATH™

Lesson 4

Objective: Read and write multi-digit numbers using base ten numerals, number names, and expanded form.

Suggested Lesson Structure

■ Fluency Practice   (13 minutes)
▨ Application Problem   (6 minutes)
▢ Concept Development   (26 minutes)
■ Student Debrief   (15 minutes)

  Total Time   **(60 minutes)**

Fluency Practice (13 minutes)

- Skip-Counting **3.OA.4–7**   (3 minutes)
- Place Value **4.NBT.2**   (2 minutes)
- Numbers Expressed in Different Base Units **4.NBT.1**   (8 minutes)

Skip-Counting (3 minutes)

Note: Practicing skip-counting on the number line builds a foundation for accessing higher-order concepts throughout the year.

Direct students to skip-count by fours forward and backward to 48 focusing on transitions crossing the ten.

Place Value (2 minutes)

Materials: (S) Personal white board, unlabeled millions place value chart (Lesson 2 Template)

Note: Reviewing and practicing place value skills in isolation prepares students for success in writing multi-digit numbers in expanded form.

  T: Show 5 hundred thousands as place value disks, and write the number below it on the place value chart.

  S: (Draw 5 hundred thousands disks and write 500,000 below the chart.)

  T: Say the number in unit form.

  S: 5 hundred thousands.

**NOTES ON
MULTIPLE MEANS
OF REPRESENTATION:**

Place value fluency supports language acquisition as it couples meaningful visuals with valuable practice speaking the standard and unit form of numbers to 1 million.

Lesson 4:   Read and write multi-digit numbers using base ten numerals, number
                    names, and expanded form.

T: Say it in standard form.

S: 500,000.

Continue for the following possible sequence: 5 hundred thousands 3 ten thousands, 5 hundred thousands 3 hundreds, 5 ten thousands 3 hundreds, 1 hundred thousand 3 hundreds 5 tens, and 4 hundred thousands 2 ten thousands 5 tens 3 ones.

Numbers Expressed in Different Base Units (8 minutes)

Materials: (S) Personal white board

Note: This fluency activity prepares students for success in writing multi-digit numbers in expanded form.

Base Hundred Units

T: (Project 3 hundreds = _____.) Say the number in standard form.

S: 300.

Continue with a suggested sequence of 9 hundreds, 10 hundreds, 19 hundreds, 21 hundreds, 33 hundreds, 30 hundreds, 100 hundreds, 200 hundreds, 500 hundreds, 530 hundreds, 537 hundreds, and 864 hundreds.

Base Thousand Units

T: (Project 5 thousands = _____.) Say the number in standard form.

S: 5,000.

Continue with a suggested sequence of 9 thousands, 10 thousands, 20 thousands, 100 thousands, 220 thousands, and 347 thousands.

Base Ten Thousand Units

T: (Project 7 ten thousands = _____.) Say the number in standard form.

S: 70,000.

Continue with a suggested sequence of 9 ten thousands, 10 ten thousands, 12 ten thousands, 19 ten thousands, 20 ten thousands, 30 ten thousands, 80 ten thousands, 81 ten thousands, 87 ten thousands, and 99 ten thousands.

Base Hundred Thousand Units

T: (Project 3 hundred thousands = _____.) Say the number in standard form.

S: 300,000.

Continue with a suggested sequence of 2 hundred thousands, 4 hundred thousands, 5 hundred thousands, 7 hundred thousands, 8 hundred thousands, and 10 hundred thousands.

Lesson 4:   Read and write multi-digit numbers using base ten numerals, number names, and expanded form.

©2015 Great Minds. eureka-math.org
G4-M1M2-TE-BK1-1.3.1-1.2016

Application Problem (6 minutes)

There are about forty-one thousand Asian elephants and about four hundred seventy thousand African elephants left in the world. About how many Asian and African elephants are left in total?

Note: This Application Problem builds on the content of the previous lesson, requiring students to name base thousand units. It also builds from **3.NBT.2** (fluently add and subtract within 1000). Assist students by asking them to add using unit names (similar to the example), not the entire numbers as digits.

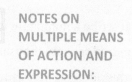

41 thousand Asian
+ 470 thousand African
———————————
511 thousand elephants

About 511,000 elephants are left.

Concept Development (26 minutes)

Materials: (S) Personal white board, unlabeled millions place value chart (Lesson 2 Template)

Problem 1: Write a four-digit number in expanded form.

T: On your place value chart, write 1,708.

T: What is the value of the 1?

S: 1 thousand.

T: (Record 1,000 under the thousands column.) What is the value of the 7?

S: 7 hundred.

T: (Record 700 under the hundreds column.) What value does the zero have?

S: Zero. → Zero tens.

T: What is the value of the 8?

S: 8 ones.

T: (Record 8 under the ones column.) What is the value of 1,000 and 700 and 8?

S: 1,708.

T: So, 1,708 is the same as 1,000 plus 700 plus 8.

T: Record that as a number sentence.

S: (Write 1,000 + 700 + 8 = 1,708.)

**NOTES ON
MULTIPLE MEANS
OF ACTION AND
EXPRESSION:**

Scaffold student composition of number words with the following options:

- Provide individual cards with number words that can be easily copied.
- Allow students to abbreviate number words.
- Set individual goals for writing number words.
- Allow English language learners their language of choice for expressing number words.

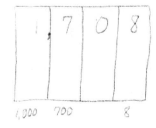

**EUREKA
MATH™**   Lesson 4:   Read and write multi-digit numbers using base ten numerals, number
                              names, and expanded form.   69

©2015 Great Minds. eureka-math.org
G4-M1M2-TE-BK1-1.3.1-1.2016

Problem 2: Write a five-digit number in word form and expanded form.

T: Now, erase your values, and write this number: 27,085.

T: Show the value of each digit at the bottom of your place value chart.

S: (Write 20,000, 7,000, 80, and 5.)

T: Why is there no term representing the hundreds?

S: Zero stands for nothing. → Zero added to a number doesn't change the value.

T: With your partner, write an addition sentence to represent 27,085.

S: 20,000 + 7,000 + 80 + 5 = 27,085.

T: Now, read the number sentence with me.

S: Twenty thousand plus seven thousand plus eighty plus five equals twenty-seven thousand, eighty-five.

T: (Write the number as you speak.) You said "twenty-seven thousand, eighty-five."

T: What do you notice about where I placed a comma in both the standard form and word form?

S: It is placed after 27 to separate the thousands in both the standard form and word form.

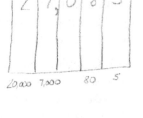

Problem 3: Transcribe a number in word form to standard and expanded form.

Display two hundred seventy thousand, eight hundred fifty.

T: Read this number. (Students read.) Tell your partner how you can match the word form to the standard form.

S: Everything you say, you should write in words. → The comma helps to separate the numbers in the thousands from the numbers in the hundreds, tens, and ones.

T: Write this number in your place value chart. Now, write this number in expanded form. Tell your partner the number sentence.

S: 200,000 plus 70,000 plus 800 plus 50 equals 270,850.

Repeat with sixty-four thousand, three.

Problem 4: Convert a number in expanded form to word and standard form.

Display 700,000 + 8,000 + 500 + 70 + 3.

T: Read this expression. (Students read.) Use digits to write this number in your place value chart.

T: My sum is 78,573. Compare your sum with mine.

S: Your 7 is in the wrong place. → The value of the 7 is 700,000. Your 7 has a value of 70,000.

MP.3

T: Read this number in standard form with me.

S: Seven hundred eight thousand, five hundred seventy-three.

T: Write this number in words. Remember to check for correct use of commas and hyphens.

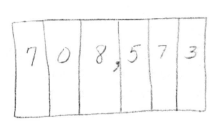

Repeat with 500,000 + 30,000 + 10 + 3.

Lesson 4:   Read and write multi-digit numbers using base ten numerals, number names, and expanded form.

©2015 Great Minds. eureka-math.org
G4-M1M2-TE-BK1-1.3.1-1.2016

EUREKA MATH™

Problem Set (10 minutes)

Students should do their personal best to complete the Problem Set within the allotted 10 minutes. For some classes, it may be appropriate to modify the assignment by specifying which problems they work on first. Some problems do not specify a method for solving. Students should solve these problems using the RDW approach used for Application Problems.

Student Debrief (15 minutes)

Lesson Objective: Read and write multi-digit numbers using base ten numerals, number names, and expanded form.

Invite students to review their solutions for the Problem Set and the totality of the lesson experience. They should check work by comparing answers with a partner before going over answers as a class. Look for misconceptions or misunderstandings that can be addressed in the Student Debrief. Guide students in a conversation to debrief the Problem Set.

Any combination of the questions below may be used to lead the discussion.

- Compare the numbers in Problems 1 and 2. What do you notice?

- As you completed the chart on Page 2, what number words were tricky to write? Which number words can be confused with other number words? Why? What strategies did you use to spell number words?

- In Problem 4, Timothy and his dad read a number word in two ways. What other numbers can be read more than one way? Which way of reading a number best helps you solve? When?

- Two students discussed the importance of zero. Nate said that zero is not important while Jill said that zero is extremely important. Who is right? Why do you think so?

- What role can zero play in a number?

- How is the expanded form related to the standard form of a number?

- When might you use expanded form to solve a calculation?

Name __Jack__   Date _____

1a. On the place value chart below, label the units and represent the number 90,523.

millions	hundred thousands	ten thousands	thousands	hundreds	tens	ones
		9	0	5	2	3

b. Write the number in word form.

Ninety thousand, five hundred twenty-three

c. Write the number in expanded form.

90,000 + 500 + 20 + 3

2a. On the place value chart below, label the units and represent the number 905,203.

millions	hundred thousands	ten thousands	thousands	hundreds	tens	ones
	9	0	5	2	0	3

b. Write the number in word form.

Nine hundred five thousand, two hundred three

c. Write the number in expanded form.

900,000 + 5,000 + 200 + 3

Exit Ticket (3 minutes)

After the Student Debrief, instruct students to complete the Exit Ticket. A review of their work will help with assessing students' understanding of the concepts that were presented in today's lesson and planning more effectively for future lessons. The questions may be read aloud to the students.

3. Complete the following chart:

Number	Word Form	Expanded Form
2,480	two thousand, four hundred eighty	2,000 + 400 + 80
20,482	twenty thousand, four hundred eighty-two	20,000 + 400 + 80 + 2
64,106	sixty-four thousand, one hundred six	60,000 + 4,000 + 100 + 6
604,016	six hundred four thousand, sixteen	600,000 + 4,000 + 10 + 6
960,060	nine hundred sixty thousand sixty	900,000 + 60,000 + 60

4. Black Rhinos are endangered, with only 4,400 left in the world. Timothy read that number as "four thousand, four hundred."   His father read the number as "44 hundred." Who read the number correctly? Use pictures, numbers or words to explain your answer.

Both Timothy and his father read the number correctly. 4,400 is "four thousand, four hundred". It can also be read as "forty-four hundred" since the 4 thousands can be regrouped as 40 hundreds. 40 hundreds plus 4 hundreds is forty-four hundreds.

Lesson 4:   Read and write multi-digit numbers using base ten numerals, number names, and expanded form.

EUREKA MATH

Name _____   Date _____

1. a.   On the place value chart below, label the units, and represent the number 90,523.

    b.   Write the number in word form.

    c.   Write the number in expanded form.

2. a.   On the place value chart below, label the units, and represent the number 905,203.

    b.   Write the number in word form.

    c.   Write the number in expanded form.

EUREKA
MATH™

Lesson 4:   Read and write multi-digit numbers using base ten numerals, number
names, and expanded form.

©2015 Great Minds. eureka-math.org
G4-M1M2-TE-BK1-1.3.1-1.2016

73

3. Complete the following chart:

Standard Form	Word Form	Expanded Form
	two thousand, four hundred eighty	
		20,000 + 400 + 80 + 2
	sixty-four thousand, one hundred six	
604,016		
960,060		

4. Black rhinos are endangered, with only 4,400 left in the world. Timothy read that number as "four thousand, four hundred." His father read the number as "44 hundred." Who read the number correctly? Use pictures, numbers, or words to explain your answer.

Lesson 4:   Read and write multi-digit numbers using base ten numerals, number names, and expanded form.

EUREKA MATH™

Name _____   Date _____

1. Use the place value chart below to complete the following:

a. Label the units on the chart.

b. Write the number 800,000 + 6,000 + 300 + 2 in the place value chart.

c. Write the number in word form.

2. Write one hundred sixty thousand, five hundred eighty-two in expanded form.

Lesson 4:   Read and write multi-digit numbers using base ten numerals, number
              names, and expanded form.

©2015 Great Minds. eureka-math.org
G4-M1M2-TE-BK1-1.3.1-1.2016

75

Name _____   Date _____

1. a.   On the place value chart below, label the units, and represent the number 50,679.

    b.   Write the number in word form.

    c.   Write the number in expanded form.

2. a.   On the place value chart below, label the units, and represent the number 506,709.

    b.   Write the number in word form.

    c.   Write the number in expanded form.

Lesson 4:   Read and write multi-digit numbers using base ten numerals, number names, and expanded form.

EUREKA MATH

©2015 Great Minds. eureka-math.org
G4-M1M2-TE-BK1-1.3.1-1.2016

3. Complete the following chart:

Standard Form	Word Form	Expanded Form
	five thousand, three hundred seventy	
		50,000 + 300 + 70 + 2
	thirty-nine thousand, seven hundred one	
309,017		
770,070		

4. Use pictures, numbers, and words to explain another way to say sixty-five hundred.

EUREKA
MATH™

Lesson 4: Read and write multi-digit numbers using base ten numerals, number names, and expanded form.

77

©2015 Great Minds. eureka-math.org
G4-M1M2-TE-BK1-1.3.1-1.2016

4
GRADE

Mathematics Curriculum

Topic B

Comparing Multi-Digit Whole Numbers

4.NBT.2

Focus Standard:	4.NBT.2	Read and write multi-digit whole numbers using base-ten numerals, number names, and expanded form. Compare two multi-digit numbers based on meanings of the digits in each place, using >, =, and < symbols to record the results of comparisons.
Instructional Days:	2	
Coherence -Links from:	G2–M3	Place Value, Counting, and Comparison of Numbers to 1,000
-Links to:	G5–M1	Place Value and Decimal Fractions

In Topic B, students use place value to compare whole numbers. Initially using the place value chart, students compare the value of each digit to surmise which number is of greater value. Moving away from dependency on models and toward fluency with numbers, students compare numbers by observing across the entire number and noticing value differences. For example, in comparing 12,566 to 19,534, it is evident 19 thousands is greater than 12 thousands because of the value of the digits in the thousands unit. Additionally, students continue with number fluency by finding what is 1, 10, or 100 thousand more or less than a given number.

A Teaching Sequence Toward Mastery of Comparing Multi-Digit Whole Numbers
Objective 1: Compare numbers based on meanings of the digits using >, <, or = to record the comparison. (Lesson 5)
Objective 2: Find 1, 10, and 100 thousand more and less than a given number. (Lesson 6)

Lesson 5

Objective: Compare numbers based on meanings of the digits using >, <, or = to record the comparison.

Suggested Lesson Structure

■ Fluency Practice   (14 minutes)
■ Application Problem   (6 minutes)
□ Concept Development   (30 minutes)
■ Student Debrief   (10 minutes)
  Total Time   **(60 minutes)**

Fluency Practice (14 minutes)

- Sprint: Multiply by 4 **3.OA.7**   (10 minutes)
- Unit Skip-Counting **4.NBT.1**   (2 minutes)
- Place Value **4.NBT.2**   (2 minutes)

Sprint: Multiply by 4 (10 minutes)

Materials: (S) Multiply by 4 Sprint

Note: This fluency activity reviews a foundational Grade 3 standard that helps students learn standard **4.NBT.5**.

Unit Skip-Counting (2 minutes)

Note: This activity applies skip-counting fluency that was built during the first four lessons and applies to concepts from the multiplying by ten lessons.

    T: Count by twos to 20.
    S: 2, 4, 6, 8, 10, 12, 14, 16, 18, 20.
    T: Now, count by 2 tens to 20 tens. Stop counting and raise your hand when you see me raise my hand.
    S: 2 tens, 4 tens, 6 tens.
    T/S: (Raise hand.)
    T: Say the number in standard form.
    S: 60.

Continue, stopping students at 12 tens, 16 tens, and 20 tens.

Repeat the process. This time, count by threes to 30 and by 3 ten thousands to 30 ten thousands.

©2015 Great Minds. eureka-math.org
G4-M1M2-TE-BK1-1.3.1-1.2016

Place Value (2 minutes)

Note: Reviewing and practicing place value skills in isolation prepares students for success in comparing numbers during the lesson.

T: (Write 3,487.) Say the number.

S: 3,487.

T: What digit is in the tens place?

S: 8.

T: (Underline 8.) What's the value of the 8?

S: 80.

T: State the value of the 3.

S: 3,000.

T: 4?

S: 400.

Repeat for the following possible sequence: 59,607; 287,493; and 742,952.

Application Problem (6 minutes)

Draw and label the units on the place value chart to hundred thousands. Use each of the digits 9, 8, 7, 3, 1, and 0 once to create a number that is between 7 hundred thousands and 9 hundred thousands. In word form, write the number you created.

hundred Thousands	ten thousands	thousands	hundreds	tens	ones
8	3	7	9	1	0

eight hundred thirty-seven thousand, nine hundred ten

Extension: Create two more numbers following the same directions as above.

Note: This Application Problem builds on the content of the previous lesson, requiring students to read and write multi-digit numbers in expanded, word, and unit forms.

Concept Development (30 minutes)

Materials: (S) Personal white board, unlabeled hundred thousands place value chart (Template)

Problem 1: Comparing two numbers with the same largest unit.

Display: 3,010 ◯ 2,040.

T: Let's compare two numbers. Say the standard form to your partner, and model each number on your place value chart.

S: Three thousand, ten. Two thousand, forty.

         Lesson 5:   Compare numbers based on meanings of the digits using >, <, or = to record the comparison.

©2015 Great Minds. eureka-math.org
G4-M1M2-TE-BK1-1.3.1-1.2016

T: What is the name of the unit with the greatest value?

S: Thousands.

T: Compare the value of the thousands.

S: 3 thousands is greater than 2 thousands. → 2 thousands is less than 3 thousands.

T: Tell your partner what would happen if we only compared tens rather than the unit with the greatest value.

S: We would say that 2,040 is greater than 3,010, but that isn't right. → The number with more of the largest unit being compared is greater. → We don't need to compare the tens because the thousands are different.

T: Thousands is our largest unit. 3 thousands is greater than 2 thousands, so 3,010 is greater than 2,040. (Write the comparison symbol > in the circle.) Write this comparison statement on your board, and say it to your partner in two different ways.

S: (Write 3,010 > 2,040.) 3,010 is greater than 2,040. 2,040 is less than 3,010.

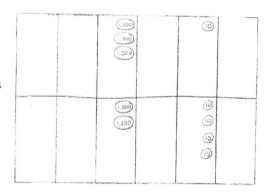

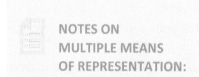

NOTES ON MULTIPLE MEANS OF REPRESENTATION:

Provide sentence frames for students to refer to when using comparative statements.

Problem 2: Comparing two numbers with an equal amount of the largest units.

Display: 43,021 ◯ 45,302.

T: Model and read each number. How is this comparison different from our first comparison?

S: Before, our largest unit was thousands. Now, our largest unit is ten thousands. → In this comparison, both numbers have the same number of ten thousands.

T: If the digits of the largest unit are equal, how do we compare?

S: We compare the thousands. → We compare the next largest unit. → We compare the digit one place to the right.

T: Write your comparison statement on your board. Say the comparison statement in two ways.

S: (Write 43,021 < 45,302 and 45,302 > 43,021.) 43,021 is less than 45,302. 45,302 is greater than 43,021.

Repeat the comparison process using 2,305 and 2,530 and then 970,461 and 907,641.

T: Write your own comparison problem for your partner to solve. Create a two-number comparison problem in which the largest unit in both numbers is the same.

Lesson 5: Compare numbers based on meanings of the digits using >, <, or = to record the comparison.

©2015 Great Minds. eureka-math.org
G4-M1M2-TE-BK1-1.3.1-1.2016

81

Problem 3: Comparing values of multiple numbers using a place value chart.

Display: 32,434, 32,644, and 32,534.

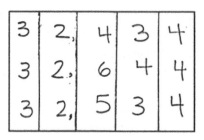

T: Write these numbers in your place value chart. Whisper the value of each digit as you do so.

T: When you compare the value of these three numbers, what do you notice?

S: All three numbers have 3 ten thousands. → All three numbers have 2 thousands. → We can compare the hundreds because they are different.

MP.1

T: Which number has the greatest value?

S: 32,644.

T: Tell your partner which number has the least value and how you know.

S: 32,434 is the smallest of the three numbers because it has the least number of hundreds.

T: Write the numbers from greatest to least. Use comparison symbols to express the relationships of the numbers.

S: (Write 32,644 > 32,534 > 32,434.)

Problem 4: Comparing numbers in different number forms.

Display: Compare 700,000 + 30,000 + 20 + 8 and 735,008.

T: Discuss with your partner how to solve and write your comparison.

S: I will write the numerals in my place value chart to compare. → Draw disks for each number. → I'll write the first number in standard form and then compare.

S: (Write 730,028 < 735,008.)

T: Tell your partner which units you compared and why.

S: I compared thousands because the larger units were the same. 5 thousands are greater than 0 thousands, so 735,008 is greater than 730,028.

Repeat with 4 hundred thousands 8 thousands 9 tens and 40,000 + 8,000 + 90.

NOTES ON MULTIPLE MEANS OF ACTION AND EXPRESSION:

For students who have difficulty converting numbers from expanded form into standard form, demonstrate using a place value chart to show how each number can be represented and then how the numbers can be added together. Alternatively, use place value cards (known as Hide Zero cards in the primary grades) to allow students to see the value of each digit that composes a number. The cards help students manipulate and visually display both the expanded form and the standard form of any number.

$$\boxed{700,000} + \boxed{30,000} + \boxed{20} + \boxed{8} = \boxed{730,028}$$
place value cards

Lesson 5:   Compare numbers based on meanings of the digits using >, <, or = to record the comparison.

©2015 Great Minds. eureka-math.org
G4-M1M2-TE-BK1-1.3.1-1.2016

EUREKA MATH

Problem Set (10 minutes)

Students should do their personal best to complete the Problem Set within the allotted 10 minutes. For some classes, it may be appropriate to modify the assignment by specifying which problems they work on first. Some problems do not specify a method for solving. Students should solve these problems using the RDW approach used for Application Problems.

Student Debrief (10 minutes)

Lesson Objective: Compare numbers based on meanings of the digits using >, <, or = to record the comparison.

Invite students to review their solutions for the Problem Set and the totality of the lesson experience. They should check work by comparing answers with a partner before going over answers as a class. Look for misconceptions or misunderstandings that can be addressed in the Student Debrief. Guide students in a conversation to debrief the Problem Set.

Any combination of the questions below may be used to lead the discussion.

- When comparing numbers, which is more helpful to you: lining up digits or lining up place value disks in a place value chart? Explain.

- How is comparing numbers in Problem 1(a) different from Problem 1(b)?

- How does your understanding of place value help to compare and order numbers?

- How can ordering numbers apply to real life?

- What challenges arise in comparing numbers when the numbers are written in different forms, such as in Problem 2?

Exit Ticket (3 minutes)

After the Student Debrief, instruct students to complete the Exit Ticket. A review of their work will help with assessing students' understanding of the concepts that were presented in today's lesson and planning more effectively for future lessons. The questions may be read aloud to the students.

Lesson 5:   Compare numbers based on meanings of the digits using >, <, or = to record the comparison.

©2015 Great Minds. eureka-math.org
G4-M1M2-TE-BK1-1.3.1-1.2016

83

A

Number Correct: _____

Multiply by 4

1.	1 × 4 =	
2.	4 × 1 =	
3.	2 × 4 =	
4.	4 × 2 =	
5.	3 × 4 =	
6.	4 × 3 =	
7.	4 × 4 =	
8.	5 × 4 =	
9.	4 × 5 =	
10.	6 × 4 =	
11.	4 × 6 =	
12.	7 × 4 =	
13.	4 × 7 =	
14.	8 × 4 =	
15.	4 × 8 =	
16.	9 × 4 =	
17.	4 × 9 =	
18.	10 × 4 =	
19.	4 × 10 =	
20.	4 × 3 =	
21.	1 × 4 =	
22.	2 × 4 =	

23.	10 × 4 =	
24.	9 × 4 =	
25.	4 × 4 =	
26.	8 × 4 =	
27.	4 × 3 =	
28.	7 × 4 =	
29.	6 × 4 =	
30.	4 × 10 =	
31.	4 × 5 =	
32.	4 × 6 =	
33.	4 × 1 =	
34.	4 × 9 =	
35.	4 × 4 =	
36.	4 × 3 =	
37.	4 × 2 =	
38.	4 × 7 =	
39.	4 × 8 =	
40.	11 × 4 =	
41.	4 × 11 =	
42.	12 × 4 =	
43.	4 × 12 =	
44.	13 × 4 =	

Lesson 5: Compare numbers based on meanings of the digits using >, <, or = to record the comparison.

B

Number Correct: _____

Improvement: _____

Multiply by 4

1.	4 × 1 =	
2.	1 × 4 =	
3.	4 × 2 =	
4.	2 × 4 =	
5.	4 × 3 =	
6.	3 × 4 =	
7.	4 × 4 =	
8.	4 × 5 =	
9.	5 × 4 =	
10.	4 × 6 =	
11.	6 × 4 =	
12.	4 × 7 =	
13.	7 × 4 =	
14.	4 × 8 =	
15.	8 × 4 =	
16.	4 × 9 =	
17.	9 × 4 =	
18.	4 × 10 =	
19.	10 × 4 =	
20.	1 × 4 =	
21.	10 × 4 =	
22.	2 × 4 =	

23.	9 × 4 =	
24.	3 × 4 =	
25.	8 × 4 =	
26.	4 × 4 =	
27.	7 × 4 =	
28.	5 × 4 =	
29.	6 × 4 =	
30.	4 × 5 =	
31.	4 × 10 =	
32.	4 × 1 =	
33.	4 × 6 =	
34.	4 × 4 =	
35.	4 × 9 =	
36.	4 × 2 =	
37.	4 × 7 =	
38.	4 × 3 =	
39.	4 × 8 =	
40.	11 × 4 =	
41.	4 × 11 =	
42.	12 × 4 =	
43.	4 × 12 =	
44.	13 × 4 =	

Lesson 5:   Compare numbers based on meanings of the digits using >, <, or = to
record the comparison.

85

©2015 Great Minds. eureka-math.org
G4-M1M2-TE-BK1-1.3.1-1.2016

Name _____   Date _____

1. Label the units in the place value chart. Draw place value disks to represent each number in the place value chart. Use <, >, or = to compare the two numbers. Write the correct symbol in the circle.

a.   600,015 ( ) 60,015

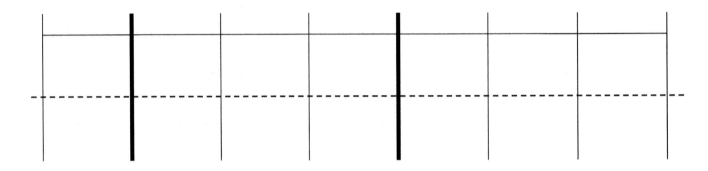

b.   409,004 ( ) 440,002

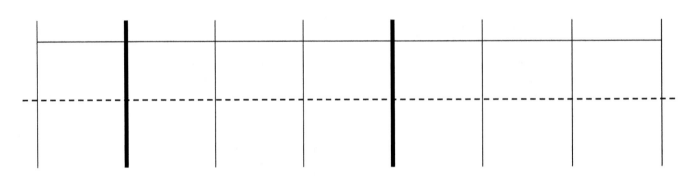

2. Compare the two numbers by using the symbols <, >, and =. Write the correct symbol in the circle.

a. 342,001 ( ) 94,981

b. 500,000 + 80,000 + 9,000 + 100 ( ) five hundred eight thousand, nine hundred one

Lesson 5:   Compare numbers based on meanings of the digits using >, <, or = to record the comparison.

EUREKA
MATH™

c.   9 hundred thousands 8 thousands 9 hundreds 3 tens ◯ 908,930

d.   9 hundreds 5 ten thousands 9 ones ◯ 6 ten thousands 5 hundreds 9 ones

3.   Use the information in the chart below to list the height in feet of each mountain from least to greatest. Then, name the mountain that has the lowest elevation in feet.

Name of Mountain	Elevation in Feet (ft)
Allen Mountain	4,340 ft
Mount Marcy	5,344 ft
Mount Haystack	4,960 ft
Slide Mountain	4,240 ft

EUREKA
MATH™

Lesson 5:   Compare numbers based on meanings of the digits using >, <, or = to record the comparison.

©2015 Great Minds. eureka-math.org
G4-M1M2-TE-BK1-1.3.1-1.2016

87

4. Arrange these numbers from least to greatest: 8,002   2,080   820   2,008   8,200

5. Arrange these numbers from greatest to least: 728,000   708,200   720,800   87,300

6. One astronomical unit, or 1 AU, is the approximate distance from Earth to the sun. The following are the approximate distances from Earth to nearby stars given in AUs:

   Alpha Centauri is 275,725 AUs from Earth.
   Proxima Centauri is 268,269 AUs from Earth.
   Epsilon Eridani is 665,282 AUs from Earth.
   Barnard's Star is 377,098 AUs from Earth.
   Sirius is 542,774 AUs from Earth.

   List the names of the stars and their distances in AUs in order from closest to farthest from Earth.

EUREKA
MATH™

Name _____   Date _____

1. Four friends played a game. The player with the most points wins. Use the information in the table below to order the number of points each player earned from least to greatest. Then, name the person who won the game.

Player Name	Points Earned
Amy	2,398 points
Bonnie	2,976 points
Jeff	2,709 points
Rick	2,699 points

2. Use each of the digits 5, 4, 3, 2, 1 exactly once to create two different five-digit numbers.

   a. Write each number on the line, and compare the two numbers by using the symbols < or >. Write the correct symbol in the circle.

   b. Use words to write a comparison statement for the problem above.

EUREKA MATH™

Lesson 5:   Compare numbers based on meanings of the digits using >, <, or = to record the comparison.

©2015 Great Minds. eureka-math.org
G4-M1M2-TE-BK1-1.3.1-1.2016

89

Name _____ Date _____

1. Label the units in the place value chart. Draw place value disks to represent each number in the place value chart. Use <, >, or = to compare the two numbers. Write the correct symbol in the circle.

   a.   909,013 ◯ 90,013

   b.   210,005 ◯ 220,005

Compare numbers based on meanings of the digits using >, <, or = to record the comparison.

©2015 Great Minds. eureka-math.org
G4-M1M2-TE-BK1-1.3.1-1.2016

EUREKA
MATH™

2. Compare the two numbers by using the symbols <, >, and =. Write the correct symbol in the circle.

a. 501,107 ( ) 89,171

b. 300,000 + 50,000 + 1,000 + 800 ( ) six hundred five thousand, nine hundred eight

c. 3 hundred thousands 3 thousands 8 hundreds 4 tens ( ) 303,840

d. 5 hundreds 6 ten thousands 2 ones ( ) 3 ten thousands 5 hundreds 1 one

3. Use the information in the chart below to list the height, in feet, of each skyscraper from shortest to tallest. Then, name the tallest skyscraper.

Name of Skyscraper	Height of Skyscraper (ft)
Willis Tower	1,450 ft
One World Trade Center	1,776 ft
Taipei 101	1,670 ft
Petronas Towers	1,483 ft

4. Arrange these numbers from least to greatest: 7,550   5,070   750   5,007   7,505

5. Arrange these numbers from greatest to least: 426,000   406,200   640,020   46,600

6. The areas of the 50 states can be measured in square miles.

California is 158,648 square miles. Nevada is 110,567 square miles. Arizona is 114,007 square miles. Texas is 266,874 square miles. Montana is 147,047 square miles, and Alaska is 587,878 square miles.

Arrange the states in order from least area to greatest area.

Lesson 5:   Compare numbers based on meanings of the digits using >, <, or = to record the comparison.

EUREKA
MATH™

unlabeled hundred thousands place value chart

Lesson 5:   Compare numbers based on meanings of the digits using >, <, or = to
record the comparison.

©2015 Great Minds. eureka-math.org
G4-M1M2-TE-BK1-1.3.1-1.2016

93

Lesson 6

Objective: Find 1, 10, and 100 thousand more and less than a given number.

Suggested Lesson Structure

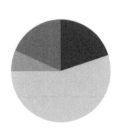

■ Fluency Practice   (12 minutes)
■ Application Problem   (4 minutes)
■ Concept Development   (33 minutes)
■ Student Debrief   (11 minutes)

   Total Time   **(60 minutes)**

Fluency Practice (12 minutes)

■ Unit Skip-Counting **4.NBT.1**   (3 minutes)
■ Rename the Units **4.NBT.2**   (5 minutes)
■ Compare Numbers **4.NBT.2**   (4 minutes)

Unit Skip-Counting (3 minutes)

Note: This activity applies skip-counting fluency to the multiplying by ten lessons.

   T: Count by threes to 30.

   S: 3, 6, 9, 12, 15, 18, 21, 24, 27, 30.

   T: Now, count by 3 ten thousands to 30 ten thousands. Stop counting and raise your hand when you see me raise my hand.

   S: 3 ten thousands, 6 ten thousands, 9 ten thousands.

   T/S: (Raise hand.)

   T: Say the number in standard form.

   S: 90,000.

NOTES ON MULTIPLE MEANS OF ACTION AND EXPRESSION:

Before directing the students to count by *3 ten thousands*, direct them first to count by *3 cats*. Then, direct them to count by *3 hundreds*. Finally, bridge the directions to counting by *3 ten thousands*.

Continue, stopping students at 15 ten thousands, 21 ten thousands, and 30 ten thousands.

Repeat the process. This time, count by fours to 40 and by 4 hundred thousands to 40 hundred thousands.

©2015 Great Minds. eureka-math.org
G4-M1M2-TE-BK1-1.3.1-1.2016

Rename the Units (5 minutes)

Note: This fluency activity applies students' place value skills in a new context that helps them better access the lesson's content.

Materials: (S) Personal white board

T: (Write 54,783.) Say the number.

S: 54,783.

T: How many thousands are in 54,783?

S: 54 thousands.

T: (Write 54,783 = _____ thousands ____ ones.) On your personal white board, fill in the equation.

S: (Write 54,783 = 54 thousands 783 ones.)

T: How many ten thousands are in 54,783?

S: 5 ten thousands.

T: (Write 54,783 = _____ ten thousands ____ hundreds ____ ones.) On your board, fill in the equation.

S: (Write 54,783 = 5 ten thousands 47 hundreds 83 ones.)

Follow the same process and sequence for 234,673.

Compare Numbers (4 minutes)

Materials: (S) Personal white board

Note: This fluency activity reviews comparing number concepts learned in Lesson 5.

T: (Write 231,005 _____ 83,872.) On your personal white board, compare the numbers by writing the greater than, less than, or equal to symbol.

S: (Write 231,005 > 83,872.)

Repeat using the following sequence: 6 thousands 4 hundreds 9 tens _____5 ten thousands 4 hundreds 9 ones and 8 hundred thousands 7 thousands 8 hundreds 2 tens _____ 807,820.

Application Problem (4 minutes)

Use the digits 5, 6, 8, 2, 4, and 1 to create two six-digit numbers. Be sure to use each of the digits within both numbers. Express the numbers in word form, and use a comparison symbol to show their relationship.

Note: This Application Problem builds on the content of the previous two lessons.

Example: 586,241   412,685
five hundred eighty-six thousand, two hundred forty-one >
four hundred twelve thousand, six hundred eighty-five

EUREKA
MATH™

Lesson 6:   Find 1, 10, and 100 thousand more and less than a given number.

95

©2015 Great Minds. eureka-math.org
G4-M1M2-TE-BK1-1.3.1-1.2016

Concept Development (33 minutes)

Materials: (T) Unlabeled hundred thousands place value chart (Lesson 5 Template) (S) Personal white board, unlabeled hundred thousands place value chart (Lesson 5 Template)

Problem 1: Find 1 thousand more and 1 thousand less.

T: (Draw 2 thousands disks in the place value chart.) How many thousands do you count?

S: Two thousands.

T: What number is one thousand more? (Draw 1 more thousand.)

S: Three thousands.

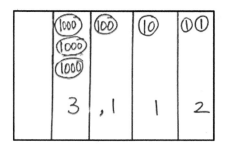

T: (Write 3 thousands 112 ones.) Model this number with disks, and write its expanded and standard form.

S: (Write 3,000 + 100 + 10 + 2. 3,112.)

T: Draw 1 more unit of one thousand. What number is 1 thousand more than 3,112?

MP.5

S: 4,112 is 1 thousand more than 3,112.

T: 1 thousand less than 3,112?

S: 2,112.

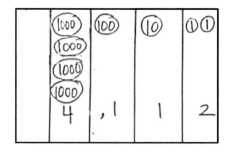

T: Draw 1 ten thousands disk. What number do you have now?

S: 14,112.

T: Show 1 less unit of 1 thousand. What number is 1 thousand less than 14,112?

S: 13,112.

T: 1 thousand more than 14,112?

S: 15,112.

T: Did the largest unit change? Discuss with your partner.

S: (Discuss.)

T: Show 19,112. (Pause as students draw.) What is 1 thousand less? 1 thousand more than 19,112?

S: 18,112. 20,112.

T: Did the largest unit change? Discuss with your partner.

S: (Discuss.)

T: Show 199,465. (Pause as they do so.) What is 1 thousand less? 1 thousand more than 199,465?

S: 198,465. 200,465.

T: Did the largest unit change? Discuss with your partner.

S: (Discuss.)

Lesson 6:   Find 1, 10, and 100 thousand more and less than a given number.

EUREKA MATH™

Problem 2: Find 10 thousand more and 10 thousand less.

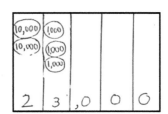

T: Use numbers and disks to model 2 ten thousands 3 thousands. Read and write the expanded form.

S: (Model, read, and write 20,000 + 3,000 = 23,000.)

T: What number is 10 thousand more than 2 ten thousands 3 thousands? Draw, read, and write the expanded form.

S: (Model, read, and write 20,000 + 10,000 + 3,000 = 33,000.)

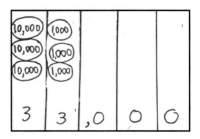

T: (Display 100,000 + 30,000 + 4,000.) Use disks and numbers to model the sum. What number is 10 thousand more than 134,000? Say your answer as an addition sentence.

S: 10,000 plus 134,000 is 144,000.

T: (Display 25,130 – 10,000.) What number is 10 thousand less than 25,130? Work with your partner to use numbers and disks to model the difference. Write and whisper to your partner an equation in unit form to verify your answer.

S: (Model, read, and write 2 ten thousands 5 thousands 1 hundred 3 tens minus 1 ten thousand is 1 ten thousand 5 thousands 1 hundred 3 tens.)

Problem 3: Find 100 thousand more and 100 thousand less.

T: (Display 200,352.) Work with your partner to find the number that is 100 thousand more than 200,352. Write an equation to verify your answer.

S: (Write 200,352 + 100,000 = 300,352.)

T: (Display 545,000 and 445,000 and 345,000.) Read these three numbers to your partner. Predict the next number in my pattern, and explain your reasoning.

S: I predict the next number will be 245,000. I notice the numbers decrease by 100,000. 345,000 minus 100,000 is 245,000. → I notice the hundred thousand units decreasing: 5 hundred thousands, 4 hundred thousands, 3 hundred thousands. I predict the next number will have 2 hundred thousands. I notice the other units do not change, so the next number will be 2 hundred thousands 4 ten thousands 5 thousands.

> **NOTES ON MULTIPLE MEANS OF ENGAGEMENT:**
>
> After students predict the next number in the pattern, ask students to create their own pattern using the strategy of one thousand more or less, ten thousand more or less, or one hundred thousand more or less. Then, ask students to challenge their classmates to predict the next number in the pattern.

Problem Set (10 minutes)

Students should do their personal best to complete the Problem Set within the allotted 10 minutes. For some classes, it may be appropriate to modify the assignment by specifying which problems they work on first. Some problems do not specify a method for solving. Students should solve these problems using the RDW approach used for Application Problems.

Student Debrief (11 minutes)

Lesson Objective: Find 1, 10, and 100 thousand more and less than a given number.

Invite students to review their solutions for the Problem Set and the totality of the lesson experience. They should check work by comparing answers with a partner before going over answers as a class. Look for misconceptions or misunderstandings that can be addressed in the Student Debrief. Guide students in a conversation to debrief the Problem Set.

Any combination of the questions below may be used to lead the discussion.

- When drawing place value disks in the Problem Set, how did you show that a number was added or that a number was taken away? If you used symbols, which symbols did you use?

- Look at Problem 2 in the Problem Set. How did you solve? Compare your method to your partner's. How else could you model?

- Why were Problem 3 (e) and (f) more challenging than the rest? How did you use your place value knowledge to solve?

- Look at Problem 4. What strategy did you use to complete the pattern? How many ways can we model to solve? Which way is best? Why do you think so?

- Compare Problem 3 and Problem 4. Which was easier to solve? Why?

- How does your understanding of place value help you add or subtract 1,000, 10,000, and 100,000?

- What place value patterns have we discovered?

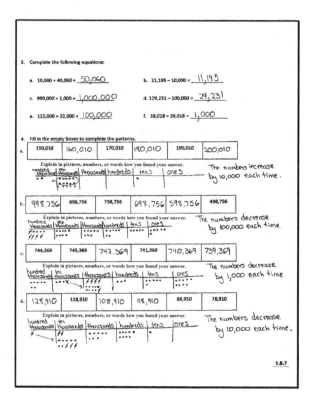

Exit Ticket (3 minutes)

After the Student Debrief, instruct students to complete the Exit Ticket. A review of their work will help with assessing students' understanding of the concepts that were presented in today's lesson and planning more effectively for future lessons. The questions may be read aloud to the students.

Lesson 6:   Find 1, 10, and 100 thousand more and less than a given number.

©2015 Great Minds. eureka-math.org
G4-M1M2-TE-BK1-1.3.1-1.2016

99

Name _____ Date _____

1. Label the place value chart. Use place value disks to find the sum or difference. Write the answer in standard form on the line.

   a. 10,000 more than six hundred five thousand, four hundred seventy-two is _____.

   b. 100 thousand less than 400,000 + 80,000 + 1,000 + 30 + 6 is _____.

   c. 230,070 is _____ than 130,070.

2. Lucy plays an online math game. She scored 100,000 more points on Level 2 than on Level 3. If she scored 349,867 points on Level 2, what was her score on Level 3? Use pictures, words, or numbers to explain your thinking.

100

Lesson 6: Find 1, 10, and 100 thousand more and less than a given number.

EUREKA MATH

3. Fill in the blank for each equation.

   a. 10,000 + 40,060 = _____

   b. 21,195 − 10,000 = _____

   c. 999,000 + 1,000 = _____

   d. 129,231 − 100,000 = _____

   e. 122,000 = 22,000 + _____

   f. 38,018 = 39,018 − _____

4. Fill in the empty boxes to complete the patterns.

   a.

150,010		170,010		190,010	

   Explain in pictures, numbers, or words how you found your answers.

   b.

	898,756	798,756			498,756

   Explain in pictures, numbers, or words how you found your answers.

Lesson 6: Find 1, 10, and 100 thousand more and less than a given number.

101

©2015 Great Minds. eureka-math.org
G4-M1M2-TE-BK1-1.3.1-1.2016

c.

744,369	743,369		741,369		

Explain in pictures, numbers, or words how you found your answers.

d.

	118,910			88,910	78,910

Explain in pictures, numbers, or words how you found your answers.

Name _____   Date _____

1. Fill in the empty boxes to complete the pattern.

468,235			471,235	472,235	

Explain in pictures, numbers, or words how you found your answers.

2. Fill in the blank for each equation.

    a. 1,000 + 56,879 = _____   b. 324,560 – 100,000 = _____

    c. 456,080 – 10,000 = _____   d. 10,000 + 786,233 = _____

3. The population of Rochester, NY, in the 2000 Census was 219,782. The 2010 Census found that the population decreased by about 10,000. About how many people lived in Rochester in 2010? Explain in pictures, numbers, or words how you found your answer.

Name _____   Date _____

1. Label the place value chart. Use place value disks to find the sum or difference. Write the answer in standard form on the line.

   a. 100,000 less than five hundred sixty thousand, three hundred thirteen is _____.

   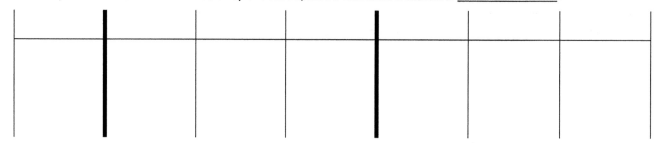

   b. Ten thousand more than 300,000 + 90,000 + 5,000 + 40 is _____.

   c. 447,077 is _____ than 347,077.

2. Fill in the blank for each equation:

   a. 100,000 + 76,960 = _____   b. 13,097 − 1,000 = _____

   c. 849,000 − 10,000 = _____   d. 442,210 + 10,000 = _____

   e. 172,090 = 171,090 + _____   f. 854,121 = 954,121 − _____

Lesson 6:   Find 1, 10, and 100 thousand more and less than a given number.

EUREKA MATH

3. Fill in the empty boxes to complete the patterns.

a.

145,555		147,555		149,555	

Explain in pictures, numbers, or words how you found your answers.

b.

	764,321	774,321			804,321

Explain in pictures, numbers, or words how you found your answers.

c.

125,876	225,876		425,876		

Explain in pictures, numbers, or words how you found your answers.

EUREKA MATH

Lesson 6:   Find 1, 10, and 100 thousand more and less than a given number.

105

©2015 Great Minds. eureka-math.org
G4-M1M2-TE-BK1-1.3.1-1.2016

d.

	254,445			224,445	214,445

Explain in pictures, numbers, or words how you found your answers.

4. In 2012, Charlie earned an annual salary of $54,098. At the beginning of 2013, Charlie's annual salary was raised by $10,000. How much money will Charlie earn in 2013? Use pictures, words, or numbers to explain your thinking.

EUREKA
MATH™

©2015 Great Minds. eureka-math.org
G4-M1M2-TE-BK1-1.3.1-1.2016

Mathematics Curriculum

4 GRADE

Topic C

Rounding Multi-Digit Whole Numbers

4.NBT.3

Focus Standard:	4.NBT.3	Use place value understanding to round multi-digit whole numbers to any place.
Instructional Days:	4	
Coherence -Links from:	G3–M2	Place Value and Problem Solving with Units of Measure
-Links to:	G5–M1	Place Value and Decimal Fractions

In Topic C, students round to any place using the vertical number line and approximation. The vertical number line allows students to line up place values of the numbers they are comparing. In Grade 3, students rounded to the nearest 10 or 100 using place value understanding. Now, they extend this understanding rounding to the nearest thousand, ten thousand, and hundred thousand. Uniformity in the base ten system easily transfers understanding from the Grade 3 (**3.NBT.1**) to Grade 4 (**4.NBT.3**) standard.

Rounding to the leftmost unit is easiest for students, but Grade 4 students learn the advantages to rounding to any place value, which increases accuracy. Students move from dependency on the number line and learn to round a number to a particular unit. To round 34,108 to the nearest thousand, students find the nearest multiple, 34,000 or 35,000, by seeing if 34,108 is more than or less than halfway between the multiples. The final lesson of Topic C presents complex and real world examples of rounding, including instances where the number requires rounding down, but the context requires rounding up.

A Teaching Sequence Toward Mastery of Rounding Multi-Digit Whole Numbers
Objective 1: Round multi-digit numbers to the thousands place using the vertical number line. (Lesson 7)
Objective 2: Round multi-digit numbers to any place using the vertical number line. (Lesson 8)
Objective 3: Use place value understanding to round multi-digit numbers to any place value. (Lesson 9)
Objective 4: Use place value understanding to round multi-digit numbers to any place value using real world applications. (Lesson 10)

Lesson 7

Objective: Round multi-digit numbers to the thousands place using the vertical number line.

Suggested Lesson Structure

■ Fluency Practice   (15 minutes)
■ Application Problem   (6 minutes)
☐ Concept Development   (27 minutes)
■ Student Debrief   (12 minutes)

   Total Time   **(60 minutes)**

Fluency Practice (15 minutes)

▪ Change Place Value **4.NBT.1**   (5 minutes)
▪ Number Patterns **4.NBT.1**   (5 minutes)
▪ Find the Midpoint **4.NBT.3**   (5 minutes)

Change Place Value (5 minutes)

Materials: (S) Personal white board, unlabeled hundred thousands place value chart (Lesson 5 Template)

Note: This fluency activity reviews Lesson 6's content.

   T: (Project place value chart. Write 3 hundred thousands, 5 ten thousands, 2 thousands, 1 hundred, 5 tens, and 4 ones.) On your personal white board, draw place value disks, and write the numbers beneath it.
   S: (Draw disks and write 352,154.)
   T: Show 100 more.
   S: (Draw 1 more 100 disk, erase the number 1 in the hundreds place, and replace it with a 2 so that their boards now read 352,254.)

Possible further sequence: 10,000 less; 100,000 more; 1 less; and 10 more.

Repeat with the following: 7,385; 297,084; and 306,032.

Number Patterns (5 minutes)

Materials: (S) Personal white board

Note: This activity synthesizes skip-counting fluency with Lesson 6's content and applies it in a context that lays a foundation for rounding multi-digit numbers to the thousands place.

T: (Project 50,300; 60,300; 70,300; _____.) What is the place value of the digit that's changing?
S: Ten thousand.
T: Count with me saying the value of the digit I'm pointing to. (Point at the ten thousand digit as students count.)
S: 50,000; 60,000; 70,000.
T: On your personal board, write what number would come after 70,300.
S: (Write 80,300.)

Repeat for the following possible sequence, using place value disks if students are struggling:

92,010	82,010	72,010	_____
135,004	136,004	137,004	_____
832,743	832,643	832,543	_____
271,543	281,543	291,543	_____

Find the Midpoint (5 minutes)

Materials: (S) Personal white board

Note: Practicing this skill in isolation lays a foundation to conceptually understand rounding on a vertical number line and reviews Grade 3 skills in anticipation of this lesson.

Project a vertical number line with endpoints 10 and 20.

T: What's halfway between 10 and 20?
S: 15.
T: (Write 15 halfway between 10 and 20. Draw a second line with 1,000 and 2,000 as the endpoints.)
MP.2   How many hundreds are in 1,000?
S: 10 hundreds.
T: (Below 1,000, write 10 hundreds.) How many hundreds are in 2,000?
S: 20 hundreds.
T: (Write 20 hundreds below 2,000.) What's halfway between 10 hundreds and 20 hundreds?
S: 15 hundreds.
T: (Write 1,500 halfway between 1,000 and 2,000. Below 1,500, write 15 hundreds.) On your personal board, draw a vertical number line with two endpoints and a midpoint.
S: (Draw number line with two endpoints and a midpoint.)

number line

Lesson 7:   Round multi-digit numbers to the thousands place using the vertical number line.

©2015 Great Minds. eureka-math.org
G4-M1M2-TE-BK1-1.3.1-1.2016

109

T: Label 31,000 and 32,000 as endpoints.

S: (Label 31,000 and 32,000 as endpoints.)

MP.2

T: How many hundreds are in 31,000?

S: 310 hundreds.

T: How many hundreds are in 32,000?

S: 320 hundreds.

T: Identify the midpoint.

S: (Write 31,500.)

Repeat the process and procedure to find the midpoint of 831,000 and 832,000; 63,000 and 64,000; 264,000 and 265,000; and 99,000 and 100,000.

Application Problem (6 minutes)

According to their pedometers, Mrs. Alsup's class took a total of 42,619 steps on Tuesday. On Wednesday, they took ten thousand more steps than they did on Tuesday. On Thursday, they took one thousand fewer steps than they did on Wednesday. How many steps did Mrs. Alsup's class take on Thursday?

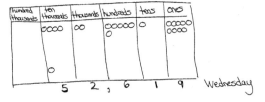 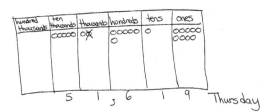

Mrs. Alsup's class took 51,619 steps on Thursday.

Note: This Application Problem builds on the concept of the previous lesson requiring students to find 1 thousand, 10 thousand, or 100 thousand more or less than a given number.

Concept Development (27 minutes)

Materials: (S) Personal white board

Problem 1: Use a vertical number line to round four-digit numbers to the nearest thousand.

T: (Draw a vertical number line with 2 endpoints.) We are going to round 4,100 to the nearest thousand. How many thousands are in 4,100?

S: 4 thousands.

T: (Mark the lower endpoint with 4 thousands.) And 1 more thousand would be?

S: 5 thousands.

T: (Mark the upper endpoint with 5 thousands.) What's halfway between 4 thousands and 5 thousands?

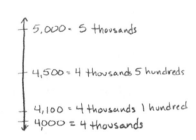

Lesson 7:   Round multi-digit numbers to the thousands place using the vertical
                                   number line.

©2015 Great Minds. eureka-math.org
G4-M1M2-TE-BK1-1.3.1-1.2016

**EUREKA
MATH**

S: 4,500.

T: (Label 4,500 on the number line.) Where should I label 4,100? Tell me where to stop. (Move your marker up the line.)

S: Stop!

T: (Label 4,100 on the number line.) Is 4,100 nearer to 4 thousands or 5 thousands?

S: 4,100 is nearer to 4 thousands.

T: True. We say 4,100 rounded to the nearest thousand is 4,000.

T: (Label 4,700 on the number line.) What about 4,700?

S: 4,700 is nearer to 5 thousands.

T: Therefore, we say 4,700 rounded to the nearest thousand is 5,000.

NOTES ON MULTIPLE MEANS OF REPRESENTATION:

For those students who have trouble conceptualizing *halfway*, demonstrate *halfway* using students as models. Two students represent the thousands. A third student represents halfway. A fourth student represents the number being rounded. Discuss: Where do they belong? To whom are they nearer? To which number would they round?

Problem 2: Use a vertical number line to round five- and six-digit numbers to the nearest thousand.

T: Let's round 14,500 to the nearest thousand. How many thousands are there in 14,500?

S: 14 thousands.

T: What's 1 more thousand?

S: 15 thousands.

T: Designate the endpoints on your number line. What is halfway between 14,000 and 15,000?

S: 14,500. Hey, that's the number that we are trying to round to the nearest thousand.

T: True. 14,500 is right in the middle. It is the halfway point. It is not closer to either number. The rule is that we round up. 14,500 rounded to the nearest thousand is 15,000.

T: With your partner, mark 14,990 on your number line, and round it to the nearest thousand.

S: 14,990 is nearer to 15 thousands or 15,000.

T: Mark 14,345 on your number line. Talk with your partner about how to round it to the nearest thousand.

15,000 = 15 thousands

14,500 = 14 thousands 5 hundreds
14,345 = 14 thousands 3 hundreds
14,000 = 14 thousands

S: 14,345 is nearer to 14 thousands. → 14,345 is nearer to 14,000. → 14,345 rounded to the nearest thousand is 14,000.

T: Is 14,345 greater than or less than the halfway point?

S: Less than.

T: We can look to see if 14,345 is closer to 14,000 or 15,000, and we can also look to see if it is greater than or less than the halfway point. If it is less than the halfway point, it is closer to 14,000.

Repeat using the numbers 215,711 and 214,569. Round to the nearest thousand, and name how many thousands are in each number.

Lesson 7:   Round multi-digit numbers to the thousands place using the vertical number line.

©2015 Great Minds. eureka-math.org
G4-M1M2-TE-BK1-1.3.1-1.2016

111

Problem Set (10 minutes)

Students should do their personal best to complete the Problem Set within the allotted 10 minutes. For some classes, it may be appropriate to modify the assignment by specifying which problems they work on first. Some problems do not specify a method for solving. Students should solve these problems using the RDW approach used for Application Problems.

Student Debrief (12 minutes)

Lesson Objective: Round multi-digit numbers to the thousands place using the vertical number line.

Invite students to review their solutions for the Problem Set and the totality of the lesson experience. They should check work by comparing answers with a partner before going over answers as a class. Look for misconceptions or misunderstandings that can be addressed in the Student Debrief. Guide students in a conversation to debrief the Problem Set.

Any combination of the questions below may be used to lead the discussion.

- Look at Problem 1 in the Problem Set. Compare how you rounded 6,700 and 16,401. Explain how your rounding to the nearest thousand differed even though both numbers have a 6 in the thousands place.

- What was your strategy for solving Problem 4? How did the vertical number line support your thinking?

- What makes 5 special in rounding?

- How does the number line help you round numbers? Is there another way you prefer? Why?

- What is the purpose of rounding?

- When might we use rounding or estimation?

Exit Ticket (3 minutes)

After the Student Debrief, instruct students to complete the Exit Ticket. A review of their work will help with assessing students' understanding of the concepts that were presented in today's lesson and planning more effectively for future lessons. The questions may be read aloud to the students.

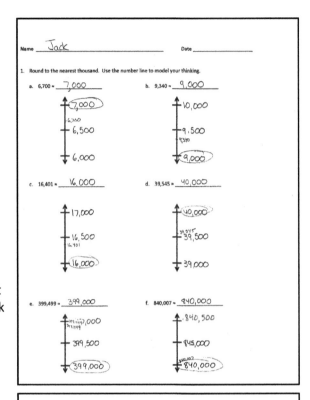

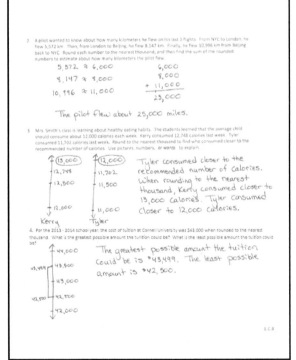

EUREKA MATH™

Name _____ Date _____

1. Round to the nearest thousand. Use the number line to model your thinking.

a. 6,700 ≈ _____

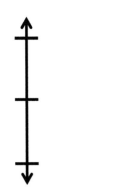

b. 9,340 ≈ _____

c. 16,401 ≈ _____

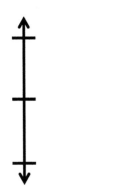

d. 39,545 ≈ _____

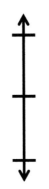

e. 399,499 ≈ _____

f. 840,007 ≈ _____

EUREKA
MATH™

Lesson 7: Round multi-digit numbers to the thousands place using the vertical number line.

©2015 Great Minds. eureka-math.org
G4-M1M2-TE-BK1-1.3.1-1.2016

113

2. A pilot wanted to know about how many kilometers he flew on his last 3 flights. From NYC to London, he flew 5,572 km. Then, from London to Beijing, he flew 8,147 km. Finally, he flew 10,996 km from Beijing back to NYC. Round each number to the nearest thousand, and then find the sum of the rounded numbers to estimate about how many kilometers the pilot flew.

3. Mrs. Smith's class is learning about healthy eating habits. The students learned that the average child should consume about 12,000 calories each week. Kerry consumed 12,748 calories last week. Tyler consumed 11,702 calories last week. Round to the nearest thousand to find who consumed closer to the recommended number of calories. Use pictures, numbers, or words to explain.

4. For the 2013-2014 school year, the cost of tuition at Cornell University was $43,000 when rounded to the nearest thousand. What is the greatest possible amount the tuition could be? What is the least possible amount the tuition could be?

Lesson 7:   Round multi-digit numbers to the thousands place using the vertical number line.

©2015 Great Minds. eureka-math.org
G4-M1M2-TE-BK1-1.3.1-1.2016

EUREKA
MATH™

Name _____ Date _____

1. Round to the nearest thousand. Use the number line to model your thinking.

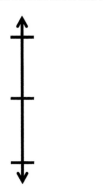 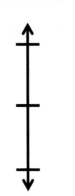 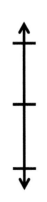

   a. 7,621 ≈ _____   b. 12,502 ≈ _____   c. 324,087 ≈ _____

2. It takes 39,090 gallons of water to manufacture a new car. Sammy thinks that rounds up to about 40,000 gallons. Susie thinks it is about 39,000 gallons. Who rounded to the nearest thousand, Sammy or Susie? Use pictures, numbers, or words to explain.

Lesson 7:   Round multi-digit numbers to the thousands place using the vertical number line.

©2015 Great Minds. eureka-math.org
G4-M1M2-TE-BK1-1.3.1-1.2016

115

Name _____   Date _____

1.   Round to the nearest thousand. Use the number line to model your thinking.

a.   5,900 ≈ _____

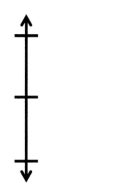

b.   4,180 ≈ _____

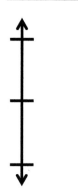

c.   32,879 ≈ _____

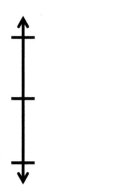

d.   78,600 ≈ _____

e.   251,031 ≈ _____

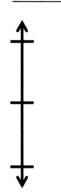

f.   699,900 ≈ _____

Lesson 7:   Round multi-digit numbers to the thousands place using the vertical
number line.

©2015 Great Minds. eureka-math.org
G4-M1M2-TE-BK1-1.3.1-1.2016

EUREKA
MATH™

2. Steven put together 981 pieces of a puzzle. About how many pieces did he put together? Round to the nearest thousand. Use what you know about place value to explain your answer.

3. Louise's family went on vacation to Disney World. Their vacation cost $5,990. Sophia's family went on vacation to Niagara Falls. Their vacation cost $4,720. Both families budgeted about $5,000 for their vacation. Whose family stayed closer to the budget? Round to the nearest thousand. Use what you know about place value to explain your answer.

4. Marsha's brother wanted help with the first question on his homework. The question asked the students to round 128,902 to the nearest thousand and then to explain the answer. Marsha's brother thought that the answer was 128,000. Was his answer correct? How do you know? Use pictures, numbers, or words to explain.

EUREKA
MATH™

Lesson 7: Round multi-digit numbers to the thousands place using the vertical number line.

©2015 Great Minds. eureka-math.org
G4-M1M2-TE-BK1-1.3.1-1.2016

117

Lesson 8

Objectives: Round multi-digit numbers to any place using the vertical number line.

Suggested Lesson Structure

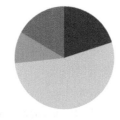

■ Fluency Practice   (12 minutes)
■ Application Problem   (6 minutes)
■ Concept Development   (32 minutes)
■ Student Debrief   (10 minutes)
   Total Time   **(60 minutes)**

Fluency Practice (12 minutes)

- Sprint: Find the Midpoint **4.NBT.3**   (9 minutes)
- Rename the Units **4.NBT.2**   (3 minutes)

Sprint: Find the Midpoint (9 minutes)

Materials: (S) Find the Midpoint Sprint

Note: Practicing this skill in isolation lays a foundation to conceptually understand rounding on a vertical number line.

Rename the Units (3 minutes)

Materials: (S) Personal white board

Note: This fluency activity applies students' place value skills in a new context that helps them better access the lesson's content.

- T: (Write 357,468.) Say the number.
- S: 357,468.
- T: (Write 357,468 = ____ thousands 468 ones.) On your personal white boards, fill in the equation.
- S: (Write 357,468 = 357 thousands 468 ones.)

Repeat process for 357,468 = ____ ten thousands 7,468 ones; 357,468 = ____ hundreds 6 tens 8 ones; and 357,468 = ____ tens 8 ones.

EUREKA MATH

Application Problem (6 minutes)

Jose's parents bought a used car, a new motorcycle, and a used snowmobile. The car cost $8,999. The motorcycle cost $9,690. The snowmobile cost $4,419. About how much money did they spend on the three items?

Note: This Application Problem builds on the content of previous lessons. Students are required to round and then to add base thousand units.

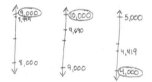

Car $8,999 ≈ $9,000
Motorcycle $9,690 ≈ $10,000
Snowmobile $4,419 ≈ $4,000
9 thousands + 10 thousands + 4 thousands = 23 thousands
Jose's parents spent about $23,000.

Concept Development (32 minutes)

Materials: (S) Personal white board

Problem 1: Use a vertical number line to round five- and six-digit numbers to the nearest ten thousand.

(Display a number line with endpoints 70,000 and 80,000.)

80 000 = 8 ten thousands
75,000 = 7 ten thousands 5 thousands
72,744 = 7 ten thousands 2 thousands
70,000 = 7 ten thousands

T: We are going to round 72,744 to the nearest ten thousand. How many ten thousands are in 72,744?

S: 7 ten thousands.

T: (Mark the lower endpoint with 7 ten thousands.) And 1 more ten thousand would be…?

S: 8 ten thousands.

T: (Mark the upper endpoint with 8 ten thousands.) What's halfway between 7 ten thousands and 8 ten thousands?

S: 7 ten thousands 5 thousands. → 75,000.

T: (Mark 75,000 on the number line.) Where should I label 72,744? Tell me where to stop. (Move your marker up the line.)

S: Stop.

T: (Mark 72,744 on the number line.)

T: Is 72,744 nearer to 70,000 or 80,000?

S: 72,744 is nearer to 70,000.

NOTES ON MULTIPLE MEANS OF REPRESENTATIONS:

An effective scaffold when working in the thousands period is to first work with an analogous number in the ones period. For example:

T: Let's round 72 to the nearest ten.

T: How many tens are in 72?

S: 7 tens.

T: What is 1 more ten?

S: 8 tens.

T: 7 tens and 8 tens are the endpoints of my number line.

T: What is the value of the halfway point?

S: 7 tens 5 ones. → Seventy-five.

T: Tell me where to stop on my number line. (Start at 70 and move up.)

S: Stop!

T: Is 72 less than halfway or more than halfway to 8 tens or 80?

S: Less than halfway.

T: We say 72 rounded to the nearest ten is 70.

T: We use the exact same process when rounding 72 thousand to the nearest ten thousand.

T: We say 72,744 rounded to the nearest ten thousand is 70,000.

Repeat with 337,601 rounded to the nearest ten thousand.

Problem 2: Use a vertical number line to round six-digit numbers to the nearest hundred thousand.

T: (Draw a number line to round 749,085 to the nearest hundred thousand.) We are going to round 749,085 to the nearest hundred thousand. How many hundred thousands are in 749,085?

S: 7 hundred thousands.

T: What's 1 more hundred thousand?

S: 8 hundred thousands.

T: Label your endpoints on the number line. What is halfway between 7 hundred thousands and 8 hundred thousands?

S: 7 hundred thousands 5 ten thousands. → 750,000.

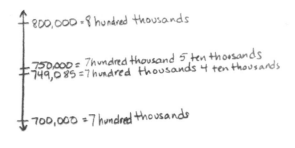

T: Designate the midpoint on the number line. With your partner, mark 749,085 on the number line, and round it to the nearest hundred thousand.

S: 749,085 is nearer to 7 hundred thousands. → 749,085 is nearest to 700,000. → 749,085 rounded to the nearest hundred thousand is 700,000.

Repeat with 908,899 rounded to the nearest hundred thousand.

Problem 3: Estimating with addition and subtraction.

T: (Write 505,341 + 193,841.) Without finding the exact answer, I can estimate the answer by first rounding each addend to the nearest hundred thousand and then adding the rounded numbers.

T: Use a number line to round both numbers to the nearest hundred thousand.

S: (Round 505,341 to 500,000. Round 193,841 to 200,000.)

MP.2

T: Now add 500,000 + 200,000.

S: 700,000.

T: So, what's a good estimate for the sum of 505,341 and 193,841?

S: 700,000.

T: (Write 35,555 − 26,555.) How can we use rounding to estimate the answer?

S: Let's round each number before we subtract.

T: Good idea. Discuss with your partner how you will round to estimate the difference.

S: I can round each number to the nearest ten thousand. That way I'll have mostly zeros in my numbers. 40,000 minus 30,000 is 10,000. → 35,555 minus 26,555 is like 35 minus 26, which is 9. 35,000 minus 26,000 is 9,000. → It's more accurate to round up. 36,000 minus 27,000 is 9,000. Hey, it's the same answer!

> **NOTES ON MULTIPLE MEANS OF ENGAGEMENT:**
>
> Make the lesson relevant to students' lives. Discuss everyday instances of estimation. Elicit examples of when a general idea about a sum or difference is necessary, rather than an exact answer. Ask, "When is it appropriate to estimate? When do we need an exact answer?"

EUREKA
MATH™

T: What did you discover?

S: It's easier to find an estimate rounded to the largest unit. → We found the same estimate even though you rounded up and I rounded down. → We got two different estimates!

T: Which estimate do you suppose is closer to the actual difference?

S: I think 9,000 is closer because we changed fewer numbers when we rounded.

T: How might we find an estimate even closer to the actual difference?

S: We could round to the nearest hundred or ten.

Problem Set (10 minutes)

Students should do their personal best to complete the Problem Set within the allotted 10 minutes. For some classes, it may be appropriate to modify the assignment by specifying which problems they work on first. Some problems do not specify a method for solving. Students should solve these problems using the RDW approach used for Application Problems.

Student Debrief (10 minutes)

Lesson Objective: Round multi-digit numbers to any place value using the vertical number line.

Invite students to review their solutions for the Problem Set and the totality of the lesson experience. They should check work by comparing answers with a partner before going over answers as a class. Look for misconceptions or misunderstandings that can be addressed in the Student Debrief. Guide students in a conversation to debrief the Problem Set.

Any combination of the questions below may be used to lead the discussion.

- Compare Problem 1(b) and (c). How did you determine your endpoints for each number line?

- Tell your partner your steps for rounding a number. Which step is most difficult for you? Why?

- Look at Problem 5. How did your estimates compare? What did you notice as you solved?

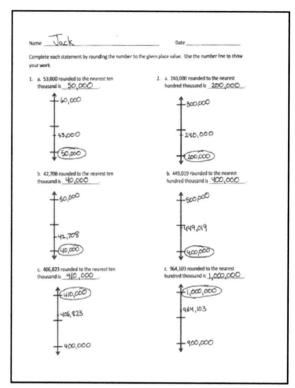

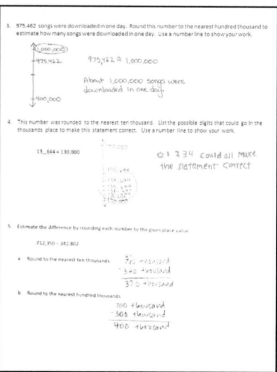

- What are the benefits and drawbacks of rounding the same number to different units (as you did in Problem 5)?
- In what real life situation might you make an estimate like Problem 5?

Write and complete one of the following statements in your math journal:

- The purpose of rounding addends is _____.
- Rounding to the nearest _____ is best when _____.

Exit Ticket (3 minutes)

After the Student Debrief, instruct students to complete the Exit Ticket. A review of their work will help with assessing students' understanding of the concepts that were presented in today's lesson and planning more effectively for future lessons. The questions may be read aloud to the students.

Lesson 8:   Round multi-digit numbers to any place using the vertical number line.

©2015 Great Minds. eureka-math.org
G4-M1M2-TE-BK1-1.3.1-1.2016

A

Number Correct: _____

Find the Midpoint

1.	0	10		23.	6000	7000	
2.	0	100		24.	600	700	
3.	0	1000		25.	60	70	
4.	10	20		26.	260	270	
5.	100	200		27.	9260	9270	
6.	1000	2000		28.	80	90	
7.	30	40		29.	90	100	
8.	300	400		30.	990	1000	
9.	400	500		31.	9990	10,000	
10.	20	30		32.	440	450	
11.	30	40		33.	8300	8400	
12.	40	50		34.	680	690	
13.	50	60		35.	9400	9500	
14.	500	600		36.	3900	4000	
15.	5000	6000		37.	2450	2460	
16.	200	300		38.	7080	7090	
17.	300	400		39.	3200	3210	
18.	700	800		40.	8630	8640	
19.	5700	5800		41.	8190	8200	
20.	70	80		42.	2510	2520	
21.	670	680		43.	4890	4900	
22.	6700	6800		44.	6660	6670	

Lesson 8:   Round multi-digit numbers to any place using the vertical number line.

123

B

G4-M1M2-TE-BK1-1.3.1-1.2016

Number Correct: _____

Improvement: _____

Find the Midpoint

1.	10	20	
2.	100	200	
3.	1000	2000	
4.	20	30	
5.	200	300	
6.	2000	3000	
7.	40	50	
8.	400	500	
9.	500	600	
10.	30	40	
11.	40	50	
12.	50	60	
13.	60	70	
14.	600	700	
15.	6000	7000	
16.	300	400	
17.	400	500	
18.	800	900	
19.	5800	5900	
20.	80	90	
21.	680	690	
22.	6800	6900	

23.	7000	8000	
24.	700	800	
25.	70	80	
26.	270	280	
27.	9270	9280	
28.	80	90	
29.	90	100	
30.	990	1000	
31.	9990	10,000	
32.	450	460	
33.	8400	8500	
34.	580	590	
35.	9500	9600	
36.	2900	3000	
37.	3450	3460	
38.	6080	6090	
39.	4200	4210	
40.	7630	7640	
41.	7190	7200	
42.	3510	3520	
43.	5890	5900	
44.	7770	7780	

Lesson 8:   Round multi-digit numbers to any place using the vertical number line.

EUREKA MATH™

Name _____ Date _____

Complete each statement by rounding the number to the given place value. Use the number line to show your work.

1. a. 53,000 rounded to the nearest ten thousand is _____.

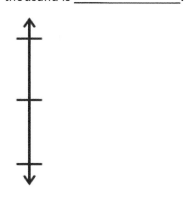

2. a. 240,000 rounded to the nearest hundred thousand is _____.

b. 42,708 rounded to the nearest ten thousand is _____.

b. 449,019 rounded to the nearest hundred thousand is _____.

c. 406,823 rounded to the nearest ten thousand is _____.

c. 964,103 rounded to the nearest hundred thousand is _____.

EUREKA MATH™

Lesson 8:   Round multi-digit numbers to any place using the vertical number line.

125

3. 975,462 songs were downloaded in one day. Round this number to the nearest hundred thousand to estimate how many songs were downloaded in one day. Use a number line to show your work.

4. This number was rounded to the nearest ten thousand. List the possible digits that could go in the thousands place to make this statement correct. Use a number line to show your work.

13_ ,644 ≈ 130,000

5. Estimate the difference by rounding each number to the given place value.

712,350 – 342,802

a. Round to the nearest ten thousands.

b. Round to the nearest hundred thousands.

Lesson 8:   Round multi-digit numbers to any place using the vertical number line.

©2015 Great Minds. eureka-math.org
G4-M1M2-TE-BK1-1.3.1-1.2016

Name _____   Date _____

1. Round to the nearest ten thousand. Use the number line to model your thinking.

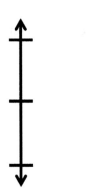

    a. 35,124 ≈ _____

    b. 981,657 ≈ _____

2. Round to the nearest hundred thousand. Use the number line to model your thinking.

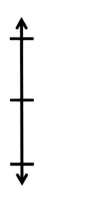

    a. 89,678 ≈ _____

    b. 999,765 ≈ _____

3. Estimate the sum by rounding each number to the nearest hundred thousand.

    257,098 + 548,765 ≈ _____

Name _____   Date _____

Complete each statement by rounding the number to the given place value. Use the number line to show your work.

1. a. 67,000 rounded to the nearest ten thousand is _____.

   b. 51,988 rounded to the nearest ten thousand is _____.

   c. 105,159 rounded to the nearest ten thousand is _____.

2. a. 867,000 rounded to the nearest hundred thousand is _____.

   b. 767,074 rounded to the nearest hundred thousand is _____.

   c. 629,999 rounded to the nearest hundred thousand is _____.

Lesson 8: Round multi-digit numbers to any place using the vertical number line.

EUREKA MATH™

3. 491,852 people went to the water park in the month of July. Round this number to the nearest hundred thousand to estimate how many people went to the park. Use a number line to show your work.

4. This number was rounded to the nearest hundred thousand. List the possible digits that could go in the ten thousands place to make this statement correct. Use a number line to show your work.

$$1\_9{,}644 \approx 100{,}000$$

5. Estimate the sum by rounding each number to the given place value.

$$164{,}215 + 216{,}088$$

a. Round to the nearest ten thousand.

b. Round to the nearest hundred thousand.

EUREKA
MATH™

Lesson 8: Round multi-digit numbers to any place using the vertical number line.

129

©2015 Great Minds. eureka-math.org
G4-M1M2-TE-BK1-1.3.1-1.2016

Lesson 9

Objective: Use place value understanding to round multi-digit numbers to any place value.

Suggested Lesson Structure

■ Fluency Practice   (12 minutes)
■ Application Problem   (8 minutes)
■ Concept Development   (30 minutes)
■ Student Debrief   (10 minutes)
  Total Time   **(60 minutes)**

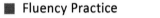

Fluency Practice (12 minutes)

- Multiply by Ten **4.NBT.1**   (5 minutes)
- Round to Different Place Values **4.NBT.3**   (7 minutes)

Multiply by Ten (5 minutes)

Materials: (S) Personal white board

Note: This fluency activity deepens the students' foundation of multiplying by ten.

T: (Write 10 × 10 =_____.) Say the multiplication sentence.
S: 10 × 10 = 100.
T: (Write 10 × _____ ten = 100.) On your personal white boards, fill in the blank.
S: (Write 10 × 1 ten = 100.)
T: (Write _____ ten × _____ ten = 100.) On your boards, fill in the blanks.
S: (Write 1 ten × 1 ten = 100.)
T: (Write _____ ten × _____ ten = _____hundred.) On your boards, fill in the blanks.
S: (Write 1 ten × 1 ten = 1 hundred.)

Repeat process for possible sequence: 1 ten × 20 =_____, 1 ten × 40 = _____ hundreds, 1 ten × _____= 700, and 4 tens × 1 ten = _____ hundreds.

Note: The use of the digit or a unit is intentional. It builds understanding of multiplying by different units (6 ones times 1 ten equals 6 tens, so 6 tens times 1 ten equals 6 hundreds, not 6 tens).

Lesson 9:   Use place value understanding to round multi-digit numbers to any
                            place value.

EUREKA MATH™

Round to Different Place Values (7 minutes)

Materials: (S) Personal white board

Note: This fluency activity reviews Lesson 8's objective and lays a foundation for today's lesson.

T: (Write 63,941.) Say the number.

S: 63,941.

T: Round 63,941 to the nearest ten thousand. Between what 2 ten thousands is 63,941?

S: 6 ten thousands and 7 ten thousands.

T: On your boards, draw a vertical number line with 60,000 and 70,000 as endpoints.

S: (Draw a vertical number line with 60,000 and 70,000 as the endpoints.)

T: What's halfway between 60,000 and 70,000?

S: 65,000.

T: Label 65,000 as the midpoint on your number line. Label 63,941 on your number line.

S: (Label 63,941 below 65,000 on their number lines.)

T: (Write 63,941 ≈ _____.) On your boards, fill in the blank, rounding 63,941 to the nearest ten thousand.

S: (Write 63,941 ≈ 60,000.)

Repeat process for 63,941 rounded to the nearest thousand; 47,261 rounded to the nearest ten thousand; 47,261 rounded to the nearest thousand; 618,409 rounded to the nearest hundred thousand; 618,409 rounded to the nearest ten thousand; and 618,904 rounded to the nearest thousand.

Application Problem (8 minutes)

34,123 people attended a basketball game. 28,310 people attended a football game. About how many more people attended the basketball game than the football game? Round to the nearest ten thousand to find the answer. Does your answer make sense? What might be a better way to compare attendance?

Note: The Application Problem builds on the concept learned in the previous lesson (**4.NBT.3**) and on **3.NBT.2**. Students are required to round and then to subtract using base thousand units. Students have not practiced an algorithm for subtracting with five digits. Due to the rounded numbers, you may show subtraction using unit form as an alternative method (34 thousand − 28 thousand, instead of 34,000 − 28,000).

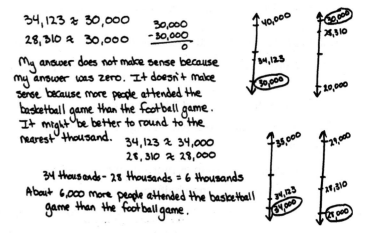

EUREKA
MATH™

Lesson 9:   Use place value understanding to round multi-digit numbers to any place value.

©2015 Great Minds. eureka-math.org
G4-M1M2-TE-BK1-1.3.1-1.2016

131

Concept Development (30 minutes)

Materials: (S) Personal white board

Problem 1: Rounding to the nearest thousand without using a number line.

T: (Write 4,333 ≈ _____.) Round to the nearest thousand. Between what two thousands is 4,333?

S: 4 thousands and 5 thousands.

T: What is halfway between 4,000 and 5,000?

S: 4,500.

T: Is 4,333 less than or more than halfway?

S: Less than.

T: So 4,333 is nearer to 4,000.

T: (Write 18,753 ≈_____.) Round to the nearest thousand. Tell your partner between what two thousands 18,753 is located.

S: 18 thousands and 19 thousands.

T: What is halfway between 18 thousands and 19 thousands?

S: 18,500.

T: Round 18,753 to the nearest thousand. Tell your partner if 18,753 is more than or less than halfway.

S: 18,753 is more than halfway. 18,753 is nearer to 19,000. → 18,753 rounded to the nearest thousand is 19,000.

NOTES ON MULTIPLE MEANS OF REPRESENTATION:

Students who have difficulty visualizing 4,333 as having 4 thousands 3 hundreds could benefit from writing the number on their place value chart. In doing so, they will be able to see that 4,333 has 43 hundreds. This same strategy could also be used for other numbers.

Repeat with 346,560 rounded to the nearest thousand.

Problem 2: Rounding to the nearest ten thousand or hundred thousand without using a vertical line.

T: (Write 65,600 ≈ _____.) Round to the nearest ten thousand. Between what two ten thousands is 65,600?

S: 6 ten thousands and 7 ten thousands.

T: What is halfway between 60,000 and 70,000?

S: 65,000.

T: Is 65,600 less than or more than halfway?

S: 65,600 is more than halfway.

T: Tell your partner what 65,600 is when rounded to the nearest ten thousand.

S: 65,600 rounded to the nearest ten thousand is 70,000.

Repeat with 548,253 rounded to the nearest ten thousand.

Lesson 9:   Use place value understanding to round multi-digit numbers to any place value.

©2015 Great Minds. eureka-math.org
G4-M1M2-TE-BK1-1.3.1-1.2016

T: (Write 676,000 ≈ _____.) Round 676,000 to the nearest hundred thousand. First tell your partner what your endpoints will be.

S: 600,000 and 700,000.

T: Determine the halfway point.

S: 650,000.

T: Is 676,000 greater than or less than the halfway point?

S: Greater than.

T: Tell your partner what 676,000 is when rounded to the nearest hundred thousand.

S: 676,000 rounded to the nearest hundred thousand is 700,000.

T: (Write 203,301 ≈ _____.) Work with your partner to round 203,301 to the nearest hundred thousand.

T: Explain to your partner how we use the midpoint to round without a number line.

S: We can't look at a number line, so we have to use mental math to find our endpoints and halfway point. → If we know the midpoint, we can see if the number is greater than or less than the midpoint. → When rounding, the midpoint helps determine which endpoint the rounded number is closer to.

Problem 3: Rounding to any value without using a number line.

T: (Write 147,591 ≈ _____.) Whisper read this number to your partner in standard form. Now, round 147,591 to the nearest hundred thousand.

S: 100,000.

T: Excellent. (Write 147,591 ≈ 100,000. Point to 100,000.) 100,000 has zero ones in the ones place, zero tens in the tens place, zero hundreds in the hundreds place, zero thousands in the thousands place, and zero ten thousands in the ten thousands place. I could add, subtract, multiply, or divide with this rounded number much easier than with 147,591. True? But, what if I wanted a more accurate estimate? Give me a number closer to 147,591 that has (point) a zero in the ones, tens, hundreds, and thousands.

S: 150,000.

T: Why not 140,000?

S: 147,591 is closer to 150,000 because it is greater than the halfway point 145,000.

T: Great. 147,591 rounded to the nearest ten thousand is 150,000. Now let's round 147,591 to the nearest thousand.

S: 148,000.

$$147,591 ≈ 100,000$$
$$147,591 ≈ 150,000$$
$$147,591 ≈ 148,000$$
$$147,591 ≈ 147,600$$
$$147,591 ≈ 147,590$$

NOTES ON MULTIPLE MEANS OF ENGAGEMENT:

Challenge students who are above grade level to look at the many ways that they rounded the number 147,591 to different place values. Have them discuss with a partner what they notice about the rounded numbers. Students should notice that when rounding to the hundred thousands, the answer is 100,000, but when rounding to all of the other places, the answers are closer to 150,000. Have them discuss what this can teach them about rounding.

Lesson 9:   Use place value understanding to round multi-digit numbers to any place value.

©2015 Great Minds. eureka-math.org
G4-M1M2-TE-BK1-1.3.1-1.2016

133

T: Work with your partner to round 147,591 to the nearest hundred and then the nearest ten.

S: 147,591 rounded to the nearest hundred is 147,600. 147,591 rounded to the nearest ten is 147,590.

MP.3

T: Compare estimates of 147,591 after rounding to different units. What do you notice? When might it be better to round to a larger unit? When might it be better to round to a smaller unit?

S: (Discuss.)

Problem Set (10 minutes)

Students should do their personal best to complete the Problem Set within the allotted 10 minutes. For some classes, it may be appropriate to modify the assignment by specifying which problems they work on first. Some problems do not specify a method for solving. Students should solve these problems using the RDW approach used for Application Problems.

Student Debrief (10 minutes)

Lesson Objective: Use place value understanding to round multi-digit numbers to any place value.

Invite students to review their solutions for the Problem Set and the totality of the lesson experience. They should check work by comparing answers with a partner before going over answers as a class. Look for misconceptions or misunderstandings that can be addressed in the Student Debrief. Guide students in a conversation to debrief the Problem Set.

Any combination of the questions below may be used to lead the discussion.

▪ Explain the reasoning behind your answer for Problem 2(e) and Problem 3(e).

▪ In Problem 2(e), you and your partner probably wrote different numbers that rounded to 30,000. Explain why your numbers were different. What is the smallest possible number that could round to 30,000 when rounded to the nearest ten

Lesson 9:   Use place value understanding to round multi-digit numbers to any place value.

©2015 Great Minds. eureka-math.org
G4-M1M2-TE-BK1-1.3.1-1.2016

EUREKA MATH

thousand? What is the largest possible number that could round to 30,000 when rounded to the nearest ten thousand? Explain your reasoning. (Use Problem 3(e) for further discussion.)

▪ Was there any difficulty in solving Problem 3(d)? Explain your strategy when solving this problem.

▪ In Problem 4(b), the newspaper rounded to the nearest hundred thousand inappropriately. What unit should the newspaper have rounded to, and why?

▪ How is rounding without a number line easier? How is it more challenging?

▪ How does knowing how to round mentally assist you in everyday life?

▪ What strategy do you use when observing a number to be rounded?

Exit Ticket (3 minutes)

After the Student Debrief, instruct students to complete the Exit Ticket. A review of their work will help with assessing students' understanding of the concepts that were presented in today's lesson and planning more effectively for future lessons. The questions may be read aloud to the students.

EUREKA MATH™

Lesson 9:   Use place value understanding to round multi-digit numbers to any place value.

©2015 Great Minds. eureka-math.org
G4-M1M2-TE-BK1-1.3.1-1.2016

135

Name _____ Date _____

1. Round to the nearest thousand.

    a. 5,300 ≈ _____

    b. 4,589 ≈ _____

    c. 42,099 ≈ _____

    d. 801,504 ≈ _____

    e. Explain how you found your answer for Part (d).

2. Round to the nearest ten thousand.

    a. 26,000 ≈ _____

    b. 34,920 ≈ _____

    c. 789,091 ≈ _____

    d. 706,286 ≈ _____

    e. Explain why two problems have the same answer. Write another number that has the same answer when rounded to the nearest ten thousand.

3. Round to the nearest hundred thousand.

    a. 840,000 ≈ _____

    b. 850,471 ≈ _____

    c. 761,004 ≈ _____

    d. 991,965 ≈ _____

    e. Explain why two problems have the same answer. Write another number that has the same answer when rounded to the nearest hundred thousand.

Lesson 9: Use place value understanding to round multi-digit numbers to any place value.

EUREKA
MATH™

4. Solve the following problems using pictures, numbers, or words.

   a. The 2012 Super Bowl had an attendance of just 68,658 people. If the headline in the newspaper the next day read, "About 70,000 People Attend Super Bowl," how did the newspaper round to estimate the total number of people in attendance?

   b. The 2011 Super Bowl had an attendance of 103,219 people. If the headline in the newspaper the next day read, "About 200,000 People Attend Super Bowl," is the newspaper's estimate reasonable? Use rounding to explain your answer.

   c. According to the problems above, about how many more people attended the Super Bowl in 2011 than in 2012? Round each number to the largest place value before giving the estimated answer.

EUREKA
MATH™

Lesson 9:   Use place value understanding to round multi-digit numbers to any
place value.

©2015 Great Minds. eureka-math.org
G4-M1M2-TE-BK1-1.3.1-1.2016

137

Name _____   Date _____

1. Round 765,903 to the given place value:

    Thousand   _____

    Ten thousand   _____

    Hundred thousand   _____

2. There are 16,850 Star coffee shops around the world. Round the number of shops to the nearest thousand and ten thousand. Which answer is more accurate? Explain your thinking using pictures, numbers, or words.

Lesson 9:   Use place value understanding to round multi-digit numbers to any
                                place value.
©2015 Great Minds. eureka-math.org
G4-M1M2-TE-BK1-1.3.1-1.2016

EUREKA
MATH™

Name _____   Date _____

1. Round to the nearest thousand.

    a. 6,842 ≈ _____   b. 2,722 ≈ _____

    c. 16,051 ≈ _____   d. 706,421 ≈ _____

    e. Explain how you found your answer for Part (d).

2. Round to the nearest ten thousand.

    a. 88,999 ≈ _____   b. 85,001 ≈ _____

    c. 789,091 ≈ _____   d. 905,154 ≈ _____

    e. Explain why two problems have the same answer. Write another number that has the same answer when rounded to the nearest ten thousand.

3. Round to the nearest hundred thousand.

    a. 89,659 ≈ _____   b. 751,447 ≈ _____

    c. 617,889 ≈ _____   d. 817,245 ≈ _____

    e. Explain why two problems have the same answer. Write another number that has the same answer when rounded to the nearest hundred thousand.

©2015 Great Minds. eureka-math.org
G4-M1M2-TE-BK1-1.3.1-1.2016

4. Solve the following problems using pictures, numbers, or words.

a. At President Obama's inauguration in 2013, the newspaper headlines stated there were about 800,000 people in attendance. If the newspaper rounded to the nearest hundred thousand, what is the largest number and smallest number of people who could have been there?

b. At President Bush's inauguration in 2005, the newspaper headlines stated there were about 400,000 people in attendance. If the newspaper rounded to the nearest ten thousand, what is the largest number and smallest number of people who could have been there?

c. At President Lincoln's inauguration in 1861, the newspaper headlines stated there were about 30,000 people in attendance. If the newspaper rounded to the nearest thousand, what is the largest number and smallest number of people who could have been there?

Lesson 9: Use place value understanding to round multi-digit numbers to any place value.

©2015 Great Minds. eureka-math.org
G4-M1M2-TE-BK1-1.3.1-1.2016

EUREKA
MATH

Lesson 10

Objective: Use place value understanding to round multi-digit numbers to any place value using real world applications.

Suggested Lesson Structure

■ Fluency Practice   (12 minutes)
■ Application Problem   (6 minutes)
□ Concept Development   (30 minutes)
■ Student Debrief   (12 minutes)

   Total Time   **(60 minutes)**

Fluency Practice (12 minutes)

▪ Sprint: Round to the Nearest 10,000 **4.NBT.3**   (9 minutes)
▪ Multiply by 10 **4.NBT.1**   (3 minutes)

Sprint: Round to the Nearest 10,000 (9 minutes)

Materials: (S) Round to the nearest 10,000 Sprint

Note: This fluency activity reviews Lesson 9's content and work toward automatizing rounding skills.

Multiply by 10 (3 minutes)

Materials: (S) Personal white board

Note: This fluency activity deepens student understanding of base ten units.

   T: (Write $10 \times 10 =$____.) Say the multiplication sentence.
   S: $10 \times 10 = 100$.
   T: (Write ____ten $\times$ 10 = 100.) On your personal white boards, fill in the blank.
   S: (Write 1 ten $\times$ 10 = 100.)
   T: (Write ____ten $\times$ ____ten = 100.) On your boards, fill in the blanks.
   S: (Write 1 ten $\times$ 1 ten = 100.)
   T: (Write ____ten $\times$ ____ten = ____hundred.) On your boards, fill in the blanks.
   S: (Write 1 ten $\times$ 1 ten = 1 hundred.)

Repeat using the following sequence: 1 ten $\times$ 50 =____, 1 ten $\times$ 80 = ____hundreds, 1 ten $\times$ ____= 600, and 3 tens $\times$ 1 ten = ____hundreds.

Note: Watch for students who say 3 tens $\times$ 4 tens is 12 tens rather than 12 hundreds.

Application Problem (6 minutes)

The post office sold 204,789 stamps last week and 93,061 stamps this week. About how many more stamps did the post office sell last week than this week? Explain how you got your answer.

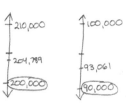

204,789 ≈ 200,000

93,061 ≈ 90,000

200 thousands - 90 thousands = 110 thousands
The post office sold about 110,000 more stamps last week than this week. I got my answer by rounding to the nearest ten thousand and then subtracting.

Note: This Application Problem builds on the concept of the previous lesson (rounding multi-digit numbers to any place value) and creates a bridge to this lesson's concept (rounding using real world applications).

Concept Development (30 minutes)

Materials: (S) Personal white board

Problem 1: Round one number to multiple units.

- T: Write 935,292 ≈ _____. Read it to your partner, and round to the nearest hundred thousand.
- S: 900,000.
- T: It is 900,000 when we round to the largest unit. What's the next largest unit we might round to?
- S: Ten thousands.
- T: Round to the ten thousands. Then, round to the thousands.
- S: 940,000. 935,000.
- T: What changes about the numbers when rounding to smaller and smaller units? Discuss with your partner.
- S: When you round to the largest unit, every other place will have a zero. → Rounding to the largest unit gives you the easiest number to add, subtract, multiply, or divide. → As you round to smaller units, there are not as many zeros in the number. → Rounding to smaller units gives an estimate that is closer to the actual value of the number.

$$935,292 \approx 900,000$$
$$935,292 \approx 940,000$$
$$935,292 \approx 935,000$$

Lesson 10:   Use place value understanding to round multi-digit numbers to any
place value using real world applications.

©2015 Great Minds. eureka-math.org
G4-M1M2-TE-BK1-1.3.1-1.2016

Problem 2: Determine the best estimate to solve a word problem.

Display: In the year 2012, there were 935,292 visitors to the White House.

T: Let's read together. Assume that each visitor is given a White House map. Now, use this information to predict the number of White House maps needed for visitors in 2013. Discuss with your partner how you made your estimate.

MP.3

S: I predict 940,000 maps are needed. I rounded to the nearest ten thousands place in order to make sure every visitor has a map. It is better to have more maps than not enough maps. → I predict more people may visit the White House in 2013, so I rounded to the nearest ten thousand—940,000—the only estimate that is greater than the actual number.

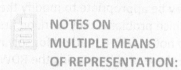

NOTES ON
MULTIPLE MEANS
OF REPRESENTATION:

For English language learners, define unfamiliar words and experiences, such as the *White House*. Give an alternative example using a more familiar tourist attraction, perhaps from their cultural experience.

Display: In the year 2011, there were 998,250 visitors to the White House.

T: Discuss with your partner how these data may change your estimate.

S: These data show the number of visitors decreased from 2011 to 2012. It may be wiser to predict 935,000 or 900,000 maps needed for 2013.

T: How can you determine the best estimate in a situation?

S: I can notice patterns or find data that might inform my estimate.

Problem 3: Choose a unit of rounding to solve a word problem.

Display: 2,837 students attend Lincoln Elementary school.

T: Discuss with your partner how you would estimate the number of chairs needed in the school.

S: I would round to the nearest thousand for an estimate of 3,000 chairs needed. If I rounded to the nearest hundred—2,800—some students may not have a seat. → I disagree. 3,000 is almost 200 too many. I would round to the nearest hundred because some students might be absent.

NOTES ON
MULTIPLE MEANS
OF ENGAGEMENT:

Challenge students working above grade level to think of at least two situations similar to that of Problem 3, where choosing the unit to which to round is important to the outcome of the problem. Have them share and discuss.

T: Compare the effect of rounding to the largest unit in this problem and Problem 2.

S: In Problem 2, rounding to the largest unit resulted in a number less than the actual number. By contrast, when we rounded to the largest unit in Problem 3, our estimate was greater.

$2{,}837 \approx 3{,}000$

$2{,}837 \approx 2{,}800$

T: What can you conclude?

$2{,}837 \approx 2{,}840$

S: Rounding to the largest unit may not always be a reliable estimate. → I will choose the unit based on the situation and what is most reasonable.

EUREKA MATH™

Lesson 10:   Use place value understanding to round multi-digit numbers to any place value using real world applications.

143

©2015 Great Minds. eureka-math.org
G4-M1M2-TE-BK1-1.3.1-1.2016

Problem Set (10 minutes)

Students should do their personal best to complete the Problem Set within the allotted 10 minutes. For some classes, it may be appropriate to modify the assignment by specifying which problems they work on first. Some problems do not specify a method for solving. Students should solve these problems using the RDW approach used for Application Problems.

Student Debrief (12 minutes)

Lesson Objective: Use place value understanding to round multi-digit numbers to any place value using real world applications.

Invite students to review their solutions for the Problem Set and the totality of the lesson experience. They should check work by comparing answers with a partner before going over answers as a class. Look for misconceptions or misunderstandings that can be addressed in the Student Debrief. Guide students in a conversation to debrief the Problem Set.

Any combination of the questions below may be used to lead the discussion.

- In Problem 3, why didn't rounding to the nearest hundred work? Would rounding to the nearest thousand have worked better? What does this show you about rounding?

- When estimating, how do you choose to which unit you will round? Would it have been more difficult to solve Problem 5 if you rounded both numbers to the hundreds? Why or why not?

- In Problem 5, how does rounding one number up and one number down affect the answer? The plane can actually make between 8 and 9 trips. How might you revise the units to which you round to estimate this answer more accurately?

- Notice, in Problem 5, that 65,000 rounded to 70,000 and that 7,460 rounded to 7,000. What is the relationship between 7,000 and 70,000? How does this relationship make it easier to determine the number of trips?

- In Problem 1, how do your estimates compare?

Name Jack _____ Date _____

1. Round 543,982 to the nearest

   a. thousand: 544,000

   b. ten thousand: 540,000

   c. hundred thousand: 500,000

2. Complete each statement by rounding the number to the given place value.

   a. 2,841 rounded to the nearest hundred is 2,800

   b. 32,851 rounded to the nearest hundred is 32,900

   c. 132,891 rounded to the nearest hundred is 132,900

   d. 6,299 rounded to the nearest thousand is 6,000

   e. 36,599 rounded to the nearest thousand is 37,000

   f. 100,699 rounded to the nearest thousand is 101,000

   g. 40,984 rounded to the nearest ten thousand is 40,000

   h. 54,984 rounded to the nearest ten thousand is 50,000

   i. 997,010 rounded to the nearest ten thousand is 1,000,000

   j. 360,034 rounded to the nearest hundred thousand is 400,000

   k. 436,709 rounded to the nearest hundred thousand is 400,000

   l. 852,442 rounded to the nearest hundred thousand is 900,000

3. Empire Elementary School needs to purchase water bottles for field day. There are 2,142 students. Principal Vadar rounded to the nearest hundred to estimate how many water bottles to order. Will there be enough water bottles for everyone? Explain.

   2,142 ≈ 2,100

   There will not be enough water bottles because 2,142 rounded to the nearest hundred is 2,100. If Principal Vadar orders 2,100, there will be 42 students without water.

4. Opening day at the New York State Fair in 2012 had an attendance of 46,753. Decide which place value to round 46,753 to if you were writing a newspaper article. Round the number and explain why it is an appropriate unit to round the attendance to.

   I would round 46,753 to the ten thousands place to get 50,000. For a newspaper article, saying approximately 50,000 were in attendance is a nice round number that is pretty close to the actual number.

5. A jet airplane holds about 65,000 gallons of gas. It uses about 7,460 gallons when flying between New York City and Los Angeles. Round each number to the largest place value. Then find about how many trips the plane can take between cities before running out of fuel.

   65,000 ≈ 70,000
   7,460 ≈ 7,000

   The plane can take about 10 trips between cities before running out of fuel

Lesson 10:   Use place value understanding to round multi-digit numbers to any place value using real world applications.

EUREKA MATH

- How do you choose a best estimate? What is the advantage of rounding to smaller and larger units?
- Why might you round up, even though the numbers tell you to round down?

Exit Ticket (3 minutes)

After the Student Debrief, instruct students to complete the Exit Ticket. A review of their work will help with assessing students' understanding of the concepts that were presented in today's lesson and planning more effectively for future lessons. The questions may be read aloud to the students.

Lesson 10: Use place value understanding to round multi-digit numbers to any place value using real world applications.

©2015 Great Minds. eureka-math.org
G4-M1M2-TE-BK1-1.3.1-1.2016

145

A

Number Correct: _____

Round to the Nearest 10,000

1.	21,000 ≈	
2.	31,000 ≈	
3.	41,000 ≈	
4.	541,000 ≈	
5.	49,000 ≈	
6.	59,000 ≈	
7.	69,000 ≈	
8.	369,000 ≈	
9.	62,000 ≈	
10.	712,000 ≈	
11.	28,000 ≈	
12.	37,000 ≈	
13.	137,000 ≈	
14.	44,000 ≈	
15.	56,000 ≈	
16.	456,000 ≈	
17.	15,000 ≈	
18.	25,000 ≈	
19.	35,000 ≈	
20.	235,000 ≈	
21.	75,000 ≈	
22.	175,000 ≈	

23.	185,000 ≈	
24.	85,000 ≈	
25.	95,000 ≈	
26.	97,000 ≈	
27.	98,000 ≈	
28.	198,000 ≈	
29.	798,000 ≈	
30.	31,200 ≈	
31.	49,300 ≈	
32.	649,300 ≈	
33.	64,520 ≈	
34.	164,520 ≈	
35.	17,742 ≈	
36.	917,742 ≈	
37.	38,396 ≈	
38.	64,501 ≈	
39.	703,280 ≈	
40.	239,500 ≈	
41.	708,170 ≈	
42.	188,631 ≈	
43.	777,499 ≈	
44.	444,919 ≈	

Lesson 10:   Use place value understanding to round multi-digit numbers to any place value using real world applications.

EUREKA
MATH

B

Number Correct: _____

Improvement: _____

Round to the Nearest 10,000

1.	11,000 ≈	
2.	21,000 ≈	
3.	31,000 ≈	
4.	531,000 ≈	
5.	39,000 ≈	
6.	49,000 ≈	
7.	59,000 ≈	
8.	359,000 ≈	
9.	52,000 ≈	
10.	612,000 ≈	
11.	18,000 ≈	
12.	27,000 ≈	
13.	127,000 ≈	
14.	34,000 ≈	
15.	46,000 ≈	
16.	346,000 ≈	
17.	25,000 ≈	
18.	35,000 ≈	
19.	45,000 ≈	
20.	245,000 ≈	
21.	65,000 ≈	
22.	165,000 ≈	

23.	185,000 ≈	
24.	85,000 ≈	
25.	95,000 ≈	
26.	96,000 ≈	
27.	99,000 ≈	
28.	199,000 ≈	
29.	799,000 ≈	
30.	21,200 ≈	
31.	39,300 ≈	
32.	639,300 ≈	
33.	54,520 ≈	
34.	154,520 ≈	
35.	27,742 ≈	
36.	927,742 ≈	
37.	28,396 ≈	
38.	54,501 ≈	
39.	603,280 ≈	
40.	139,500 ≈	
41.	608,170 ≈	
42.	177,631 ≈	
43.	888,499 ≈	
44.	444,909 ≈	

Lesson 10: Use place value understanding to round multi-digit numbers to any place value using real world applications.

147

Name _____ Date _____

1. Round 543,982 to the nearest

   a. thousand: _____.

   b. ten thousand: _____.

   c. hundred thousand: _____.

2. Complete each statement by rounding the number to the given place value.

   a. 2,841 rounded to the nearest hundred is _____.

   b. 32,851 rounded to the nearest hundred is _____.

   c. 132,891 rounded to the nearest hundred is _____.

   d. 6,299 rounded to the nearest thousand is _____.

   e. 36,599 rounded to the nearest thousand is _____.

   f. 100,699 rounded to the nearest thousand is _____.

   g. 40,984 rounded to the nearest ten thousand is _____.

   h. 54,984 rounded to the nearest ten thousand is _____.

   i. 997,010 rounded to the nearest ten thousand is _____.

   j. 360,034 rounded to the nearest hundred thousand is _____.

   k. 436,709 rounded to the nearest hundred thousand is _____.

   l. 852,442 rounded to the nearest hundred thousand is _____.

Lesson 10: Use place value understanding to round multi-digit numbers to any place value using real world applications.

©2015 Great Minds. eureka-math.org
G4-M1M2-TE-BK1-1.3.1-1.2016

3. Empire Elementary School needs to purchase water bottles for field day. There are 2,142 students. Principal Vadar rounded to the nearest hundred to estimate how many water bottles to order. Will there be enough water bottles for everyone? Explain.

4. Opening day at the New York State Fair in 2012 had an attendance of 46,753. Decide which place value to round 46,753 to if you were writing a newspaper article. Round the number and explain why it is an appropriate unit to round the attendance to.

5. A jet airplane holds about 65,000 gallons of gas. It uses about 7,460 gallons when flying between New York City and Los Angeles. Round each number to the largest place value. Then, find about how many trips the plane can take between cities before running out of fuel.

EUREKA
MATH™

Lesson 10:   Use place value understanding to round multi-digit numbers to any
             place value using real world applications.

149

©2015 Great Minds. eureka-math.org
G4-M1M2-TE-BK1-1.3.1-1.2016

Name _____ Date _____

1. There are 598,500 Apple employees in the United States.
   a. Round the number of employees to the given place value.

      thousand: _____

      ten thousand: _____

      hundred thousand: _____

   b. Explain why two of your answers are the same.

2. A company developed a student survey so that students could share their thoughts about school. In 2011, 78,234 students across the United States were administered the survey. In 2012, the company planned to administer the survey to 10 times as many students as were surveyed in 2011. About how many surveys should the company have printed in 2012? Explain how you found your answer.

Lesson 10:   Use place value understanding to round multi-digit numbers to any place value using real world applications.

©2015 Great Minds. eureka-math.org
G4-M1M2-TE-BK1-1.3.1-1.2016

EUREKA
MATH

Name _____ Date _____

1. Round 845,001 to the nearest

   a. thousand: _____.

   b. ten thousand: _____.

   c. hundred thousand: _____.

2. Complete each statement by rounding the number to the given place value.

   a. 783 rounded to the nearest hundred is _____.

   b. 12,781 rounded to the nearest hundred is _____.

   c. 951,194 rounded to the nearest hundred is _____.

   d. 1,258 rounded to the nearest thousand is _____.

   e. 65,124 rounded to the nearest thousand is _____.

   f. 99,451 rounded to the nearest thousand is _____.

   g. 60,488 rounded to the nearest ten thousand is _____.

   h. 80,801 rounded to the nearest ten thousand is _____.

   i. 897,100 rounded to the nearest ten thousand is _____.

   j. 880,005 rounded to the nearest hundred thousand is _____.

   k. 545,999 rounded to the nearest hundred thousand is _____.

   l. 689,114 rounded to the nearest hundred thousand is _____.

Lesson 10:   Use place value understanding to round multi-digit numbers to any place value using real world applications.

151

©2015 Great Minds. eureka-math.org
G4-M1M2-TE-BK1-1.3.1-1.2016

3. Solve the following problems using pictures, numbers, or words.

   a. In the 2011 New York City Marathon, 29,867 men finished the race, and 16,928 women finished the race. Each finisher was given a t-shirt. About how many men's shirts were given away? About how many women's shirts were given away? Explain how you found your answers.

   b. In the 2010 New York City Marathon, 42,429 people finished the race and received a medal. Before the race, the medals had to be ordered. If you were the person in charge of ordering the medals and estimated how many to order by rounding, would you have ordered enough medals? Explain your thinking.

   c. In 2010, 28,357 of the finishers were men, and 14,072 of the finishers were women. About how many more men finished the race than women? To determine your answer, did you round to the nearest ten thousand or thousand? Explain.

Name _____   Date _____

1. a. Arrange the following numbers in order from least to greatest:

504,054   4,450   505,045   44,500

b. Use the words *ten times* to tell how you ordered the two smallest numbers using words, pictures, or numbers.

2. Compare using >, <, or =. Write your answer inside the circle.

a. 1 hundred thousand   ◯   10,000

b. 200 thousands 4 hundreds   ◯   204,000

c. 7 hundreds + 4 thousands + 27 ones   ◯   6 thousands + 4 hundreds

d. 1,000,000   ◯   10 hundred thousands

3. The football stadium at Louisiana State University (LSU) has a seating capacity of 92,542.

   a. According to the 2010 census, the population of San Jose, CA, was approximately ten times the amount of people that LSU's stadium can seat. What was the population of San Jose in 2010?

   b. Write the seating capacity of the LSU stadium in words and in expanded form.

   c. Draw two separate number lines to round the LSU stadium's seating capacity to the nearest ten thousand and to the nearest thousand.

©2015 Great Minds. eureka-math.org
G4-M1M2-TE-BK1-1.3.1-1.2016

EUREKA
MATH

d. Compare the stadium's seating rounded to the nearest ten thousand and the seating rounded to the nearest thousand using >, <, or =.

e. Which estimate (rounding to the nearest ten thousand or nearest thousand) is more accurate? Use words and numbers to explain.

Generalize place value understanding for multi-digit whole numbers.

4.NBT.1	Recognize that in a multi-digit whole number, a digit in one place represents ten times what it represents in the place to its right. *For example, recognize that 700 ÷ 70 = 10 by applying concepts of place value and division.*
4.NBT.2	Read and write multi-digit whole numbers using base-ten numerals, number names, and expanded form. Compare two multi-digit numbers based on meanings of the digits in each place, using >, =, and < symbols to record the results of comparisons.
4.NBT.3	Use place value understanding to round multi-digit whole numbers to any place.

Evaluating Student Learning Outcomes

A Progression Toward Mastery chart is provided to describe steps that illuminate the gradually increasing understandings that students develop *on their way to proficiency.* In this chart, this progress is presented from left (Step 1) to right (Step 4). The learning goal for students is to achieve Step 4 mastery. These steps are meant to help teachers and students identify and celebrate what the students CAN do now and what they need to work on next.

A Progression Toward Mastery				
Assessment Task Item and Standards Assessed	**STEP 1** Little evidence of reasoning without a correct answer. (1 Point)	**STEP 2** Evidence of some reasoning without a correct answer. (2 Points)	**STEP 3** Evidence of some reasoning with a correct answer or evidence of solid reasoning with an incorrect answer. (3 Points)	**STEP 4** Evidence of solid reasoning with a correct answer. (4 Points)
1 **4.NBT.1**	The student arranged two numbers and provided no clear explanation for Part (b).	The student arranged two numbers in order or arranged the least and greatest numbers correctly. The student provided some explanation of *ten times*.	The student arranged three or four numbers correctly but was unable to articulate the relationship of the two smallest numbers using the words *ten times*.	The student correctly: ▪ Arranged the numbers in the following order: 4,450; 44,500; 504,054; 505,045. ▪ Used the words *ten times* to describe the relationship between 4,450 and 44,500.

EUREKA MATH™

A Progression Toward Mastery

| **2**

4.NBT.2 | The student correctly answered one problem. | The student correctly answered two problems. | The student correctly answered three problems. | The student correctly answered all four problems:

a. >
b. <
c. <
d. = |
| --- | --- | --- | --- | --- |
| **3**

4.NBT.1
4.NBT.2
4.NBT.3 | The student correctly answered one part or was able to answer some parts with partial accuracy. | The student correctly answered two of the five parts. | The student correctly answered three or four of the five parts but was unable to reason in Part (e). | The student correctly answered all five problems:

a. 925,420

b. 90,000 + 2,000 + 500 + 40 + 2. Ninety-two thousand, five hundred forty-two.

c. Draws two number lines showing the number rounded to 90,000 and 93,000.

d. 90,000 < 93,000

e. Explains rounding to the nearest thousand is more accurate because rounding to a smaller unit gives a more accurate estimate, so the difference will be closer to the exact number. |

Module 1:   Place Value, Rounding, and Algorithms for Addition and Subtraction   **157**

©2015 Great Minds. eureka-math.org
G4-M1M2-TE-BK1-1.3.1-1.2016

Name ___Jack_____   Date _____

1.

a. Arrange the following numbers in order from least to greatest.

504,054   4,450   505,045   44,500

4,450   44,500   504,054   505,045

b. Use the words "ten times" to tell how you ordered the two smallest numbers using words,
pictures and numbers.

44,500 is ten times 4,450 so it comes after 4,450 when
going from smallest to greatest

TM	Th	H	T	O
	4	4	5	0
4	4	5	0	0

Because 44,500 is
ten times 4,450,
the digits shift left
one place value

2. Compare using >, <, or =. Write your answer inside the circle.

a. 1 hundred thousand   (>)   10,000

100,000

b. 200 thousands 4 hundreds   (<)   204,000

200,400

c. 7 hundreds + 4 thousands + 2 ones   6 thousands + 4 hundreds

4,722   6,400

d. 1,000,000   (=)   10 hundred thousands

EUREKA
MATH™

3. The football stadium at Louisiana State University (LSU) has a seating capacity of 92,542.

   a. According to the 2010 census, the population of San Jose, CA was approximately ten times the amount of people that LSU's stadium can seat. What was the population of San Jose in 2010?

   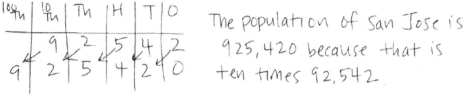

   The population of San Jose is 925,420 because that is ten times 92,542

   b. Write the seating capacity of the LSU stadium in words and in expanded form.

   90,000 + 2,000 + 500 + 40 + 2
   Ninety-two thousand five hundred forty-two.

   c. Draw two separate number lines to round the LSU stadium's seating capacity to the nearest ten thousand and to the nearest thousand.

   Ten Thousands
   ↑ 100,000
   — 92,542
   — (90,000)

   Thousands
   ↑ (93,000)
   — 92,542
   — 92,000

   d. Compare the stadium's seating rounded to the nearest ten thousand and the seating rounded to the nearest thousand using >, <, or =.
   90,000 < 93,000

   e. Which estimate (rounding to the nearest ten thousand or nearest thousand) is more accurate? Use words and numbers to explain.

   Rounding to the nearest thousands is more accurate because the actual number, 92,542, is closer to 93,000 than 90,000. Rounding to a smaller place value is more accurate because it will be closer to the actual number. That's why for this problem, rounding to the thousands gave me an estimate closer to the actual number than rounding to the ten thousands.

©2015 Great Minds. eureka-math.org
G4-M1M2-TE-BK1-1.3.1-1.2016

Topic D
Multi-Digit Whole Number Addition

4.OA.3, 4.NBT.4, 4.NBT.1, 4.NBT.2

Focus Standard:	4.OA.3	Solve multistep word problems posed with whole numbers and having whole-number answers using the four operations, including problems in which remainders must be interpreted. Represent these problems using equations with a letter standing for the unknown quantity. Assess the reasonableness of answers using mental computation and estimation strategies including rounding.
	4.NBT.4	Fluently add and subtract multi-digit whole numbers using the standard algorithm.
Instructional Days:	2	
Coherence -Links from:	G3–M2	Place Value and Problem Solving with Units of Measure
-Links to:	G5–M1	Place Value and Decimal Fractions

Moving away from special strategies for addition, students develop fluency with the standard addition algorithm (**4.NBT.4**). Students compose larger units to add like base ten units, such as composing 10 hundreds to make 1 thousand and working across the numbers unit by unit (ones with ones, thousands with thousands). Recording of regrouping occurs on the line under the addends as shown to the right. For example, in the ones column, students do not record the 0 in the ones column and the 1 above the tens column, instead students record 10, writing the 1 under the tens column and then a 0 in the ones column. They practice and apply the algorithm within the context of word problems and assess the reasonableness of their answers using rounding (**4.OA.3**). When using tape diagrams to model word problems, students use a variable to represent the unknown quantity.

$$\begin{array}{r} 755,206 \\ +89,814 \\ \hline 845,020 \end{array}$$

A Teaching Sequence Toward Mastery of Multi-Digit Whole Number Addition

Objective 1: Use place value understanding to fluently add multi-digit whole numbers using the standard addition algorithm, and apply the algorithm to solve word problems using tape diagrams.
(Lesson 11)

Objective 2: Solve multi-step word problems using the standard addition algorithm modeled with tape diagrams, and assess the reasonableness of answers using rounding.
(Lesson 12)

Lesson 11

Objective: Use place value understanding to fluently add multi-digit whole numbers using the standard addition algorithm, and apply the algorithm to solve word problems using tape diagrams.

Suggested Lesson Structure

■ Fluency Practice   (12 minutes)
■ Application Problem   (7 minutes)
□ Concept Development   (30 minutes)
■ Student Debrief   (11 minutes)

Total Time   **(60 minutes)**

Fluency Practice (12 minutes)

- Round to Different Place Values **4.NBT.3**   (5 minutes)
- Multiply by 10 **3.NBT.3**   (4 minutes)
- Add Common Units **3.NBT.2**   (3 minutes)

Round to Different Place Values (5 minutes)

Materials: (S) Personal white board

Note: This fluency activity reviews rounding skills that are building toward mastery.

    T: (Write 3,941.) Say the number. We are going to round this number to the nearest thousand.

    T: How many thousands are in 3,941?

    S: 3 thousands.

    T: (Label the lower endpoint of a vertical number line with 3,000.) And 1 more thousand is…?

    S: 4 thousands.

    T: (Mark the upper endpoint with 4,000.) Draw the same number line.

    S: (Draw number line.)

    T: What is halfway between 3,000 and 4,000?

    S: 3,500.

    T: Label 3,500 on your number line as I do the same. Now, label 3,941 on your number line.

    S: (Label 3,500 and 3,941.)

    T: Is 3,941 nearer to 3,000 or 4,000?

EUREKA
MATH™

Lesson 11:   Use place value understanding to fluently add multi-digit whole numbers using the standard addition algorithm, and apply the algorithm to solve word problems using tape diagrams.

©2015 Great Minds. eureka-math.org
G4-M1M2-TE-BK1-1.3.1-1.2016

161

T: (Write 3,941 ≈ _____.) Write your answer on your personal white board.

S: (Write 3,941 ≈ 4,000.)

Repeat the process for 3,941 rounded to the nearest hundred; 74,621 rounded to the nearest ten thousand and nearest thousand; and 681,904 rounded to the nearest hundred thousand, nearest ten thousand, and nearest thousand.

Multiply by 10 (4 minutes)

Materials: (S) Personal white board

Note: This fluency activity deepens student understanding of base ten units.

T: (Write 10 × _____ = 100.) Say the multiplication sentence.

S: 10 × 10 = 100.

T: (Write 10 × 1 ten = _____.) On your personal white boards, fill in the blank.

S: (Write 10 × 1 ten = 10 tens.)

T: (Write 10 tens = _____ hundred.) On your personal white boards, fill in the blank.

T: (Write _____ ten × _____ ten = 1 hundred.) On your boards, fill in the blanks.

S: (Write 1 ten × 1 ten = 1 hundred.)

Repeat the process for the following possible sequence: 1 ten × 60 = _____, 1 ten × 30 = _____ hundreds, 1 ten × _____ = 900, and 7 tens × 1 ten = _____ hundreds.

Note: Watch for students who say 3 tens × 4 tens is 12 tens rather than 12 hundreds.

Add Common Units (3 minutes)

Materials: (S) Personal white board

Note: This mental math fluency activity prepares students for understanding the importance of the algorithm.

T: (Project 303.) Say the number in unit form.

S: 3 hundreds 3 ones.

T: (Write 303 + 202 = _____.) Say the addition sentence, and answer in unit form.

S: 3 hundreds 3 ones + 2 hundreds 2 ones = 5 hundreds 5 ones.

T: Write the addition sentence on your personal white boards.

S: (Write 303 + 202 = 505.)

Repeat the process and sequence for 505 + 404; 5,005 + 5,004; 7,007 + 4,004; and 8,008 + 5,005.

Lesson 11:   Use place value understanding to fluently add multi-digit whole numbers using the standard addition algorithm, and apply the algorithm to solve word problems using tape diagrams.

©2015 Great Minds. eureka-math.org
G4-M1M2-TE-BK1-1.3.1-1.2016

EUREKA MATH™

Application Problem (7 minutes)

Meredith kept track of the calories she consumed for three
weeks. The first week, she consumed 12,490 calories, the
second week 14,295 calories, and the third week 11,116
calories. About how many calories did Meredith consume
altogether? Which of these estimates will produce a more
accurate answer: rounding to the nearest thousand or rounding
to the nearest ten thousand? Explain.

NOTES ON
MULTIPLE MEANS
OF REPRESENTATION:

For the Application Problem, students
working below grade level may need
further guidance in putting together
three addends. Help them to break it
down by putting two addends together
and then adding the third addend to
the total. Use manipulatives to
demonstrate.

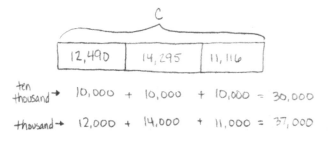

ten
thousand→   10,000 + 10,000 + 10,000 = 30,000

thousand→   12,000 + 14,000 + 11,000 = 37,000

My 2 estimates are so far apart! But rounding to
a smaller unit will always make the estimate
closer to the actual answer. So Meredith
consumed about 37,000 calories.

Note: This problem reviews rounding from Lesson 10 and can be used as an extension after the Student
Debrief to support the objective of this lesson.

Concept Development (30 minutes)

Materials: (T) Millions place value chart (Template) (S) Personal white board, millions place value chart
(Template)

Note: Using the template provided within this lesson in upcoming lessons provides students with space to
draw a tape diagram and record an addition or a subtraction problem below the place value chart.
Alternatively, the unlabeled millions place value chart template from Lesson 2 could be used along with
paper and pencil.

Problem 1: Add, renaming once, using place value disks in a place value chart.

   T: (Project vertically: 3,134 + 2,493.) Say this problem with me.
   S: Three thousand, one hundred thirty-four plus two thousand, four hundred ninety-three.
   T: Draw a tape diagram to represent this problem. What are the two parts that make up the whole?
   S: 3,134 and 2,493.
   T: Record that in the tape diagram.
   T: What is the unknown?
   S: In this case, the unknown is the whole.

Lesson 11:   Use place value understanding to fluently add multi-digit whole
numbers using the standard addition algorithm, and apply the
algorithm to solve word problems using tape diagrams.

©2015 Great Minds. eureka-math.org
G4-M1M2-TE-BK1-1.3.1-1.2016

163

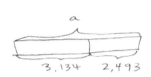

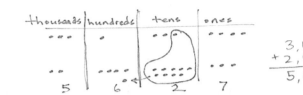

T: Show the whole above the tape diagram using a bracket and label the unknown quantity with an *a*. When a letter represents an unknown number, we call that letter a **variable**.

T: (Draw place value disks on the place value chart to represent the first part, 3,134.) Now, it is your turn. When you are done, add 2,493 by drawing more disks on your place value chart.

T: (Point to the problem.) 4 ones plus 3 ones equals?

S: 7 ones. (Count 7 ones in the chart, and record 7 ones in the problem.)

T: (Point to the problem.) 3 tens plus 9 tens equals?

S: 12 tens. (Count 12 tens in the chart.)

T: We can bundle 10 tens as 1 hundred. (Circle 10 tens disks, draw an arrow to the hundreds place, and draw the 1 hundred disk to show the regrouping.)

MP.1

T: We can represent this in writing. (Write 12 tens as 1 hundred, crossing the line, and 2 tens in the tens column so that you are writing 12 and not 2 and 1 as separate numbers. Refer to the visual above.)

T: (Point to the problem.) 1 hundred plus 4 hundreds plus 1 hundred equals?

S: 6 hundreds. (Count 6 hundreds in the chart, and record 6 hundreds in the problem.)

T: (Point to the problem.) 3 thousands plus 2 thousands equals?

S: 5 thousands. (Count 5 thousands in the chart, and record 5 thousands in the problem.)

T: Say the equation with me: 3,134 plus 2,493 equals 5,627. Label the whole in the tape diagram, above the bracket, with *a* = 5,627.

Problem 2: Add, renaming in multiple units, using the standard algorithm and the place value chart.

T: (Project vertically: 40,762 + 30,473.) With your partner, draw a tape diagram to model this problem, labeling the two known parts and the unknown whole, using the variable *B* to represent the whole. (Circulate and assist students.)

T: With your partner, write the problem, and draw disks for the first addend in your chart. Then, draw disks for the second addend.

T: (Point to the problem.) 2 ones plus 3 ones equals?

S: 5 ones. (Count the disks to confirm 5 ones, and write 5 in the ones column.)

T: 6 tens plus 7 tens equals?

EUREKA
MATH™

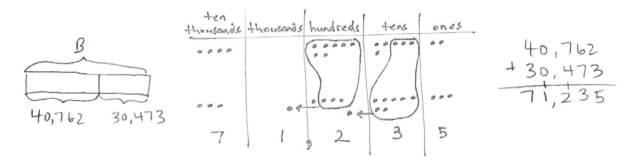

S: 13 tens. → We can group 10 tens to make 1 hundred. → We do not write two digits in one column. We can change 10 tens for 1 hundred leaving us with 3 tens.

T: (Regroup the disks.) Watch me as I record the larger unit using the addition problem. (First, record the 1 on the line in the hundreds place, and then record the 3 in the tens so that you are writing 13, not 3 then 1.)

T: 7 hundreds plus 4 hundreds plus 1 hundred equals 12 hundreds. Discuss with your partner how to record this. (Continue adding, regrouping, and recording across other units.)

T: Say the equation with me. 40,762 plus 30,473 equals 71,235. Label the whole in the tape diagram with 71,235, and write B = 71,235.

Problem 3: Add, renaming multiple units using the standard algorithm.

T: (Project: 207,426 + 128,744.) Draw a tape diagram to model this problem. Record the numbers on your personal white board.

T: With your partner, add units right to left, regrouping when necessary using the standard algorithm.

S: 207,426 + 128,744 = 336,170.

$$\begin{array}{r} 207,426 \\ + 128,744 \\ \hline 336,170 \end{array}$$

Problem 4: Solve a one-step word problem using the standard algorithm modeled with a tape diagram.

The Lane family took a road trip. During the first week, they drove 907 miles. The second week they drove the same amount as the first week plus an additional 297 miles. How many miles did they drive during the second week?

T: What information do we know?

S: We know they drove 907 miles the first week. We also know they drove 297 miles more during the second week than the first week.

T: What is the unknown information?

S: We do not know the total miles they drove in the second week.

T: Draw a tape diagram to represent the amount of miles in the first week, 907 miles. Since the Lane family drove an additional 297 miles in the second week, extend the bar for 297 more miles. What does the tape diagram represent?

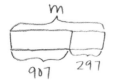

Lesson 11:   Use place value understanding to fluently add multi-digit whole numbers using the standard addition algorithm, and apply the algorithm to solve word problems using tape diagrams.

165

©2015 Great Minds. eureka-math.org
G4-M1M2-TE-BK1-1.3.1-1.2016

S: The number of miles they drove in the second week.

T: Use a bracket and label the unknown with the variable *m* for miles.

T: How do we solve for *m*?

S: $907 + 297 = m$.

T: (Check student work to see they are recording the regrouping of 10 of a smaller unit for 1 larger unit.)

T: Solve. What is *m*?

S: $m = 1,204$. (Write $m = 1,204$.)

T: Write a statement that tells your answer.

S: (Write: The Lane family drove 1,204 miles during the second week.)

Problem Set (10 minutes)

Students should do their personal best to complete the Problem Set within the allotted 10 minutes. For some classes, it may be appropriate to modify the assignment by specifying which problems they work on first. Some problems do not specify a method for solving. Students should solve these problems using the RDW approach used for Application Problems.

Student Debrief (11 minutes)

Lesson Objective: Use place value understanding to fluently add multi-digit whole numbers using the standard addition algorithm, and apply the algorithm to solve word problems using tape diagrams.

Invite students to review their solutions for the Problem Set and the totality of the lesson experience. They should check work by comparing answers with a partner before going over answers as a class. Look for misconceptions or misunderstandings that can be addressed in the Student Debrief. Guide students in a conversation to debrief the Problem Set.

Any combination of the questions below may be used to lead the discussion.

- When we are writing a sentence to express our answer, what part of the original problem helps us to tell our answer using the correct words and context?

> **NOTES ON**
> **MULTIPLE MEANS**
> **OF ACTION**
> **AND EXPRESSION:**
>
> English language learners benefit from further explanation of the word problem. Have a conversation around the following: "What do we do if we do not understand a word in the problem? What thinking can we use to figure out the answer anyway?" In this case, students do not need to know what a road trip is in order to solve. Discuss, "How is the tape diagram helpful to us?" It may be helpful to use the RDW approach: Read important information. Draw a picture. Write an equation to solve. Write the answer as a statement.

Lesson 11:   Use place value understanding to fluently add multi-digit whole numbers using the standard addition algorithm, and apply the algorithm to solve word problems using tape diagrams.

©2015 Great Minds. eureka-math.org
G4-M1M2-TE-BK1-1.3.1-1.2016

- What purpose does a tape diagram have? How does it support your work?

- What does a **variable**, like the letter *C* in Problem 2, help us do when drawing a tape diagram?

- I see different types of tape diagrams drawn for Problem 3. Some drew one bar with two parts. Some drew one bar for each addend and put the bracket for the whole on the right side of both bars. Will these diagrams result in different answers? Explain.

- In Problem 1, what did you notice was similar and different about the addends and the sums for Parts (a), (b), and (c)?

- If you have 2 addends, can you ever have enough ones to make 2 tens or enough tens to make 2 hundreds or enough hundreds to make 2 thousands? Try it out with your partner. What if you have 3 addends?

- In Problem 1(j), each addend used the numbers 2, 5, and 7 once. I do not see those digits in the sum. Why?

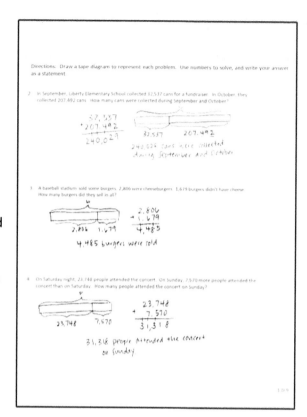

- How is recording the regrouped number in the next column when using the standard algorithm related to bundling disks?

- Have students revisit the Application Problem and solve for the actual amount of calories consumed. Which unit, when rounding, provided an estimate closer to the actual value?

Exit Ticket (3 minutes)

After the Student Debrief, instruct students to complete the Exit Ticket. A review of their work will help with assessing students' understanding of the concepts that were presented in today's lesson and planning more effectively for future lessons. The questions may be read aloud to the students.

Lesson 11:   Use place value understanding to fluently add multi-digit whole numbers using the standard addition algorithm, and apply the algorithm to solve word problems using tape diagrams.

©2015 Great Minds. eureka-math.org
G4-M1M2-TE-BK1-1.3.1-1.2016

167

Name _____   Date _____

1. Solve the addition problems below using the standard algorithm.

a.   6, 3 1 1
         +   2 6 8

b.   6, 3 1 1
         + 1, 2 6 8

c.   6, 3 1 4
         + 1, 2 6 8

d.   6, 3 1 4
         + 2, 4 9 3

e.   8, 3 1 4
         + 2, 4 9 3

f.   1 2, 3 7 8
         +   5, 4 6 3

g.   5 2, 0 9 8
         +   6, 0 4 8

h.   3 4, 6 9 8
         + 7 1, 8 4 0

i.   5 4 4, 8 1 1
         + 3 5 6, 4 4 5

j.   527 + 275 + 752

k.   38,193 + 6,376 + 241,457

Lesson 11:   Use place value understanding to fluently add multi-digit whole numbers using the standard addition algorithm, and apply the algorithm to solve word problems using tape diagrams.

©2015 Great Minds. eureka-math.org
G4-M1M2-TE-BK1-1.3.1-1.2016

EUREKA
MATH™

Draw a tape diagram to represent each problem. Use numbers to solve, and write your answer as a statement.

2. In September, Liberty Elementary School collected 32,537 cans for a fundraiser. In October, they collected 207,492 cans. How many cans were collected during September and October?

3. A baseball stadium sold some burgers. 2,806 were cheeseburgers. 1,679 burgers didn't have cheese. How many burgers did they sell in all?

4. On Saturday night, 23,748 people attended the concert. On Sunday, 7,570 more people attended the concert than on Saturday. How many people attended the concert on Sunday?

EUREKA
MATH™

Lesson 11: Use place value understanding to fluently add multi-digit whole numbers using the standard addition algorithm, and apply the algorithm to solve word problems using tape diagrams.

©2015 Great Minds. eureka-math.org
G4-M1M2-TE-BK1-1.3.1-1.2016

169

Name _____ Date _____

1. Solve the addition problems below using the standard algorithm.

   a.   2 3, 6 0 7
      + 2, 3 0 7

   b.   3, 9 4 8
      +   2 7 8

   c.   5,983 + 2,097

2. The office supply closet had 25,473 large paper clips, 13,648 medium paper clips, and 15,306 small paper clips. How many paper clips were in the closet?

Lesson 11:   Use place value understanding to fluently add multi-digit whole numbers using the standard addition algorithm, and apply the algorithm to solve word problems using tape diagrams.

EUREKA
MATH™

Name _____   Date _____

1. Solve the addition problems below using the standard algorithm.

a.   7,909
   + 1,044

b.   27,909
   + 9,740

c.   827,909
   + 42,989

d.   289,205
   + 11,845

e.   547,982
   + 114,849

f.   258,983
   + 121,897

g.   83,906
   + 35,808

h.   289,999
   + 91,849

i.   754,900
   + 245,100

EUREKA MATH™

Lesson 11:   Use place value understanding to fluently add multi-digit whole
numbers using the standard addition algorithm, and apply the
algorithm to solve word problems using tape diagrams.

©2015 Great Minds. eureka-math.org
G4-M1M2-TE-BK1-1.3.1-1.2016

171

Draw a tape diagram to represent each problem. Use numbers to solve, and write your answer as a statement.

2. At the zoo, Brooke learned that one of the rhinos weighs 4,897 pounds, one of the giraffes weighs 2,667 pounds, one of the African elephants weighs 12,456 pounds, and one of the Komodo dragons weighs 123 pounds.

    a. What is the combined weight of the zoo's African elephant and the giraffe?

    b. What is the combined weight of the zoo's African elephant and the rhino?

    c. What is the combined weight of the zoo's African elephant, the rhino, and the giraffe?

    d. What is the combined weight of the zoo's Komodo dragon and the rhino?

Lesson 11: Use place value understanding to fluently add multi-digit whole numbers using the standard addition algorithm, and apply the algorithm to solve word problems using tape diagrams.

©2015 Great Minds. eureka-math.org
G4-M1M2-TE-BK1-1.3.1-1.2016

EUREKA
MATH™

millions	hundred thousands	ten thousands	thousands	hundreds	tens	ones

millions place value chart

Lesson 11: Use place value understanding to fluently add multi-digit whole numbers using the standard addition algorithm, and apply the algorithm to solve word problems using tape diagrams.

©2015 Great Minds. eureka-math.org
G4-M1M2-TE-BK1-1.3.1-1.2016

173

Lesson 12

Objective: Solve multi-step word problems using the standard addition algorithm modeled with tape diagrams, and assess the reasonableness of answers using rounding.

Suggested Lesson Structure

■ Fluency Practice   (12 minutes)
■ Application Problem   (5 minutes)
□ Concept Development   (34 minutes)
■ Student Debrief   (9 minutes)
  Total Time   **(60 minutes)**

Fluency Practice (12 minutes)

- Round to Different Place Values **4.NBT.3**   (6 minutes)
- Find the Sum **4.NBT.4**   (6 minutes)

Round to Different Place Values (6 minutes)

Materials: (S) Personal white board

Note: This fluency activity reviews rounding skills that are building towards mastery.

  T: (Project 726,354.) Say the number.
  S: Seven hundred twenty-six thousand, three hundred fifty-four.
  T: What digit is in the hundred thousands place?
  S: 7.
  T: What is the value of the digit 7?
  S: 700,000.
  T: On your personal white boards, round the number to the nearest hundred thousand.
  S: (Write 726,354 ≈ 700,000.)

Repeat the process, rounding 726,354 to the nearest ten thousand, thousand, hundred, and ten. Follow the same process and sequence for 496,517.

Solve multi-step word problems using the standard addition algorithm modeled with tape diagrams, and assess the reasonableness of answers using rounding.
©2015 Great Minds. eureka-math.org
G4-M1M2-TE-BK1-1.3.1-1.2016

Find the Sum (6 minutes)

Materials: (S) Personal white board

Note: This fluency activity prepares students for understanding the importance of the algorithm.

- T: (Write 417 + 232 =_____.) Solve by writing horizontally or vertically.
- S: (Write 417 + 232 = 649.)

Repeat the process and sequence for 7,073 + 2,312; 13,705 + 4,412; 3,949 + 451; 538 + 385 + 853; and 23,944 + 6,056 + 159,368.

Application Problem (5 minutes)

The basketball team raised a total of $154,694 in September and $29,987 more in October than in September. How much money did they raise in October? Draw a tape diagram, and write your answer in a complete sentence.

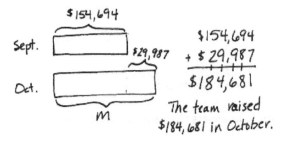

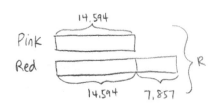

NOTES ON
MULTIPLE MEANS
OF REPRESENTATION:

Students working below grade level may have difficulty conceptualizing word problems. Use smaller numbers or familiar contexts for problems. Have students make sense of the problem, and direct them through the process of creating a tape diagram.

"The pizza shop sold five pepperoni pizzas on Friday. They sold ten more sausage pizzas than pepperoni pizzas. How many pizzas did they sell?"

Have a discussion about the two unknowns in the problem and about which unknown needs to be solved first. Students may draw a picture to help them solve. Then, relate the problem to that with bigger numbers and numbers that involve regrouping. Relay the message that it is the same process. The difference is that the numbers are bigger.

Note: This is a comparative word problem that reviews the addition algorithm practiced in the last lesson.

Concept Development (34 minutes)

Materials: (S) Personal white board

Problem 1: Solve a multi-step word problem using a tape diagram.

The city flower shop sold 14,594 pink roses on Valentine's Day. They sold 7,857 more red roses than pink roses. How many pink and red roses did the city flower shop sell altogether on Valentine's Day? Use a tape diagram to show the work.

EUREKA
MATH™

Lesson 12:   Solve multi-step word problems using the standard addition algorithm modeled with tape diagrams, and assess the reasonableness of answers using rounding.

©2015 Great Minds. eureka-math.org
G4-M1M2-TE-BK1-1.3.1-1.2016

175

T: Read the problem with me. What information do we know?

S: We know they sold 14,594 pink roses.

T: To model this, let's draw one tape to represent the pink roses. Do we know how many red roses were sold?

S: No, but we know that there were 7,857 more red roses sold than pink roses.

T: A second tape can represent the number of red roses sold. (Model on the tape diagram.)

T: What is the problem asking us to find?

S: The total number of roses.

T: We can draw a bracket to the side of both tapes. Let's label it R for pink and red roses.

MP.2

T: First, solve to find how many red roses were sold.

S: (Solve 14,594 + 7,857 = 22,451.)

T: What does the bottom tape represent?

S: The bottom tape represents the number of red roses, 22,451.

T: (Bracket and label 22,451 to show the total number of red roses.) Now, we need to find the total number of roses sold. How do we solve for R?

S: Add the totals for both tapes together. 14,594 + 22,451 = R.

T: Solve with me. What does R equal?

S: R equals 37,045.

T: (Write R = 37,045.) Let's write a statement of the answer.

S: (Write: The city flower shop sold 37,045 pink and red roses on Valentine's Day.)

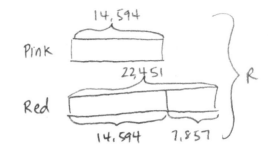

Problem 2: Solve a two-step word problem using a tape diagram, and assess the reasonableness of the answer.

On Saturday, 32,736 more bus tickets were sold than on Sunday. On Sunday, only 17,295 tickets were sold. How many people bought bus tickets over the weekend? Use a tape diagram to show the work.

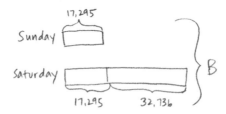

T: Tell your partner what information we know.

S: We know how many people bought bus tickets on Sunday, 17,295. We also know how many more people bought tickets on Saturday. But we do not know the total number of people that bought tickets on Saturday.

T: Let's draw a tape for Sunday's ticket sales and label it. How can we represent Saturday's ticket sales?

S: Draw a tape the same length as Sunday's, and extend it further for 32,736 more tickets.

T: What does the problem ask us to solve for?

S: The number of people that bought tickets over the weekend.

T: With your partner, finish drawing a tape diagram to model this problem. Use *B* to represent the total number of tickets bought over the weekend.

T: Before we solve, estimate to get a general sense of what our answer will be. Round each number to the nearest ten thousand.

S: (Write 20,000 + 20,000 + 30,000 = 70,000.) About 70,000 tickets were sold over the weekend.

T: Now, solve with your partner to find the actual number of tickets sold over the weekend.

S: (Solve.)

S: *B* equals 67,326.

T: (Write *B* = 67,326.)

T: Now, let's look back at the estimate we got earlier and compare with our actual answer. Is 67,326 close to 70,000?

S: Yes, 67,326 rounded to the nearest ten thousand is 70,000.

T: Our answer is reasonable.

T: Write a statement of the answer.

S: (Write: There were 67,326 people who bought bus tickets over the weekend.)

> **NOTES ON MULTIPLE MEANS OF REPRESENTATION:**
>
> English language learners may need direction in creating their answer in the form of a sentence. Direct them to look back at the question and then to verbally answer the question using some of the words in the question. Direct them to be sure to provide a label for their numerical answer.

Problem 3: Solve a multi-step word problem using a tape diagram, and assess reasonableness.

Last year, Big Bill's Department Store sold many pairs of footwear. 118,214 pairs of boots were sold, 37,092 more pairs of sandals than pairs of boots were sold, and 124,417 more pairs of sneakers than pairs of boots were sold. How many pairs of footwear were sold last year?

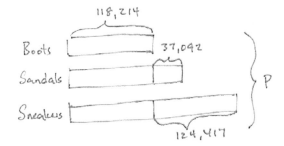

$$118{,}214 + 37{,}092 = \text{sandals} = 155{,}306$$

$$118{,}214 + 124{,}417 = \text{sneakers} = 242{,}631$$

$$155{,}306 + 242{,}631 + 118{,}214 = 516{,}151$$

516,151 pairs of footwear were sold last year.

T: Discuss with your partner the information we have and the unknown information we want to find.

S: (Discuss.)

Lesson 12:   Solve multi-step word problems using the standard addition algorithm modeled with tape diagrams, and assess the reasonableness of answers using rounding.

©2015 Great Minds. eureka-math.org
G4-M1M2-TE-BK1-1.3.1-1.2016

177

T: With your partner, draw a tape diagram to model this problem. How do you solve for *P*?

S: The tape shows me I could add the number of pairs of boots 3 times, and then add 37,092 and 124,417. → You could find the number of pairs of sandals, find the number of pairs of sneakers, and then add those totals to the number of pairs of boots.

Have students then round each addend to get an estimated answer, calculate precisely, and compare to see if their answers are reasonable.

Problem Set (10 minutes)

Students should do their personal best to complete the Problem Set within the allotted 10 minutes. For some classes, it may be appropriate to modify the assignment by specifying which problems they work on first. Some problems do not specify a method for solving. Students should solve these problems using the RDW approach used for Application Problems.

Student Debrief (9 minutes)

Lesson Objective: Solve multi-step word problems using the standard addition algorithm modeled with tape diagrams, and assess the reasonableness of answers using rounding.

The Student Debrief is intended to invite reflection and active processing of the total lesson experience.

Invite students to review their solutions for the Problem Set. They should check work by comparing answers with a partner before going over answers as a class. Look for misconceptions or misunderstandings that can be addressed in the Student Debrief. Guide students in a conversation to debrief the Problem Set and process the lesson.

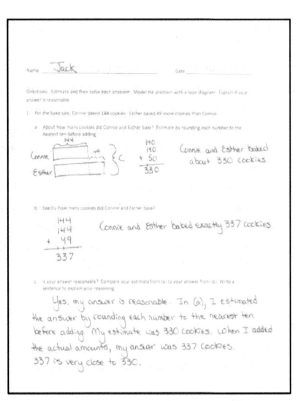

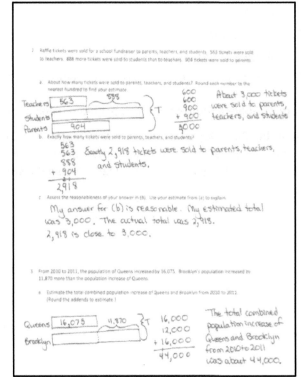

Lesson 12:   Solve multi-step word problems using the standard addition algorithm
                                modeled with tape diagrams, and assess the reasonableness of
                                answers using rounding.
                          ©2015 Great Minds. eureka-math.org
                          G4-M1M2-TE-BK1-1.3.1-1.2016

EUREKA MATH™

Any combination of the questions below may be used to lead the discussion.

- Explain why we should test to see if our answers are reasonable. (Show an example of one of the above Concept Development problems solved incorrectly to show how checking the reasonableness of an answer is important.)

- When might you need to use an estimate in real life?

- Let's check the reasonableness of our answer in the Application Problem.

    - Round to the nearest ten thousand.

    - Note that rounding to the ten thousands brings our estimate closer to the actual answer than if we were to round to the nearest hundred thousand.

    - Discuss the margin of error that occurs in estimating answers and how this relates to the place value to which you round.

- In Problem 1, how would your estimate be affected if you rounded all numbers to the nearest hundred?

- What are the next steps if your estimate is not near the actual answer? Consider the example we discussed earlier where the problem was solved incorrectly. Because we had estimated an answer, we knew that our solution was not reasonable.

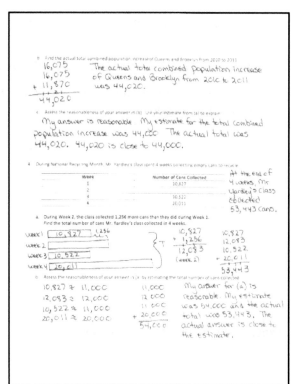

Exit Ticket (3 minutes)

After the Student Debrief, instruct students to complete the Exit Ticket. A review of their work will help with assessing students' understanding of the concepts that were presented in today's lesson and planning more effectively for future lessons. The questions may be read aloud to the students.

Lesson 12:   Solve multi-step word problems using the standard addition algorithm
modeled with tape diagrams, and assess the reasonableness of
answers using rounding.
©2015 Great Minds. eureka-math.org
G4-M1M2-TE-BK1-1.3.1-1.2016

179

Name _____ Date _____

Estimate and then solve each problem. Model the problem with a tape diagram. Explain if your answer is reasonable.

1. For the bake sale, Connie baked 144 cookies. Esther baked 49 more cookies than Connie.

    a. About how many cookies did Connie and Esther bake? Estimate by rounding each number to the nearest ten before adding.

    b. Exactly how many cookies did Connie and Esther bake?

    c. Is your answer reasonable? Compare your estimate from (a) to your answer from (b). Write a sentence to explain your reasoning.

Lesson 12: Solve multi-step word problems using the standard addition algorithm modeled with tape diagrams, and assess the reasonableness of answers using rounding.

©2015 Great Minds. eureka-math.org
G4-M1M2-TE-BK1-1.3.1-1.2016

EUREKA
MATH

2. Raffle tickets were sold for a school fundraiser to parents, teachers, and students. 563 tickets were sold to teachers. 888 more tickets were sold to students than to teachers. 904 tickets were sold to parents.

   a. About how many tickets were sold to parents, teachers, and students? Round each number to the nearest hundred to find your estimate.

   b. Exactly how many tickets were sold to parents, teachers, and students?

   c. Assess the reasonableness of your answer in (b). Use your estimate from (a) to explain.

EUREKA
MATH™

Lesson 12:   Solve multi-step word problems using the standard addition algorithm
                modeled with tape diagrams, and assess the reasonableness of
                answers using rounding.
©2015 Great Minds. eureka-math.org
G4-M1M2-TE-BK1-1.3.1-1.2016

181

3. From 2010 to 2011, the population of Queens increased by 16,075. Brooklyn's population increased by 11,870 more than the population increase of Queens.

a. Estimate the total combined population increase of Queens and Brooklyn from 2010 to 2011. (Round the addends to estimate.)

b. Find the actual total combined population increase of Queens and Brooklyn from 2010 to 2011.

c. Assess the reasonableness of your answer in (b). Use your estimate from (a) to explain.

Solve multi-step word problems using the standard addition algorithm modeled with tape diagrams, and assess the reasonableness of answers using rounding.

©2015 Great Minds. eureka-math.org
G4-M1M2-TE-BK1-1.3.1-1.2016

EUREKA
MATH

4. During National Recycling Month, Mr. Yardley's class spent 4 weeks collecting empty cans to recycle.

Week	Number of Cans Collected
1	10,827
2	
3	10,522
4	20,011

a. During Week 2, the class collected 1,256 more cans than they did during Week 1. Find the total number of cans Mr. Yardley's class collected in 4 weeks.

b. Assess the reasonableness of your answer in (a) by estimating the total number of cans collected.

EUREKA
MATH™

Lesson 12: Solve multi-step word problems using the standard addition algorithm modeled with tape diagrams, and assess the reasonableness of answers using rounding.

©2015 Great Minds. eureka-math.org
G4-M1M2-TE-BK1-1.3.1-1.2016

183

Name _____ Date _____

Model the problem with a tape diagram. Solve and write your answer as a statement.

In January, Scott earned $8,999. In February, he earned $2,387 more than in January. In March, Scott earned the same amount as in February. How much did Scott earn altogether during those three months? Is your answer reasonable? Explain.

EUREKA
MATH™

Name _____ Date _____

Estimate and then solve each problem. Model the problem with a tape diagram. Explain if your answer is reasonable.

1. There were 3,905 more hits on the school's website in January than February. February had 9,854 hits. How many hits did the school's website have during both months?

   a. About how many hits did the website have during January and February?

   b. Exactly how many hits did the website have during January and February?

   c. Is your answer reasonable? Compare your estimate from (a) to your answer from (b). Write a sentence to explain your reasoning.

Lesson 12: Solve multi-step word problems using the standard addition algorithm modeled with tape diagrams, and assess the reasonableness of answers using rounding.

©2015 Great Minds. eureka-math.org
G4-M1M2-TE-BK1-1.3.1-1.2016

185

2. On Sunday, 77,098 fans attended a New York Jets game. The same day, 3,397 more fans attended a New York Giants game than attended the Jets game. Altogether, how many fans attended the games?

   a. What was the actual number of fans who attended the games?

   b. Is your answer reasonable? Round each number to the nearest thousand to find an estimate of how many fans attended the games.

Lesson 12:   Solve multi-step word problems using the standard addition algorithm modeled with tape diagrams, and assess the reasonableness of answers using rounding.
©2015 Great Minds. eureka-math.org
G4-M1M2-TE-BK1-1.3.1-1.2016

EUREKA MATH

3. Last year on Ted's farm, his four cows produced the following number of liters of milk:

Cow	Liters of Milk Produced
Daisy	5,098
Betsy	
Mary	9,980
Buttercup	7,087

a. Betsy produced 986 more liters of milk than Buttercup. How many liters of milk did all 4 cows produce?

b. Is your answer reasonable? Explain.

EUREKA
MATH™

Lesson 12:   Solve multi-step word problems using the standard addition algorithm
modeled with tape diagrams, and assess the reasonableness of
answers using rounding.
©2015 Great Minds. eureka-math.org
G4-M1M2-TE-BK1-1.3.1-1.2016

187

Mathematics Curriculum

4
GRADE

GRADE 4 • MODULE 1

Topic E

Multi-Digit Whole Number Subtraction

4.OA.3, 4.NBT.4, 4.NBT.1, 4.NBT.2

Focus Standard:	4.OA.3	Solve multistep word problems posed with whole numbers and having whole-number answers using the four operations, including problems in which remainders must be interpreted. Represent these problems using equations with a letter standing for the unknown quantity. Assess the reasonableness of answers using mental computation and estimation strategies including rounding.
	4.NBT.4	Fluently add and subtract multi-digit whole numbers using the standard algorithm.
Instructional Days:	4	
Coherence -Links from:	G3–M2	Place Value and Problem Solving with Units of Measure
-Links to:	G5–M1	Place Value and Decimal Fractions

Following the introduction of the standard algorithm for addition in Topic D, the standard algorithm for subtraction replaces special strategies for subtraction in Topic E. Moving slowly from smaller to larger minuends, students practice decomposing larger units into smaller units. First, only one decomposition is introduced, where one zero may appear in the minuend. As in Grades 2 and 3, students continue to decompose all necessary digits before performing the algorithm, allowing subtraction from left to right, or, as taught in the lessons, from right to left. Students use the algorithm to subtract numbers from 1 million allowing for multiple decompositions (**4.NBT.4**). The topic concludes with practicing the standard algorithm for subtraction in the context of two-step word problems where students have to assess the reasonableness of their answers by rounding (**4.OA.3**). When using tape diagrams to model word problems, students use a variable to represent the unknown quantity.

$$\begin{array}{r} \overset{3}{\cancel{4}}\,\overset{11}{\cancel{1}}\,\overset{9}{\cancel{0}},\,\overset{10}{\cancel{0}}\,\overset{5}{\cancel{6}}\,\overset{11}{\cancel{1}} \\ -\ \ 56{,}328 \\ \hline 363{,}733 \end{array}$$

EUREKA
MATH™

A Teaching Sequence Toward Mastery of Multi-Digit Whole Number Subtraction

Objective 1: Use place value understanding to decompose to smaller units once using the standard subtraction algorithm, and apply the algorithm to solve word problems using tape diagrams.
(Lesson 13)

Objective 2: Use place value understanding to decompose to smaller units up to three times using the standard subtraction algorithm, and apply the algorithm to solve word problems using tape diagrams.
(Lesson 14)

Objective 3: Use place value understanding to fluently decompose to smaller units multiple times in any place using the standard subtraction algorithm, and apply the algorithm to solve word problems using tape diagrams.
(Lesson 15)

Objective 4: Solve two-step word problems using the standard subtraction algorithm fluently modeled with tape diagrams, and assess the reasonableness of answers using rounding.
(Lesson 16)

Lesson 13

Objective: Use place value understanding to decompose to smaller units once using the standard subtraction algorithm, and apply the algorithm to solve word problems using tape diagrams.

Suggested Lesson Structure

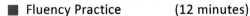

■ Fluency Practice   (12 minutes)
▨ Application Problem   (5 minutes)
▢ Concept Development   (35 minutes)
■ Student Debrief   (8 minutes)

  Total Time   **(60 minutes)**

Fluency Practice (12 minutes)

- Find the Sum **4.NBT.4**   (6 minutes)
- Subtract Common Units **4.NBT.3**   (6 minutes)

Find the Sum (6 minutes)

Materials: (S) Personal white board

Note: This math fluency activity prepares students for understanding the importance of the addition algorithm.

   T: (Write 316 + 473 =____.) Solve by writing an addition sentence horizontally or vertically.
   S: (Write 316 + 473 = 789.)

Repeat the process and sequence for 6,065 + 3,731; 13,806 + 4,393; 5,928 + 124; and 629 + 296 + 962.

Subtract Common Units (6 minutes)

Materials: (S) Personal white board

Note: This mental math fluency activity prepares students for understanding the importance of the subtraction algorithm.

   T: (Project 707.) Say the number in unit form.
   S: 7 hundreds 7 ones.
   T: (Write 707 – 202 =____.) Say the subtraction sentence and answer in unit form.
   S: 7 hundreds 7 ones – 2 hundreds 2 ones = 5 hundreds 5 ones.

Lesson 13:   Use place value understanding to decompose to smaller units once using the standard subtraction algorithm, and apply the algorithm to solve word problems using tape diagrams.

©2015 Great Minds. eureka-math.org
G4-M1M2-TE-BK1-1.3.1-1.2016

EUREKA
MATH™

T: Write the subtraction sentence on your personal white boards.

S: (Write 707 – 202 = 505.)

Repeat the process and sequence for 909 – 404; 9,009 – 5,005; 11,011 – 4,004; and 13,013 – 8,008.

Application Problem (5 minutes)

Jennifer texted 5,849 times in January. In February, she texted 1,263 more times than in January. What was the total number of texts that Jennifer sent in the two months combined? Explain how to know if the answer is reasonable.

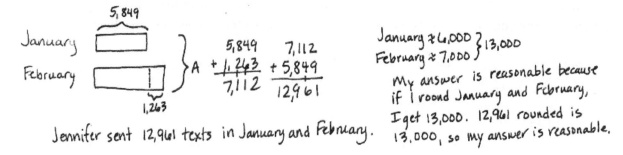

Note: This Application Problem reviews content from the previous lesson of a multi-step addition problem.

Concept Development (35 minutes)

Materials: (T) Millions place value chart (Lesson 11 Template) (S) Personal white board, millions place value chart (Lesson 11 Template)

Problem 1: Use a place value chart and place value disks to model subtracting alongside the algorithm, regrouping 1 hundred into 10 tens.

Display 4,259 – 2,171 vertically on the board.

T: Say this problem with me. (Read problem together.)

T: Watch as I draw a tape diagram to represent this problem. What is the whole?

S: 4,259.

T: We record that above the tape as the whole and record the known part of 2,171 under the tape. It is your turn to draw a tape diagram. Mark the unknown part of the diagram with the variable *A*.

T: Model the whole, 4,259, using place value disks on your place value chart.

T: Do we model the part we are subtracting?

S: No, just the whole.

Lesson 13:   Use place value understanding to decompose to smaller units once using the standard subtraction algorithm, and apply the algorithm to solve word problems using tape diagrams.

©2015 Great Minds. eureka-math.org
G4-M1M2-TE-BK1-1.3.1-1.2016

191

T: First, let's determine if we are ready to subtract. We look across the top number, from right to left, to see if there are enough units in each column. Let's look at the ones column. Are there enough ones in the top number to subtract the ones in the bottom number? (Point to the 9 and the 1 in the problem.)

S: Yes, 9 is greater than 1.

T: That means we are ready to subtract in the ones column. Let's look at the tens column. Are there enough tens in the top number to subtract the tens in the bottom number?

S: No, 5 is less than 7.

MP.6

T: (Show regrouping on the place value chart.) We ungroup or unbundle 1 unit from the hundreds to make 10 tens. I now have 1 hundred and 15 tens. Let's rename and represent the change in writing using the algorithm. (Cross out the hundreds and tens to rename them in the problem.)

T: Show the change with your disks. (Cross off 1 hundred, and change it for 10 tens as shown below.)

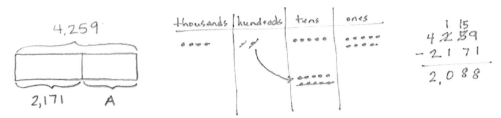

T: Are there enough hundreds in the top number to subtract the hundreds in the bottom number?

S: Yes, 1 is equal to 1.

T: Are there enough thousands in the top number to subtract the thousands in the bottom number?

S: Yes, 4 is greater than 2.

T: Are we ready to subtract?

S: Yes, we are ready to subtract.

T: (Point to the problem.) 9 ones minus 1 one?

S: 8 ones.

T: (Cross off 1 disk; write an 8 in the problem.)

T: 15 tens minus 7 tens?

S: 8 tens.

T: (Cross off 7 disks; write an 8 in the problem.)

Continue subtracting through the hundreds and thousands.

T: Say the number sentence.

S: 4,259 – 2,171 = 2,088.

T: The value of the A in our tape diagram is 2,088. We write A = 2,088 below the tape diagram. What can be added to 2,171 to result in the sum of 4,259?

S: 2,088.

Repeat the process for 6,314 – 3,133.

Lesson 13:   Use place value understanding to decompose to smaller units once using the standard subtraction algorithm, and apply the algorithm to solve word problems using tape diagrams.

©2015 Great Minds. eureka-math.org
G4-M1M2-TE-BK1-1.3.1-1.2016

EUREKA
MATH

Problem 2: Regroup 1 thousand into 10 hundreds using the subtraction algorithm.

Display 23,422 – 11,510 vertically on the board.

T: With your partner, read this problem and draw a tape diagram. Label the whole, the known part, and use the variable *B* for the unknown part.

T: Record the problem on your personal white board.

T: Look across the digits. Are we ready to subtract?

S: No.

T: Are there enough ones in the top number to subtract the ones in the bottom number? (Point to the 2 and the 0.)

S: Yes, 2 is greater than 0.

T: Are there enough tens in the top number to subtract the tens in the bottom number?

S: Yes, 2 is greater than 1.

T: Are there enough hundreds in the top number to subtract the hundreds in the bottom number?

S: No, 4 is less than 5.

T: Tell your partner how to make enough hundreds to subtract.

S: I unbundle 1 thousand to make 10 hundreds. I now have 2 thousands and 14 hundreds. → I change 1 thousand for 10 hundreds. → I rename 34 hundreds as 20 hundreds and 14 hundreds.

T: Watch as I record that. Now it is your turn.

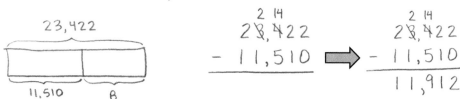

Repeat questioning for the thousands and ten thousands columns.

T: Are we ready to subtract?

S: Yes, we are ready to subtract.

T: 2 ones minus 0 ones?

S: 2 ones. (Record 2 in the ones column.)

Continue subtracting across the number from right to left, always naming the units.

T: Tell your partner what must be added to 11,510 to result in the sum of 23,422.

T: How do we check a subtraction problem?

S: We can add the difference to the part we knew at first to see if the sum we get equals the whole.

T: Please add 11,912 and 11,510. What sum do you get?

S: 23,422, so our answer to the subtraction problem is correct.

T: Label your tape diagram as *B* = 11,912.

Repeat for 29,014 – 7,503.

Lesson 13:   Use place value understanding to decompose to smaller units once using the standard subtraction algorithm, and apply the algorithm to solve word problems using tape diagrams.

©2015 Great Minds. eureka-math.org
G4-M1M2-TE-BK1-1.3.1-1.2016   **193**

Problem 3: Solve a subtraction word problem, regrouping 1 ten thousand into 10 thousands.

The paper mill produced 73,658 boxes of paper. 8,052 boxes have been sold. How many boxes remain?

T: Draw a tape diagram to represent the boxes of paper produced and sold. I will use the letter *P* to represent the boxes of paper remaining. Record the subtraction problem. Check to see that you lined up all units.

T: Am I ready to subtract?

S: No.

T: Work with your partner, asking if there are enough units in each column to subtract. Regroup when needed. Then ask, "Am I ready to subtract?" before you begin subtracting. Use the standard algorithm. (Students work.)

S: $73{,}658 - 8{,}052 = 65{,}606$.

T: The value of *P* is 65,606. In a statement, tell your partner how many boxes remain.

S: 65,606 boxes remain.

T: To check and see if your answer is correct, add the two values of the tape, 8,052 and your answer of 65,606, to see if the sum is the value of the tape, 73,658.

S: (Add to find that the sum matches the value of the tape.)

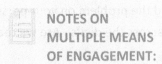

NOTES ON MULTIPLE MEANS OF ENGAGEMENT:

Ask students to look at the numbers in the subtraction problem and to think about how the numbers are related. Ask them how they might use their discovery to check to see if their answer is correct. Use the tape diagram to show if 8,052 was subtracted from 73,658 to find the unknown part of the tape diagram, the value of the unknown, 65,606, can be added to the known part of the tape diagram, 8,052. If the sum is the value of the whole tape diagram, the answer is correct.

$$\begin{array}{r} ^{6\ 13}\\ \cancel{7}\cancel{3}{,}658\\ -\ \ 8{,}052\\ \hline 65{,}606 \end{array}$$

Check

$$\begin{array}{r} 65{,}606\\ +\ \ 8{,}052\\ \hline 73{,}658\ \checkmark \end{array}$$

Repeat with the following: The library has 50,819 books. 4,506 are checked out. How many books remain in the library?

Lesson 13: Use place value understanding to decompose to smaller units once using the standard subtraction algorithm, and apply the algorithm to solve word problems using tape diagrams.

EUREKA MATH

Problem Set (10 minutes)

Students should do their personal best to complete the Problem Set within the allotted 10 minutes. For some classes, it may be appropriate to modify the assignment by specifying which problems they work on first. Some problems do not specify a method for solving. Students should solve these problems using the RDW approach used for Application Problems.

Student Debrief (8 minutes)

Lesson Objective: Use place value understanding to decompose to smaller units once using the standard subtraction algorithm, and apply the algorithm to solve word problems using tape diagrams.

The Student Debrief is intended to invite reflection and active processing of the total lesson experience.

Invite students to review their solutions for the Problem Set. They should check work by comparing answers with a partner before going over answers as a class. Look for misconceptions or misunderstandings that can be addressed in the Student Debrief. Guide students in a conversation to debrief the Problem Set and process the lesson.

Any combination of the questions below may be used to lead the discussion.

- Compare your answers for Problem 1(a) and (b). How are your answers the same when the problems are different?

- Why do the days and months matter when solving Problem 3?

- Compare Problem 1(a) and (f). Does having a larger whole in 1(a) give an answer greater than or less than 1(f)?

- In Problem 4, you used subtraction, but I can say, "I can add 52,411 to 15,614 to result in the sum of 68,025." How can we add and subtract using the same problem?

- Why do we ask, "Are we ready to subtract?"

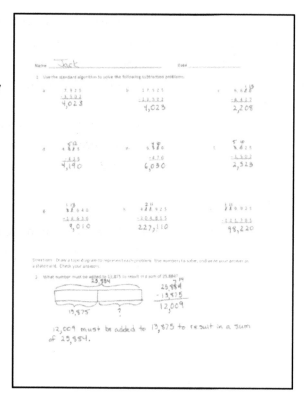

EUREKA
MATH™

Lesson 13:   Use place value understanding to decompose to smaller units once using the standard subtraction algorithm, and apply the algorithm to solve word problems using tape diagrams.

195

©2015 Great Minds. eureka-math.org
G4-M1M2-TE-BK1-1.3.1-1.2016

- After we get our top number ready to subtract, do we have to subtract in order from right to left?
- When do we need to unbundle to subtract?
- What are the benefits to modeling subtraction using place value disks?
- Why must the units line up when subtracting? How might our answer change if the digits were not aligned?
- What happens when there is a zero in the top number of a subtraction problem?
- What happens when there is a zero in the bottom number of a subtraction problem?
- When you are completing word problems, how can you tell that you need to subtract?

Exit Ticket (3 minutes)

After the Student Debrief, instruct students to complete the Exit Ticket. A review of their work will help with assessing students' understanding of the concepts that were presented in today's lesson and planning more effectively for future lessons. The questions may be read aloud to the students.

Lesson 13: Use place value understanding to decompose to smaller units once using the standard subtraction algorithm, and apply the algorithm to solve word problems using tape diagrams.

©2015 Great Minds. eureka-math.org
G4-M1M2-TE-BK1-1.3.1-1.2016

Name _____ Date _____

1. Use the standard algorithm to solve the following subtraction problems.

   a.   7, 5 2 5
       − 3, 5 0 2

   b.   1 7, 5 2 5
       − 1 3, 5 0 2

   c.   6, 6 2 5
       − 4, 4 1 7

   d.   4, 6 2 5
       −   4 3 5

   e.   6, 5 0 0
       −   4 7 0

   f.   6, 0 2 5
       − 3, 5 0 2

   g.   2 3, 6 4 0
       − 1 4, 6 3 0

   h.   4 3 1, 9 2 5
       − 2 0 4, 8 1 5

   i.   2 1 9, 9 2 5
       − 1 2 1, 7 0 5

Draw a tape diagram to represent each problem. Use numbers to solve, and write your answer as a statement. Check your answers.

2. What number must be added to 13,875 to result in a sum of 25,884?

EUREKA MATH

Lesson 13: Use place value understanding to decompose to smaller units once using the standard subtraction algorithm, and apply the algorithm to solve word problems using tape diagrams.

©2015 Great Minds. eureka-math.org
G4-M1M2-TE-BK1-1.3.1-1.2016

197

3. Artist Michelangelo was born on March 6, 1475. Author Mem Fox was born on March 6, 1946. How many years after Michelangelo was born was Fox born?

4. During the month of March, 68,025 pounds of king crab were caught. If 15,614 pounds were caught in the first week of March, how many pounds were caught in the rest of the month?

5. James bought a used car. After driving exactly 9,050 miles, the odometer read 118,064 miles. What was the odometer reading when James bought the car?

Lesson 13: Use place value understanding to decompose to smaller units once using the standard subtraction algorithm, and apply the algorithm to solve word problems using tape diagrams.

©2015 Great Minds. eureka-math.org
G4-M1M2-TE-BK1-1.3.1-1.2016

EUREKA
MATH

Name _____   Date _____

1. Use the standard algorithm to solve the following subtraction problems.

a.   8,512
     − 2,501

b.   18,042
     − 4,122

c.   8,072
     − 1,561

Draw a tape diagram to represent the following problem. Use numbers to solve. Write your answer as a statement. Check your answer.

2. What number must be added to 1,575 to result in a sum of 8,625?

EUREKA
MATH™

Lesson 13:   Use place value understanding to decompose to smaller units once
                   using the standard subtraction algorithm, and apply the algorithm to
                   solve word problems using tape diagrams.

©2015 Great Minds. eureka-math.org
G4-M1M2-TE-BK1-1.3.1-1.2016

199

Name _____   Date _____

1. Use the standard algorithm to solve the following subtraction problems.

   a.   2 , 4 3 1
        −   3 4 1

   b.   4 2 2 , 4 3 1
        −   1 4 , 3 2 1

   c.   4 2 2 , 4 3 1
        −   9 2 , 4 2 0

   d.   4 2 2 , 4 3 1
        −   3 9 2 , 4 2 0

   e.   9 8 2 , 4 3 0
        −   9 2 , 3 0 0

   f.   2 4 3 , 0 8 9
        −   1 3 7 , 0 7 9

   g.   2,431 − 920 =

   h . 892,431 − 520,800 =

2. What number must be added to 14,056 to result in a sum of 38,773?

Use place value understanding to decompose to smaller units once
using the standard subtraction algorithm, and apply the algorithm to
solve word problems using tape diagrams.

EUREKA
MATH™

Draw a tape diagram to model each problem. Use numbers to solve, and write your answers as a statement.
Check your answers.

3. An elementary school collected 1,705 bottles for a recycling program. A high school also collected some
    bottles. Both schools collected 3,627 bottles combined. How many bottles did the high school collect?

4. A computer shop sold $356,291 worth of computers and accessories. It sold $43,720 worth of
    accessories. How much did the computer shop sell in computers?

EUREKA
MATH™

Lesson 13:   Use place value understanding to decompose to smaller units once
using the standard subtraction algorithm, and apply the algorithm to
solve word problems using tape diagrams.

©2015 Great Minds. eureka-math.org
G4-M1M2-TE-BK1-1.3.1-1.2016

201

5. The population of a city is 538,381. In that population, 148,170 are children.

   a. How many adults live in the city?

   b. 186,101 of the adults are males. How many adults are female?

Use place value understanding to decompose to smaller units once using the standard subtraction algorithm, and apply the algorithm to solve word problems using tape diagrams.

EUREKA
MATH

Lesson 14

Objective: Use place value understanding to decompose to smaller units up to three times using the standard subtraction algorithm, and apply the algorithm to solve word problems using tape diagrams.

Suggested Lesson Structure

■ Fluency Practice   (10 minutes)
▨ Application Problem   (6 minutes)
▨ Concept Development   (35 minutes)
■ Student Debrief   (9 minutes)

   Total Time   **(60 minutes)**

Fluency Practice (10 minutes)

▪ Base Ten Thousand Units **4.NBT.2**   (2 minutes)
▪ Find the Difference **4.NBT.4**   (4 minutes)
▪ Convert Units **4.MD.1**   (4 minutes)

Base Ten Thousand Units (2 minutes)

Materials: (S) Personal white board

Note: This fluency activity helps students work towards mastery of understanding base ten units.

   T: (Project 8 ten thousands = _____.) Write the number in standard form.
   S: 80,000.

Continue with the following possible sequence: 9 ten thousands, 10 ten thousands, 13 ten thousands, 19 ten thousands, 20 ten thousands, 30 ten thousands, 70 ten thousands, 71 ten thousands, 90 ten thousands, and 100 ten thousands.

EUREKA MATH™

Lesson 14:   Use place value understanding to decompose to smaller units up to
              three times using the standard subtraction algorithm, and apply the
              algorithm to solve word problems using tape diagrams.

©2015 Great Minds. eureka-math.org
G4-M1M2-TE-BK1-1.3.1-1.2016

203

Find the Difference (4 minutes)

Materials: (S) Personal white board

Note: This math fluency activity prepares students for understanding the importance of the subtraction algorithm.

T: (Write 735 – 203 =_____.) Write a subtraction sentence horizontally or vertically.

S: (Write 735 – 203 = 532.)

Repeat process and sequence for 7,045 – 4,003; 845 – 18; 5,725 – 915; and 34,736 – 2,806.

Convert Units (4 minutes)

Note: Reviewing the relationship between meters and centimeters learned in Grade 3 helps prepare students to solve problems with metric measurement and to understand metric measurement's relationship to place value.

T: (Write 1 m = ___ cm.) How many centimeters are in a meter?

S: 1 m = 100 cm.

Repeat the process for 2 m, 3 m, 8 m, 8 m 50 cm, 7 m 50 cm, and 4 m 25 cm.

T: (Write 100 cm = ___ m.) Say the answer.

S: 100 cm = 1 m.

T: (Write 150 cm = ___ m ___ cm.) Say the answer.

S: 150 cm = 1 m 50 cm.

Repeat the process for 250 cm, 350 cm, 950 cm, and 725 cm.

Application Problem (6 minutes)

In one year, the animal shelter bought 25,460 pounds of dog food. That amount was 10 times the amount of cat food purchased in the month of July. How much cat food was purchased in July?

Extension: If the cats ate 1,462 pounds of the cat food, how much cat food was left?

25,460 is 10 times as many as 2,546.

2,546 pounds of cat food was purchased in the month of July.

Extension:

$$\begin{array}{r} 2\,\overset{4}{\cancel{5}}\overset{14}{\cancel{4}}6 \\ -\ 1{,}462 \\ \hline 1{,}084 \end{array}$$ 1,084 pounds of cat food was left.

Note: This Application Problem incorporates prior knowledge of 10 times as many with the objective of decomposing to smaller units in order to subtract.

Lesson 14:   Use place value understanding to decompose to smaller units up to
                                                 three times using the standard subtraction algorithm, and apply the
                                                 algorithm to solve word problems using tape diagrams.
                                      ©2015 Great Minds. eureka-math.org
                                      G4-M1M2-TE-BK1-1.3.1-1.2016

Concept Development (35 minutes)

Materials: (S) Personal white board

Problem 1: Subtract, decomposing twice.

Write 22,397 − 3,745 vertically on the board.

- T: Let's read this subtraction problem together. Watch as I draw a tape diagram labeling the whole, the known part, and the unknown part using a variable, *A*. Now, it is your turn.
- T: Record the problem on your personal white board.
- T: Look across the digits. Am I ready to subtract?
- S: No.
- T: We look across the top number to see if I have enough units in each column. Are there enough ones in the top number to subtract the ones in the bottom number?
- S: Yes, 7 ones is greater than 5 ones.
- T: Are there enough tens in the top number to subtract the tens in the bottom number?
- S: Yes, 9 tens is greater than 4 tens.
- T: Are there enough hundreds in the top number to subtract the hundreds in the bottom number?
- S: No, 3 hundreds is less than 7 hundreds. We can unbundle 1 thousand as 10 hundreds to make 1 thousand and 13 hundreds. I can subtract the hundreds column now.
- T: Watch as I record that. Now, it is your turn to record the change.
- T: Are there enough thousands in the top number to subtract the thousands in the bottom number?
- S: No, 1 thousand is less than 3 thousands. We can unbundle 1 ten thousand to 10 thousands to make 1 ten thousand and 11 thousands. I can subtract in the thousands column now.
- T: Watch as I record. Now, it is your turn to record the change.
- T: Are there enough ten thousands in the top number to subtract the ten thousands in the bottom number?
- S: Yes.
- T: Are we ready to subtract?
- S: Yes, we are ready to subtract.

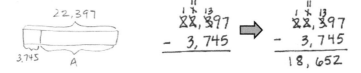

- T: 7 ones minus 5 ones?
- S: 2 ones. (Record 2 in the ones column.)

Continue subtracting across the problem, always naming the units.

- T: Say the equation with me.
- S: 22,397 minus 3,745 equals 18,652.

Lesson 14:   Use place value understanding to decompose to smaller units up to three times using the standard subtraction algorithm, and apply the algorithm to solve word problems using tape diagrams.

©2015 Great Minds. eureka-math.org
G4-M1M2-TE-BK1-1.3.1-1.2016

205

T: Check your answer using addition.

S: Our answer is correct because 18,652 plus 3,745 equals 22,397.

T: What is the value of A in the tape diagram?

S: A equals 18,652.

Problem 2: Subtract, decomposing three times.

Write 210,290 – 45,720 vertically on the board.

T: With your partner, draw a tape diagram to represent the whole, the known part, and the unknown part.

T: Record the subtraction problem on your board.

T: Look across the digits. Are we ready to subtract?

S: No.

T: Look across the top number's digits to see if we have enough units in each column. Are there enough ones in the top number to subtract the ones in the bottom number? (Point to the zeros in the ones column.)

S: Yes, 0 equals 0.

T: We are ready to subtract in the ones column. Are there enough tens in the top number to subtract the tens in the bottom number?

S: Yes, 9 is greater than 2.

T: We are ready to subtract in the tens column. Are there enough hundreds in the top number to subtract the hundreds in the bottom number?

MP.5

S: No, 2 hundreds is less than 7 hundreds.

T: There are no thousands to unbundle, so we look to the ten thousands. We can unbundle 1 ten thousand to 10 thousands. Unbundle 10 thousands to make 9 thousands and 12 hundreds. Now we can subtract the hundreds column.

Repeat questioning for the thousands, ten thousands, and hundred thousands place, recording the renaming of units in the problem.

T: Are we ready to subtract?

S: Yes, we are ready to subtract.

T: 0 ones minus 0 ones?

S: 0 ones.

T: 9 tens minus 2 tens?

S: 7 tens.

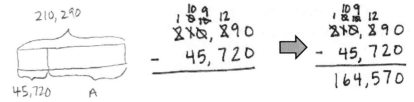

Have partners continue using the algorithm, reminding them to work right to left, always naming the units.

T: Read the equation to your partner and complete your tape diagram by labeling the variable.

S: 210,290 minus 45,720 is 164,570. (A = 164,570.)

Use place value understanding to decompose to smaller units up to three times using the standard subtraction algorithm, and apply the algorithm to solve word problems using tape diagrams.

EUREKA
MATH

Problem 3: Use the subtraction algorithm to solve a word problem, modeled with a tape diagram, decomposing units 3 times.

Bryce needed to purchase a large order of computer supplies for his company. He was allowed to spend $859,239 on computers. However, he ended up only spending $272,650. How much money was left?

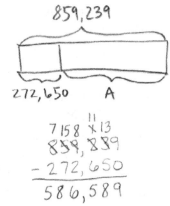

T: Read the problem with me. Tell your partner the information we know.

S: We know he can spend $859,239, and we know he only spent $272,650.

T: Draw a tape diagram to represent the information in the problem. Label the whole, the known part, and the unknown part using a variable.

T: Tell me the problem we must solve, and write it on your board.

S: $859,239 – $272,650.

T: Work with your partner to move across the digits. Are there enough in each column to subtract? Regroup when needed. Then ask, "Are we ready to subtract?" before you begin subtracting. Use the standard algorithm.

S: $859,239 – $272,650 = $586,589.

T: Say your answer as a statement.

S: $586,589 was left.

Problem Set (10 minutes)

Students should do their personal best to complete the Problem Set within the allotted 10 minutes. For some classes, it may be appropriate to modify the assignment by specifying which problems they work on first. Some problems do not specify a method for solving. Students should solve these problems using the RDW approach used for Application Problems.

Student Debrief (9 minutes)

Lesson Objective: Use place value understanding to decompose to smaller units up to three times using the standard subtraction algorithm, and apply the algorithm to solve word problems using tape diagrams.

The Student Debrief is intended to invite reflection and active processing of the total lesson experience.

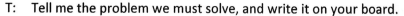

Lesson 14:   Use place value understanding to decompose to smaller units up to three times using the standard subtraction algorithm, and apply the algorithm to solve word problems using tape diagrams.   207

©2015 Great Minds. eureka-math.org
G4-M1M2-TE-BK1-1.3.1-1.2016

Invite students to review their solutions for the Problem Set. They should check work by comparing answers with a partner before going over answers as a class. Look for misconceptions or misunderstandings that can be addressed in the Student Debrief. Guide students in a conversation to debrief the Problem Set and process the lesson.

Any combination of the questions below may be used to lead the discussion.

- What pattern did you notice between Problem 1(a) and (b)?

- Explain to your partner how to solve Problem 1(e). How can you make more ones when there are not any tens from which to regroup?

- How was setting up the problem to complete Problem 4 different from setting up the other problems? What did you need to be sure to do? Why?

- How is the complexity of this lesson different from the complexity of Lesson 13?

- In which column can you begin subtracting when you are ready to subtract? (Any column.)

- You are using a variable, or a letter, to represent the unknown in each tape diagram. Tell your partner how you determine what variable to use and how it helps you to solve the problem.

- How can you check a subtraction problem?

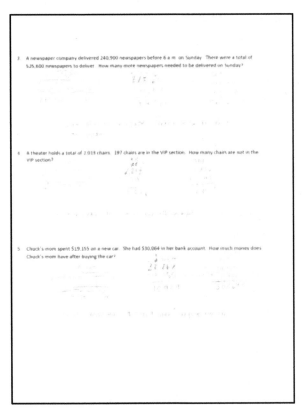

Exit Ticket (3 minutes)

After the Student Debrief, instruct students to complete the Exit Ticket. A review of their work will help with assessing students' understanding of the concepts that were presented in today's lesson and planning more effectively for future lessons. The questions may be read aloud to the students.

Lesson 14:   Use place value understanding to decompose to smaller units up to three times using the standard subtraction algorithm, and apply the algorithm to solve word problems using tape diagrams.

Name _____   Date _____

1. Use the standard algorithm to solve the following subtraction problems.

a.
$$\begin{array}{r} 2,460 \\ -1,370 \\ \hline \end{array}$$

b.
$$\begin{array}{r} 2,460 \\ -1,470 \\ \hline \end{array}$$

c.
$$\begin{array}{r} 97,684 \\ -49,700 \\ \hline \end{array}$$

d.
$$\begin{array}{r} 2,460 \\ -1,472 \\ \hline \end{array}$$

e.
$$\begin{array}{r} 124,306 \\ -31,117 \\ \hline \end{array}$$

f.
$$\begin{array}{r} 97,684 \\ -4,705 \\ \hline \end{array}$$

g.
$$\begin{array}{r} 124,006 \\ -121,117 \\ \hline \end{array}$$

h.
$$\begin{array}{r} 97,684 \\ -47,705 \\ \hline \end{array}$$

i.
$$\begin{array}{r} 124,060 \\ -31,117 \\ \hline \end{array}$$

Draw a tape diagram to represent each problem. Use numbers to solve, and write your answer as a statement. Check your answers.

2. There are 86,400 seconds in one day. If Mr. Liegel is at work for 28,800 seconds a day, how many seconds a day is he away from work?

EUREKA
MATH™

Lesson 14:   Use place value understanding to decompose to smaller units up to three times using the standard subtraction algorithm, and apply the algorithm to solve word problems using tape diagrams.

209

©2015 Great Minds. eureka-math.org
G4-M1M2-TE-BK1-1.3.1-1.2016

3. A newspaper company delivered 240,900 newspapers before 6 a.m. on Sunday. There were a total of 525,600 newspapers to deliver. How many more newspapers needed to be delivered on Sunday?

4. A theater holds a total of 2,013 chairs. 197 chairs are in the VIP section. How many chairs are not in the VIP section?

5. Chuck's mom spent $19,155 on a new car. She had $30,064 in her bank account. How much money does Chuck's mom have after buying the car?

Lesson 14:   Use place value understanding to decompose to smaller units up to three times using the standard subtraction algorithm, and apply the algorithm to solve word problems using tape diagrams.

EUREKA
MATH

Name _____ Date _____

Use the standard algorithm to solve the following subtraction problems.

1.
$$\begin{array}{r} 1\,9\,,3\,5\,0 \\ -\ \ 5\,,7\,6\,1 \\ \hline \end{array}$$

2. $32,010 - 2,546$

Draw a tape diagram to represent the following problem. Use numbers to solve, and write your answer as a statement. Check your answer.

3. A doughnut shop sold 1,232 doughnuts in one day. If they sold 876 doughnuts in the morning, how many doughnuts were sold during the rest of the day?

Lesson 14:   Use place value understanding to decompose to smaller units up to three times using the standard subtraction algorithm, and apply the algorithm to solve word problems using tape diagrams.

©2015 Great Minds. eureka-math.org
G4-M1M2-TE-BK1-1.3.1-1.2016

211

Name _____   Date _____

1 . Use the standard algorithm to solve the following subtraction problems.

a.   71,989
     −21,492

b.   371,989
     − 96,492

c.   371,089
     −25,192

d. 879,989
    −721,492

e.   879,009
     − 788,492

f.   879,989
     − 21,070

g. 879,000
    − 21,989

h.   279,389
    −191,492

i.   500,989
    −242,000

    Lesson 14:   Use place value understanding to decompose to smaller units up to
                        three times using the standard subtraction algorithm, and apply the
                        algorithm to solve word problems using tape diagrams.

©2015 Great Minds. eureka-math.org
G4-M1M2-TE-BK1-1.3.1-1.2016

EUREKA
MATH™

Draw a tape diagram to represent each problem. Use numbers to solve, and write your answer as a statement. Check your answers.

2. Jason ordered 239,021 pounds of flour to be used in his 25 bakeries. The company delivering the flour showed up with 451,202 pounds. How many extra pounds of flour were delivered?

3. In May, the New York Public Library had 124,061 books checked out. Of those books, 31,117 were mystery books. How many of the books checked out were not mystery books?

4. A Class A dump truck can haul 239,000 pounds of dirt. A Class C dump truck can haul 600,200 pounds of dirt. How many more pounds can a Class C truck haul than a Class A truck?

EUREKA
MATH™

Lesson 14: Use place value understanding to decompose to smaller units up to three times using the standard subtraction algorithm, and apply the algorithm to solve word problems using tape diagrams.

©2015 Great Minds. eureka-math.org
G4-M1M2-TE-BK1-1.3.1-1.2016

213

Lesson 15

Objective: Use place value understanding to fluently decompose to smaller units multiple times in any place using the standard subtraction algorithm, and apply the algorithm to solve word problems using tape diagrams.

Suggested Lesson Structure

■ Fluency Practice   (11 minutes)
■ Application Problem   (6 minutes)
□ Concept Development   (32 minutes)
■ Student Debrief   (11 minutes)

   Total Time   **(60 minutes)**

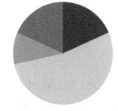

Fluency Practice (11 minutes)

- Place Value **4.NBT.2**   (3 minutes)
- Find the Difference **4.NBT.4**   (4 minutes)
- Convert Units **4.MD.1**   (4 minutes)

Place Value (3 minutes)

Materials: (T) Personal white board

Note: Practicing these skills in isolation helps lay a foundation for conceptually understanding this lesson's content.

T: (Write 4,598.) Say the number.
S: 4,598.
T: What digit is in the tens place?
S: 9.
T: (Underline 9.) What is the value of the 9?
S: 90.
T: State the value of the digit 4.
S: 4,000.
T: 5?
S: 500.

Repeat using the following possible sequence: 69,708; 398,504; and 853,967.

Lesson 15:   Use place value understanding to fluently decompose to smaller units
              multiple times in any place using the standard subtraction algorithm,
              and apply the algorithm to solve word problems using tape diagrams.

©2015 Great Minds. eureka-math.org
G4-M1M2-TE-BK1-1.3.1-1.2016

Find the Difference (4 minutes)

Materials: (S) Personal white board

Note: This math fluency activity prepares students for understanding the importance of the subtraction algorithm.

  T: (Write 846 – 304 =_____.) Write a subtraction sentence horizontally or vertically.
  S: (Write 846 – 304 = 542.)

Repeat process and sequence for 8,056 – 5,004; 935 – 17; 4,625 – 815; and 45,836 – 2,906.

Convert Units (4 minutes)

Note: This material is a review of Grade 2 and Grade 3 and helps prepare students to solve problems with meters and centimeters in Grade 4, Module 2, Topic A.

Materials: (S) Personal white board

  T: Count by 20 centimeters. When you get to 100 centimeters, say 1 meter. When you get to 200 centimeters, say 2 meters.
  S: 20 cm, 40 cm, 60 cm, 80 cm, 1 m, 120 cm, 140 cm, 160 cm, 180 cm, 2 m.

Repeat process, this time pulling out the meter (e.g., 1 m 20 cm, 1 m 40 cm).

  T: (Write 130 cm = ___ m ___ cm.) On your personal white boards, fill in the blanks.
  S: (Write 130 cm = 1 m 30 cm.)

Repeat process for 103 cm, 175 cm, 345 cm, and 708 cm for composing to meters.

Application Problem (6 minutes)

When the amusement park opened, the number on the counter at the gate read 928,614. At the end of the day, the counter read 931,682. How many people went through the gate that day?

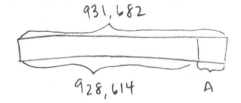

Note: At times, students are asked to use a specific strategy, and at other times, their independent work is observed. This question engages students in MP.5 by leaving open the solution path.

Lesson 15:   Use place value understanding to fluently decompose to smaller units
multiple times in any place using the standard subtraction algorithm,
and apply the algorithm to solve word problems using tape diagrams.   215

©2015 Great Minds. eureka-math.org
G4-M1M2-TE-BK1-1.3.1-1.2016

Concept Development (32 minutes)

Materials: (T) Millions place value chart (Lesson 11) (S) Personal white board, millions place value chart
(Lesson 11 Template)

Problem 1: Regroup units 5 times to subtract.

Write 253,421 – 75,832 vertically on the board.

T: Say this problem with me.

T: Work with your partner to draw a tape diagram representing this problem.

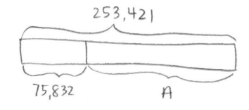
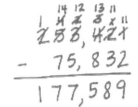

T: What is the whole amount?

S: 253,421.

T: What is the part?

S: 75,832.

T: Look across the top number, 253,421, to see if we have
enough units in each column to subtract 75,832.
Are we ready to subtract?

S: No.

T: Are there enough ones in the top number to subtract
the ones in the bottom number? (Point to the 1 and 2
in the ones column.)

S: No, 1 one is less than 2 ones.

T: What should we do?

S: Change 1 ten for 10 ones. That means you have 1 ten
and 11 ones.

T: Are there enough tens in the top number to subtract the tens in the bottom number? (Point to tens
column.)

S: No, 1 ten is less than 3 tens.

T: What should we do?

S: Change 1 hundred for 10 tens. You have 3 hundreds and 11 tens.

T: The tens column is ready to subtract.

Have partners continue questioning if there are enough units to subtract in each column, regrouping where
needed.

> **NOTES ON
> MULTIPLE MEANS
> OF ENGAGEMENT:**
>
> Students of all abilities will benefit
> from using addition to check
> subtraction. Students should see that
> if the sum does not match the whole,
> the subtraction (or calculation) is
> faulty. They must subtract again and
> then check with addition. Challenge
> students to think about how they use
> this check strategy in everyday life. We
> use it all of the time when we add up to
> another number.

Lesson 15:   Use place value understanding to fluently decompose to smaller units
multiple times in any place using the standard subtraction algorithm,
and apply the algorithm to solve word problems using tape diagrams.

©2015 Great Minds. eureka-math.org
G4-M1M2-TE-BK1-1.3.1-1.2016

T: Are we ready to subtract?

S: Yes, we are ready to subtract.

T: Go ahead and subtract. State the difference to your partner. Label the unknown part in your tape diagram.

S: The difference between 253,421 and 75,832 is 177,589. (Label A = 177,589.)

T: Add the difference to the part you knew to see if your answer is correct.

S: It is. The sum of the parts is 253,421.

Problem 2: Decompose numbers from 1 thousand and 1 million into smaller units to subtract, modeled with place value disks.

Write 1,000 – 528 vertically on the board.

T: With your partner, read this problem, and draw a tape diagram. Label what you know and the unknown.

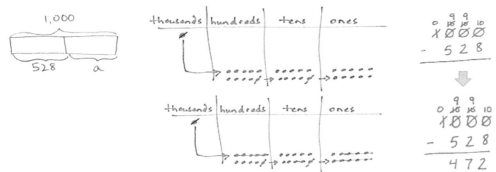
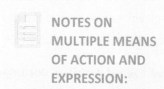

MP.6

T: Record the problem on your personal white board.

T: Look across the units in the top number. Are we ready to subtract?

S: No.

T: Are there enough ones in the top number to subtract the ones in the bottom number? (Point to 0 and 8 in the ones column.)

S: No. 0 ones is less than 8 ones.

T: I need to ungroup 1 unit from the tens. What do you notice?

S: There are no tens to ungroup.

T: We can look to the hundreds. (There are no hundreds to ungroup either.)

T: In order to get 10 ones, we need to regroup 1 thousand. Watch as I represent the ungrouping in my subtraction problem. (Model using place value disks and, rename units in the problem simultaneously.) Now it is your turn.

NOTES ON
MULTIPLE MEANS
OF ACTION AND
EXPRESSION:

Encourage students who notice a pattern of repeated nines when subtracting across multiple zeros to express this pattern in writing. Allow students to identify why this happens using manipulatives or in writing. Allow students to slowly transition into recording this particular unbundling across zeros as nines as they become fluent with using the algorithm.

Lesson 15: Use place value understanding to fluently decompose to smaller units multiple times in any place using the standard subtraction algorithm, and apply the algorithm to solve word problems using tape diagrams.

©2015 Great Minds. eureka-math.org
G4-M1M2-TE-BK1-1.3.1-1.2016

217

T: Are we ready to subtract?

S: Yes, we are ready to subtract.

T: Solve for 9 hundreds 9 tens 10 ones minus 5 hundreds 2 tens 8 ones.

S: 1,000 – 528 is 472.

T: Check our answer.

S: The sum of 472 and 528 is 1,000.

Write 1,000,000 – 345,528 vertically on the board.

T: Read this problem, and draw a tape diagram to represent the subtraction problem.

T: Record the subtraction problem on your board.

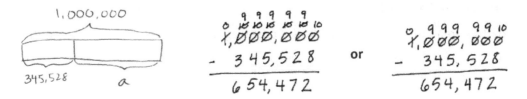

T: What do you notice when you look across the top number?

S: There are a lot more zeros. → We will have to regroup 6 times. → We are not ready to subtract. We will have to regroup 1 million to solve the problem.

T: Work with your partner to get 1,000,000 ready to subtract. Rename your units in the subtraction problem.

S: 9 hundred thousands 9 ten thousands 9 thousands 9 hundreds 9 tens 10 ones. We are ready to subtract.

S: 1,000,000 minus 345,528 equals 654,472.

T: To check your answer, add the parts to see if you get the correct whole amount.

S: We did! We got one million when we added the parts.

Problem 3: Solve a word problem, decomposing units multiple times.

Last year, there were 620,073 people in attendance at a local parade. This year, there were 456,795 people in attendance. How many more people were in attendance last year?

T: Read with me.

T: Represent this information in a tape diagram.

T: Work with your partner to write a subtraction problem using the information in the tape diagram.

T: Look across the units in the top number. Are you ready to subtract?

S: No, I do not have enough ones in the top number. I need to unbundle 1 ten to make 10 ones. Then I have 6 tens and 13 ones.

T: Continue to check if you are ready to subtract in each column. When you are ready to subtract, solve.

S: 620,073 minus 456,795 equals 163,278. There were 163,278 more people in attendance last year.

EUREKA
MATH™

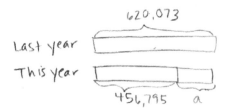

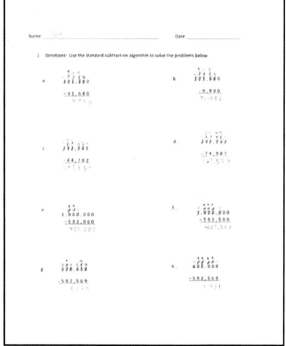

Problem Set (10 minutes)

Students should do their personal best to complete the Problem Set within the allotted 10 minutes. For some classes, it may be appropriate to modify the assignment by specifying which problems they work on first. Some problems do not specify a method for solving. Students should solve these problems using the RDW approach used for Application Problems.

Student Debrief (11 minutes)

Lesson Objective: Use place value understanding to fluently decompose to smaller units multiple times in any place using the standard subtraction algorithm, and apply the algorithm to solve word problems using tape diagrams.

The Student Debrief is intended to invite reflection and active processing of the total lesson experience.

Invite students to review their solutions for the Problem Set. They should check work by comparing answers with a partner before going over answers as a class. Look for misconceptions or misunderstandings that can be addressed in the Student Debrief. Guide students in a conversation to debrief the Problem Set and process the lesson.

Any combination of the questions below may be used to lead the discussion.

- Problems 1(e) and (f) were similar. Did anyone notice a pattern that could be used to solve these problems?

- How did your tape diagrams differ in Problems 2, 3, and 4?

- How do you know when you are ready to subtract across the problem?

- How can you check your answer when subtracting?

- Is there a number that you can subtract from 1,000,000 without decomposing across to the ones (other than 1,000,000)? 100,000? 10,000?

Lesson 15:   Use place value understanding to fluently decompose to smaller units multiple times in any place using the standard subtraction algorithm, and apply the algorithm to solve word problems using tape diagrams.

©2015 Great Minds. eureka-math.org
G4-M1M2-TE-BK1-1.3.1-1.2016

219

- How can decomposing multiple times be challenging?
- How does the tape diagram help you determine which operation to use to find the answer?

Exit Ticket (3 minutes)

After the Student Debrief, instruct students to complete the Exit Ticket. A review of their work will help with assessing students' understanding of the concepts that were presented in today's lesson and planning more effectively for future lessons. The questions may be read aloud to the students.

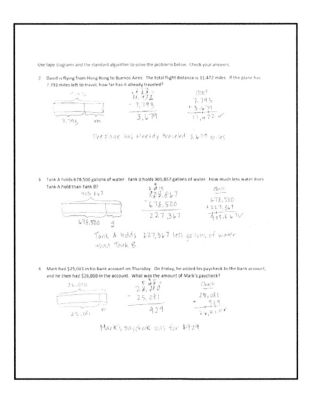

Use place value understanding to fluently decompose to smaller units multiple times in any place using the standard subtraction algorithm, and apply the algorithm to solve word problems using tape diagrams.

©2015 Great Minds. eureka-math.org
G4-M1M2-TE-BK1-1.3.1-1.2016

EUREKA
MATH™

Name _____ Date _____

1. Use the standard subtraction algorithm to solve the problems below.

a.
```
    1 0 1, 6 6 0
  -    9 1, 6 8 0
```

b.
```
    1 0 1, 6 6 0
  -     9, 9 8 0
```

c.
```
    2 4 2, 5 6 1
  -    4 4, 7 0 2
```

d.
```
    2 4 2, 5 6 1
  -    7 4, 9 8 7
```

e.
```
  1, 0 0 0, 0 0 0
  -   5 9 2, 0 0 0
```

f.
```
  1, 0 0 0, 0 0 0
  -   5 9 2, 5 0 0
```

g.
```
    6 0 0, 6 5 8
  - 5 9 2, 5 6 9
```

h.
```
    6 0 0, 0 0 0
  - 5 9 2, 5 6 9
```

EUREKA
MATH™

Lesson 15: Use place value understanding to fluently decompose to smaller units multiple times in any place using the standard subtraction algorithm, and apply the algorithm to solve word problems using tape diagrams.

©2015 Great Minds. eureka-math.org
G4-M1M2-TE-BK1-1.3.1-1.2016

221

Use tape diagrams and the standard algorithm to solve the problems below. Check your answers.

2. David is flying from Hong Kong to Buenos Aires. The total flight distance is 11,472 miles. If the plane has 7,793 miles left to travel, how far has it already traveled?

3. Tank A holds 678,500 gallons of water. Tank B holds 905,867 gallons of water. How much less water does Tank A hold than Tank B?

4. Mark had $25,081 in his bank account on Thursday. On Friday, he added his paycheck to the bank account, and he then had $26,010 in the account. What was the amount of Mark's paycheck?

Lesson 15:   Use place value understanding to fluently decompose to smaller units multiple times in any place using the standard subtraction algorithm, and apply the algorithm to solve word problems using tape diagrams.

©2015 Great Minds. eureka-math.org
G4-M1M2-TE-BK1-1.3.1-1.2016

EUREKA
MATH™

Name _____   Date _____

Draw a tape diagram to model each problem and solve.

1. 956,204 − 780,169 =_____

2. A construction company was building a stone wall on Main Street. 100,000 stones were delivered to the site. On Monday, they used 15,631 stones. How many stones remain for the rest of the week? Write your answer as a statement.

EUREKA MATH

Lesson 15:   Use place value understanding to fluently decompose to smaller units multiple times in any place using the standard subtraction algorithm, and apply the algorithm to solve word problems using tape diagrams.

©2015 Great Minds. eureka-math.org
G4-M1M2-TE-BK1-1.3.1-1.2016

223

Name _____ Date _____

1. Use the standard subtraction algorithm to solve the problems below.

a.
```
    9,656
-     838
```

b.
```
   59,656
-   5,880
```

c.
```
  759,656
- 579,989
```

d.
```
  294,150
- 166,370
```

e.
```
  294,150
- 239,089
```

f.
```
  294,150
-  96,400
```

g.
```
  800,500
-  79,989
```

h.
```
  800,500
-  45,500
```

i.
```
  800,500
- 276,664
```

Use tape diagrams and the standard algorithm to solve the problems below. Check your answers.

2. A fishing boat was out to sea for 6 months and traveled a total of 8,578 miles. In the first month, the boat traveled 659 miles. How many miles did the fishing boat travel during the remaining 5 months?

Lesson 15: Use place value understanding to fluently decompose to smaller units multiple times in any place using the standard subtraction algorithm, and apply the algorithm to solve word problems using tape diagrams.

EUREKA
MATH™

3. A national monument had 160,747 visitors during the first week of September. A total of 759,656 people visited the monument in September. How many people visited the monument in September after the first week?

4. Shadow Software Company earned a total of $800,000 selling programs during the year 2012. $125,300 of that amount was used to pay expenses of the company. How much profit did Shadow Software Company make in the year 2012?

5. At the local aquarium, Bubba the Seal ate 25,634 grams of fish during the week. If, on the first day of the week, he ate 6,987 grams of fish, how many grams of fish did he eat during the remainder of the week?

EUREKA MATH

Lesson 15: Use place value understanding to fluently decompose to smaller units multiple times in any place using the standard subtraction algorithm, and apply the algorithm to solve word problems using tape diagrams.

©2015 Great Minds. eureka-math.org
G4-M1M2-TE-BK1-1.3.1-1.2016

225

Lesson 16

Objective: Solve two-step word problems using the standard subtraction algorithm fluently modeled with tape diagrams, and assess the reasonableness of answers using rounding.

Suggested Lesson Structure

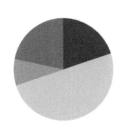

■ Fluency Practice   (12 minutes)
■ Application Problem   (5 minutes)
■ Concept Development   (30 minutes)
■ Student Debrief   (13 minutes)

Total Time   **(60 minutes)**

Fluency Practice (12 minutes)

▪ Sprint: Convert Meters and Centimeters to Centimeters **4.MD.1**   (8 minutes)
▪ Compare Numbers **4.NBT.2**   (4 minutes)

Sprint: Convert Meters and Centimeters to Centimeters (8 minutes)

Materials: (S) Convert Meters and Centimeters to Centimeters Sprint

Note: Reviewing unit conversions that were learned in Grade 3 helps to prepare students to solve problems with meters and centimeters in Module 2, Topic A.

Compare Numbers (4 minutes)

Materials: (S) Personal white board

Note: Reviewing this concept helps students work toward mastery of comparing numbers.

T: (Project 342,006 _____ 94,983.) On your personal white boards, compare the numbers by writing the greater than, less than, or equal symbol.

S: (Write 342,006 > 94,893.)

Repeat with the following possible sequence: 7 thousands 5 hundreds 8 tens _____ 6 ten thousands 5 hundreds 8 ones, and 9 hundred thousands 8 thousands 9 hundreds 3 tens _____ 807,820.

Lesson 16:   Solve two-step word problems using the standard subtraction
algorithm fluently modeled with tape diagrams, and assess the
reasonableness of answers using rounding.

©2015 Great Minds. eureka-math.org
G4-M1M2-TE-BK1-1.3.1-1.2016

EUREKA MATH™

Application Problem (5 minutes)

For the weekend basketball playoffs, a total of 61,941 tickets were sold. 29,855 tickets were sold for Saturday's games. The rest of the tickets were sold for Sunday's games. How many tickets were sold for Sunday's games?

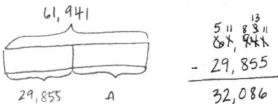

32,086 tickets were sold for Sunday's games.

Note: This Application Problem reviews content from the prior lesson of using the subtraction algorithm with multiple regroupings.

Concept Development (30 minutes)

Materials: (S) Personal white board

Problem 1: Solve a two-step word problem, modeled with a tape diagram, assessing reasonableness of the answer using rounding.

A company has 3 locations with 70,010 employees altogether. The first location has 34,857 employees. The second location has 17,595 employees. How many employees work in the third location?

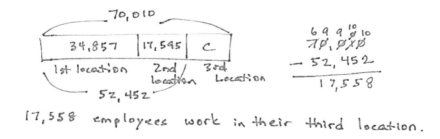

17,558 employees work in their third location.

T: Read with me. Take 2 minutes to draw and label a tape diagram. (Circulate and encourage the students: "Can you draw something?" "What can you draw?")

T: (After 2 minutes.) Tell your partner what you understand and what you still do not understand.

S: We know the total number of employees and the employees at the first and second locations. We do not know how many employees are at the third location.

Lesson 16:   Solve two-step word problems using the standard subtraction algorithm fluently modeled with tape diagrams, and assess the reasonableness of answers using rounding.

227

©2015 Great Minds. eureka-math.org
G4-M1M2-TE-BK1-1.3.1-1.2016

T: Use your tape diagram to estimate the number of employees at the third location. Explain your reasoning to your partner.

S: I rounded the number of employees. 30,000 + 20,000 = 50,000, and I know that the total number of employees is about 70,000. That means that there would be about 20,000 employees at the third location.

T: Now, find the precise answer. Work with your partner to do so. (Give students time to work.)

T: Label the unknown part on your diagram, and make a statement of the solution.

S: There are 17,558 employees at the third location.

T: Is your answer reasonable?

S: Yes, because 17,558 rounded to the nearest ten thousand is 20,000, and that was our estimate.

NOTES ON MULTIPLE MEANS OF ACTION AND EXPRESSION:

Students working below grade level may not consider whether their answer makes sense. Guide students to choose the sensible operation and check their answers. Encourage students to reread the problem after solving and to ask themselves, "Does my answer make sense?" If not, ask, "What else can I try?"

Problem 2: Solve two-step word problems, modeled with a tape diagram, assessing reasonableness of the answer using rounding.

Owen's goal is to have 1 million people visit his new website within the first four months of it being launched. Below is a chart showing the number of visitors each month. How many more visitors does he need in Month 4 to reach his goal?

Month	Month 1	Month 2	Month 3	Month 4
Visitors	228,211	301,856	299,542	

T: With your partner, draw a tape diagram. Tell your partner your strategy for solving this problem.

S: We can find the sum of the number of visitors during the first 3 months. Then, we subtract that from 1 million to find how many more visitors are needed to reach his goal.

T: Make an estimate for the number of visitors in Month 4. Explain your reasoning to your partner.

Lesson 16:   Solve two-step word problems using the standard subtraction algorithm fluently modeled with tape diagrams, and assess the reasonableness of answers using rounding.

©2015 Great Minds. eureka-math.org
G4-M1M2-TE-BK1-1.3.1-1.2016

EUREKA MATH

S: I can round to the nearest hundred thousand and estimate. Owen will need about 200,000 visitors to reach his goal. → I rounded to the nearest ten thousand to get a closer estimate of 170,000 visitors.

T: Find the total for the first 3 months. What is the precise sum?

S: 829,609.

T: Compare the actual and estimated solutions. Is your answer reasonable?

S: Yes, because our estimate of 200,000 is near 170,391. → Rounded to the nearest hundred thousand, 170,391 is 200,000. → 170,391 rounded to the nearest ten thousand is 170,000, which was also our estimate, so our solution is reasonable.

NOTES ON MULTIPLE MEANS OF ENGAGEMENT:

Challenge students working above grade level to expand their thinking and to figure out another way to solve the two-step problem. Is there another strategy that would work?

Problem 3: Solve a two-step, *compare with smaller unknown* word problem.

There were 12,345 people at a concert on Saturday night. On Sunday night, there were 1,795 fewer people at the concert than on Saturday night. How many people attended the concert on both nights?

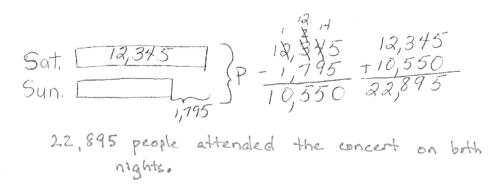

T: For 2 minutes, with your partner, draw a tape diagram. (Circulate and encourage students as they work. You might choose to call two pairs of students to draw on the board while others work at their seats. Have the pairs then present their diagrams to the class.)

T: Now how can you calculate to solve the problem?

S: We can find the number of people on Sunday night, and then add that number to the people on Saturday night.

T: Make an estimate of the solution. Explain your reasoning to your partner.

S: Rounding to the nearest thousand, the number of people on Saturday night was about 12,000. The number of people fewer on Sunday night can be rounded to 2,000, so the estimate for the number of people on Sunday is 10,000. 12,000 + 10,000 is 22,000.

T: Find the exact number of people who attended the concert on both nights. What is the exact sum?

S: 22,895.

Lesson 16: Solve two-step word problems using the standard subtraction algorithm fluently modeled with tape diagrams, and assess the reasonableness of answers using rounding.

©2015 Great Minds. eureka-math.org
G4-M1M2-TE-BK1-1.3.1-1.2016

229

T: Compare the actual and estimated solutions. Is your answer reasonable?

S: Yes, because 22,895 is near our estimate of 22,000.

T: Be sure to write a statement of your solution.

Problem Set (10 minutes)

Students should do their personal best to complete the Problem Set within the allotted 10 minutes. For some classes, it may be appropriate to modify the assignment by specifying which problems they work on first. Some problems do not specify a method for solving. Students should solve these problems using the RDW approach used for Application Problems.

Student Debrief (13 minutes)

Lesson Objective: Solve two-step word problems using the standard subtraction algorithm fluently modeled with tape diagrams, and assess the reasonableness of answers using rounding.

The Student Debrief is intended to invite reflection and active processing of the total lesson experience.

Invite students to review their solutions for the Problem Set. They should check work by comparing answers with a partner before going over answers as a class. Look for misconceptions or misunderstandings that can be addressed in the Student Debrief. Guide students in a conversation to debrief the Problem Set and process the lesson.

Any combination of the questions below may be used to lead the discussion.

- How did your estimate help you determine that your exact answer was reasonable in Problem 1?

- In Problem 2, how close was your actual answer to your estimate?

- Why was the estimate so much smaller than the exact answer in Problem 2?

- In Problem 3, to which place did you round? Why?

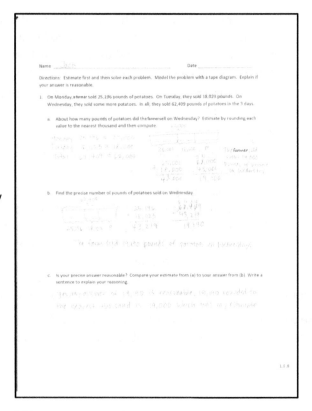

Lesson 16:   Solve two-step word problems using the standard subtraction algorithm fluently modeled with tape diagrams, and assess the reasonableness of answers using rounding.

©2015 Great Minds. eureka-math.org
G4-M1M2-TE-BK1-1.3.1-1.2016

- How did your tape diagram help you solve Problem 5?

- How do you determine what place value to round to when finding an estimate?

- What is the benefit of checking the reasonableness of your answer?

- Describe the difference between rounding and estimating.

Exit Ticket (3 minutes)

After the Student Debrief, instruct students to complete the Exit Ticket. A review of their work will help with assessing students' understanding of the concepts that were presented in today's lesson and planning more effectively for future lessons. The questions may be read aloud to the students.

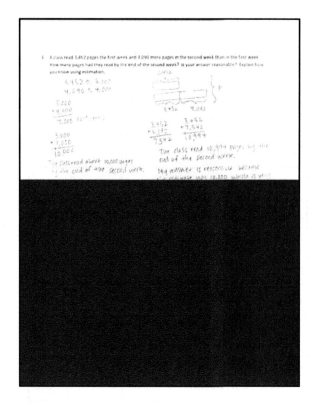

Lesson 16:   Solve two-step word problems using the standard subtraction algorithm fluently modeled with tape diagrams, and assess the reasonableness of answers using rounding.

©2015 Great Minds. eureka-math.org
G4-M1M2-TE-BK1-1.3.1-1.2016

231

A

Number Correct: _____

Convert Meters and Centimeters to Centimeters

1.	2 m =	cm	23.	1 m 2 cm =	cm
2.	3 m =	cm	24.	1 m 3 cm =	cm
3.	4 m =	cm	25.	1 m 4 cm =	cm
4.	9 m =	cm	26.	1 m 7 cm =	cm
5.	1 m =	cm	27.	2 m 7 cm =	cm
6.	7 m =	cm	28.	3 m 7 cm =	cm
7.	5 m =	cm	29.	8 m 7 cm =	cm
8.	8 m =	cm	30.	8 m 4 cm =	cm
9.	6 m =	cm	31.	4 m 9 cm =	cm
10.	1 m 20 cm =	cm	32.	6 m 8 cm =	cm
11.	1 m 30 cm =	cm	33.	9 m 3 cm =	cm
12.	1 m 40 cm =	cm	34.	2 m 60 cm =	cm
13.	1 m 90 cm =	cm	35.	3 m 75 cm =	cm
14.	1 m 95 cm =	cm	36.	6 m 33 cm =	cm
15.	1 m 85 cm =	cm	37.	8 m 9 cm =	cm
16.	1 m 84 cm =	cm	38.	4 m 70 cm =	cm
17.	1 m 73 cm =	cm	39.	7 m 35 cm =	cm
18.	1 m 62 cm =	cm	40.	4 m 17 cm =	cm
19.	2 m 62 cm =	cm	41.	6 m 4 cm =	cm
20.	7 m 62 cm =	cm	42.	10 m 4 cm =	cm
21.	5 m 27 cm =	cm	43.	10 m 40 cm =	cm
22.	3 m 87 cm =	cm	44.	11 m 84 cm =	cm

Lesson 16: Solve two-step word problems using the standard subtraction algorithm fluently modeled with tape diagrams, and assess the reasonableness of answers using rounding.

EUREKA MATH

B

Convert Meters and Centimeters to Centimeters

Number Correct: _____

Improvement: _____

1.	1 m =	cm
2.	2 m =	cm
3.	3 m =	cm
4.	7 m =	cm
5.	5 m =	cm
6.	9 m =	cm
7.	4 m =	cm
8.	8 m =	cm
9.	6 m =	cm
10.	1 m 10 cm =	cm
11.	1 m 20 cm =	cm
12.	1 m 30 cm =	cm
13.	1 m 70 cm =	cm
14.	1 m 75 cm =	cm
15.	1 m 65 cm =	cm
16.	1 m 64 cm =	cm
17.	1 m 53 cm =	cm
18.	1 m 42 cm =	cm
19.	2 m 42 cm =	cm
20.	8 m 42 cm =	cm
21.	5 m 29 cm =	cm
22.	3 m 89 cm =	cm

23.	1 m 1 cm =	cm
24.	1 m 2 cm =	cm
25.	1 m 3 cm =	cm
26.	1 m 9 cm =	cm
27.	2 m 9 cm =	cm
28.	3 m 9 cm =	cm
29.	7 m 9 cm =	cm
30.	7 m 4 cm =	cm
31.	4 m 8 cm =	cm
32.	6 m 3 cm =	cm
33.	9 m 5 cm =	cm
34.	2 m 50 cm =	cm
35.	3 m 85 cm =	cm
36.	6 m 31 cm =	cm
37.	6 m 7 cm =	cm
38.	4 m 60 cm =	cm
39.	7 m 25 cm =	cm
40.	4 m 13 cm =	cm
41.	6 m 2 cm =	cm
42.	10 m 3 cm =	cm
43.	10 m 30 cm =	cm
44.	11 m 48 cm =	cm

Lesson 16:   Solve two-step word problems using the standard subtraction algorithm fluently modeled with tape diagrams, and assess the reasonableness of answers using rounding.   **233**

©2015 Great Minds. eureka-math.org
G4-M1M2-TE-BK1-1.3.1-1.2016

Name _____   Date _____

Estimate first, and then solve each problem. Model the problem with a tape diagram. Explain if your answer is reasonable.

1. On Monday, a farmer sold 25,196 pounds of potatoes. On Tuesday, he sold 18,023 pounds. On Wednesday, he sold some more potatoes. In all, he sold 62,409 pounds of potatoes.

   a. About how many pounds of potatoes did the farmer sell on Wednesday? Estimate by rounding each value to the nearest thousand, and then compute.

   b. Find the precise number of pounds of potatoes sold on Wednesday.

   c. Is your precise answer reasonable? Compare your estimate from (a) to your answer from (b). Write a sentence to explain your reasoning.

Lesson 16:   Solve two-step word problems using the standard subtraction algorithm fluently modeled with tape diagrams, and assess the reasonableness of answers using rounding.

©2015 Great Minds. eureka-math.org
G4-M1M2-TE-BK1-1.3.1-1.2016

EUREKA
MATH™

2. A gas station had two pumps. Pump A dispensed 241,752 gallons. Pump B dispensed 113,916 more gallons than Pump A.

a. About how many gallons did both pumps dispense? Estimate by rounding each value to the nearest hundred thousand and then compute.

b. Exactly how many gallons did both pumps dispense?

c. Assess the reasonableness of your answer in (b). Use your estimate from (a) to explain.

EUREKA
MATH™

Lesson 16: Solve two-step word problems using the standard subtraction algorithm fluently modeled with tape diagrams, and assess the reasonableness of answers using rounding.

©2015 Great Minds. eureka-math.org
G4-M1M2-TE-BK1-1.3.1-1.2016

235

3. Martin's car had 86,456 miles on it. Of that distance, Martin's wife drove 24,901 miles, and his son drove 7,997 miles. Martin drove the rest.

a. About how many miles did Martin drive? Round each value to estimate.

b. Exactly how many miles did Martin drive?

c. Assess the reasonableness of your answer in (b). Use your estimate from (a) to explain.

Lesson 16: Solve two-step word problems using the standard subtraction algorithm fluently modeled with tape diagrams, and assess the reasonableness of answers using rounding.

©2015 Great Minds. eureka-math.org
G4-M1M2-TE-BK1-1.3.1-1.2016

EUREKA
MATH

4. A class read 3,452 pages the first week and 4,090 more pages in the second week than in the first week. How many pages had they read by the end of the second week? Is your answer reasonable? Explain how you know using estimation.

5. A cargo plane weighed 500,000 pounds. After the first load was taken off, the airplane weighed 437,981 pounds. Then 16,478 more pounds were taken off. What was the total number of pounds of cargo removed from the plane? Is your answer reasonable? Explain.

EUREKA
MATH™

Lesson 16: Solve two-step word problems using the standard subtraction algorithm fluently modeled with tape diagrams, and assess the reasonableness of answers using rounding.

©2015 Great Minds. eureka-math.org
G4-M1M2-TE-BK1-1.3.1-1.2016

237

Name _____   Date _____

Quarterback Brett Favre passed for 71,838 yards between the years 1991 and 2011. His all-time high was 4,413 passing yards in one year. In his second highest year, he threw 4,212 passing yards.

1. About how many passing yards did he throw in the remaining years? Estimate by rounding each value to the nearest thousand and then compute.

2. Exactly how many passing yards did he throw in the remaining years?

3. Assess the reasonableness of your answer in (b). Use your estimate from (a) to explain.

Lesson 16:   Solve two-step word problems using the standard subtraction algorithm fluently modeled with tape diagrams, and assess the reasonableness of answers using rounding.

©2015 Great Minds. eureka-math.org
G4-M1M2-TE-BK1-1.3.1-1.2016

EUREKA MATH

Name _____   Date _____

1. Zachary's final project for a college course took a semester to write and had 95,234 words. Zachary wrote 35,295 words the first month and 19,240 words the second month.

   a. Round each value to the nearest ten thousand to estimate how many words Zachary wrote during the remaining part of the semester.

   b. Find the exact number of words written during the remaining part of the semester.

   c. Use your answer from (a) to explain why your answer in (b) is reasonable.

EUREKA
MATH™

Lesson 16:   Solve two-step word problems using the standard subtraction
             algorithm fluently modeled with tape diagrams, and assess the
             reasonableness of answers using rounding.

©2015 Great Minds. eureka-math.org
G4-M1M2-TE-BK1-1.3.1-1.2016

239

2. During the first quarter of the year, 351,875 people downloaded an app for their smartphones. During the second quarter of the year, 101,949 fewer people downloaded the app than during the first quarter. How many downloads occurred during the two quarters of the year?

a. Round each number to the nearest hundred thousand to estimate how many downloads occurred during the first two quarters of the year.

b. Determine exactly how many downloads occurred during the first two quarters of the year.

c. Determine if your answer is reasonable. Explain.

Lesson 16:   Solve two-step word problems using the standard subtraction algorithm fluently modeled with tape diagrams, and assess the reasonableness of answers using rounding.

©2015 Great Minds. eureka-math.org
G4-M1M2-TE-BK1-1.3.1-1.2016

EUREKA
MATH

3. A local store was having a two-week Back to School sale. They started the sale with 36,390 notebooks. During the first week of the sale, 7,424 notebooks were sold. During the second week of the sale, 8,967 notebooks were sold. How many notebooks were left at the end of the two weeks? Is your answer reasonable?

Lesson 16: Solve two-step word problems using the standard subtraction algorithm fluently modeled with tape diagrams, and assess the reasonableness of answers using rounding.

©2015 Great Minds. eureka-math.org
G4-M1M2-TE-BK1-1.3.1-1.2016

241

Mathematics Curriculum

Topic F

Addition and Subtraction Word Problems

4.OA.3, 4.NBT.1, 4.NBT.2, 4.NBT.4

Focus Standard:	4.OA.3	Solve multistep word problems posed with whole numbers and having whole-number answers using the four operations, including problems in which remainders must be interpreted. Represent these problems using equations with a letter standing for the unknown quantity. Assess the reasonableness of answers using mental computation and estimation strategies including rounding.
Instructional Days:	3	
Coherence -Links from:	G3–M2	Place Value and Problem Solving with Units of Measure
-Links to:	G5–M1	Place Value and Decimal Fractions

Module 1 culminates with multi-step addition and subtraction word problems in Topic F (**4.OA.3**). In these lessons, the format for the Concept Development is different from the traditional vignette. Instead of following instruction, the Problem Set facilitates the problems and discussion of the Concept Development.

Throughout the module, tape diagrams are used to model word problems, and students continue to use tape diagrams to solve *additive comparative* word problems. Students also continue using a variable to represent an unknown quantity.

To culminate the module, students are given tape diagrams or equations and are encouraged to use creativity and the mathematics learned during this module to write their own word problems to solve using place value understanding and the algorithms for addition and subtraction. The module facilitates deeper comprehension and supports determining the reasonableness of an answer. Solving multi-step word problems using multiplication and division is addressed in later modules.

©2015 Great Minds. eureka-math.org
G4-M1M2-TE-BK1-1.3.1-1.2016

A Teaching Sequence Toward Mastery of Addition and Subtraction Word Problems

Objective 1: Solve *additive compare* word problems modeled with tape diagrams.
(Lesson 17)

Objective 2: Solve multi-step word problems modeled with tape diagrams, and assess the reasonableness of answers using rounding.
(Lesson 18)

Objective 3: Create and solve multi-step word problems from given tape diagrams and equations.
(Lesson 19)

Lesson 17

Objective: Solve *additive compare* word problems modeled with tape diagrams.

Suggested Lesson Structure

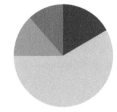

■ Fluency Practice   (10 minutes)
■ Application Problem   (8 minutes)
■ Concept Development   (35 minutes)
■ Student Debrief   (7 minutes)
   Total Time   **(60 minutes)**

Fluency Practice (10 minutes)

- Change Place Value **4.NBT.2**   (5 minutes)
- Convert Units **4.MD.1**   (5 minutes)

Change Place Value (5 minutes)

Materials: (S) Personal white board, labeled millions place value chart (Lesson 11 Template)

Note: This fluency activity helps students work toward mastery of using place value skills to add and subtract different units.

    T: (Project the place value chart to the millions place. Write 4 hundred thousands, 6 ten thousands, 3 thousands, 2 hundreds, 6 tens, 5 ones.) On your personal white board, write the number.

    S: (Write 463,265.)

    T: Show 100 more.

    S: (Write 463,365.)

Possible further sequence: 10,000 less, 100,000 more, 1 less, and 10 more.

    T: (Write 400 + 90 + 3 = _____.) On your place value chart, write the number.

Possible further sequence: 7,000 + 300 + 80 + 5; 20,000 + 700,000 + 5 + 80; 30,000 + 600,000 + 3 + 20.

Convert Units (5 minutes)

Note: This fluency activity strengthens understanding of the relationship between kilograms and grams learned in Grade 3 and prepares students to use this relationship to solve problems in Module 2, Topic A. Use a number bond to support understanding the relationship of grams and kilograms.

    T: (Write 1 kg = ___ g.) How many grams are in 1 kilogram?

    S: 1 kg = 1,000 g.

Repeat the process for 2 kg, 3 kg, 8 kg, 8 kg 500 g, 7 kg 500 g, and 4 kg 250 g.

  T: (Write 1,000 g = ___ kg.) Say the answer.
  S: 1,000 grams equals 1 kilogram.
  T: (Write 1,500 g = ___ kg ___ g.) Say the answer.
  S: 1,500 grams equals 1 kilogram 500 grams.
Repeat the process for 2,500 g, 3,500 g, 9,500 g, and 7,250 g.

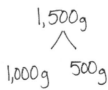

Application Problem (8 minutes)

A bakery used 12,674 kg of flour. Of that, 1,802 kg was whole wheat and 888 kg was rice flour. The rest was all-purpose flour. How much all-purpose flour did they use? Solve and check the reasonableness of your answer.

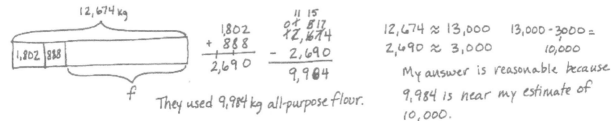

Note: This problem leads into today's lesson and bridges as it goes back into the work from Lesson 16.

Concept Development (35 minutes)

Materials: (S) Problem Set

Suggested Delivery of Instruction for Solving Topic F's Word Problems

1. Model the problem.

Have two pairs of students (choose as models those students who are likely to successfully solve the problem) work at the board while the others work independently or in pairs at their seats. Review the following questions before solving the first problem.

  ▪   Can you draw something?
  ▪   What can you draw?
  ▪   What conclusions can you make from your drawing?

As students work, circulate. Reiterate the questions above.

After two minutes, have the two pairs of students share *only* their labeled diagrams.

For about one minute, have the demonstrating students receive and respond to feedback and questions from their peers.

2. Calculate to solve and write a statement.

Give everyone two minutes to finish work on the problem, sharing their work and thinking with a peer. All should then write their equations and statements for the answer.

3. Assess the solution for reasonableness.

Give students one to two minutes to assess and explain the reasonableness of their solutions.

Note: In Lessons 17–19, the Problem Set comprises word problems from the lesson and is, therefore, to be used during the lesson itself.

Problem 1: Solve a single-step word problem using *how much more*.

Sean's school raised $32,587. Leslie's school raised $18,749. How much more money did Sean's school raise?

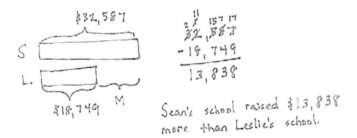

Support students in realizing that though the question is asking, "How much more?" the tape diagram shows that the unknown is a missing part, and therefore, subtraction is necessary to find the answer.

Problem 2: Solve a single-step word problem using *how many fewer*.

At a parade, 97,853 people sat in bleachers. 388,547 people stood along the street. How many fewer people were in the bleachers than standing along the street?

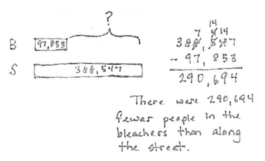

Circulate and support students to realize that the unknown number of how many fewer people is the difference between the two tape diagrams. Encourage them to write a statement using the word *fewer* when talking about separate things. For example, I have *fewer* apples than you do and *less* juice.

246   Lesson 17:   Solve *additive compare* word problems modeled with tape diagrams.

©2015 Great Minds. eureka-math.org
G4-M1M2-TE-BK1-1.3.1-1.2016

Problem 3: Solve a two-step problem using *how much more*.

A pair of hippos weighs 5,201 kilograms together. The female weighs 2,038 kilograms. How much more does the male weigh than the female?

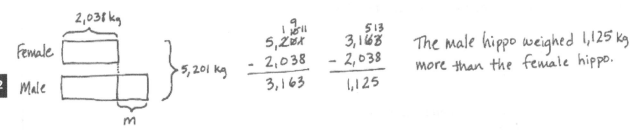

MP.2

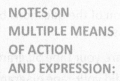

The male hippo weighed 1,125 kg more than the female hippo.

Many students may want to draw this as a single tape showing the combined weight to start. That works. However, the second step most likely requires a new double tape to compare the weights of the male and female. If no one comes up with the model pictured, it can be shown quickly. Students generally do not choose to draw a bracket with the known total to the side until they are very familiar with two-step comparison models. However, be aware that students have modeled this problem type since Grade 2.

Problem 4: Solve a three-step problem using *how much longer*.

A copper wire was 240 meters long. After 60 meters was cut off, it was double the length of a steel wire. How much longer was the copper wire than the steel wire at first?

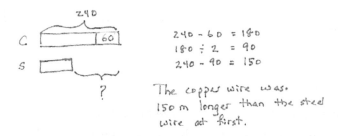

$$240 - 60 = 180$$
$$180 \div 2 = 90$$
$$240 - 90 = 150$$

The copper wire was 150 m longer than the steel wire at first.

> **NOTES ON**
> **MULTIPLE MEANS**
> **OF ACTION**
> **AND EXPRESSION:**
>
> For students who may find Problem 4 challenging, remind them of the work done earlier in this module with multiples of 10. For example, 180 is ten times as much as 18. If 18 divided by 2 is 9, then 180 divided by 2 is 90.

T: Read the problem, draw a model, write equations both to estimate and calculate precisely, and write a statement. I'll give you five minutes.

Circulate, using the bulleted questions to guide students. When students get stuck, encourage them to focus on what they can learn from their drawings.

- Show me the copper wire at first.
- In your model, show me what happened to the copper wire.
- In your model, show me what you know about the steel wire.
- What are you comparing? Where is that difference in your model?

Notice the number size is quite small here. The calculations are not the issue but rather the relationships. Students will eventually solve similar problems with larger numbers, but they will begin here at a simple level numerically.

Problem Set

Please note that in Topic F, the Problem Sets are used in the Concept Developments. As a result, the 10 minutes usually allotted for the completion of the Problem Set are not needed.

Student Debrief (7 minutes)

Lesson Objective: Solve *additive compare* word problems modeled with tape diagrams.

The Student Debrief is intended to invite reflection and active processing of the total lesson experience.

Invite students to review their solutions for the Problem Set. They should check work by comparing answers with a partner before going over answers as a class. Look for misconceptions or misunderstandings that can be addressed in the Student Debrief. Guide students in a conversation to debrief the Problem Set and process the lesson.

Any combination of the questions below may be used to lead the discussion.

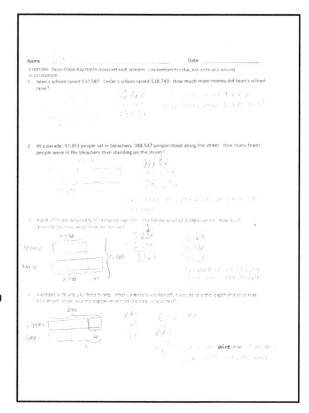

- How are your tape diagrams for Problem 1 and Problem 2 similar?
- How did your tape diagrams vary across all problems?
- In Problem 3, how did drawing a double tape diagram help you to visualize the problem?
- What was most challenging about drawing the tape diagram for Problem 4? What helped you find the best diagram to solve the problem?
- What different ways are there to draw a tape diagram to solve comparative problems?
- What does the word *compare* mean?
- What phrases do you notice repeated through many of today's problems that help you to see the problem as a comparative problem?

Exit Ticket (3 minutes)

After the Student Debrief, instruct students to complete the Exit Ticket. A review of their work will help with assessing students' understanding of the concepts that were presented in today's lesson and planning more effectively for future lessons. The questions may be read aloud to the students.

EUREKA MATH™

Name _____ Date _____

Draw a tape diagram to represent each problem. Use numbers to solve, and write your answer as a statement.

1. Sean's school raised $32,587. Leslie's school raised $18,749. How much more money did Sean's school raise?

2. At a parade, 97,853 people sat in bleachers, and 388,547 people stood along the street. How many fewer people were in the bleachers than standing on the street?

EUREKA MATH

Lesson 17: Solve *additive compare* word problems modeled with tape diagrams.

249

©2015 Great Minds. eureka-math.org
G4-M1M2-TE-BK1-1.3.1-1.2016

3. A pair of hippos weighs 5,201 kilograms together. The female weighs 2,038 kilograms. How much more does the male weigh than the female?

4. A copper wire was 240 meters long. After 60 meters was cut off, it was double the length of a steel wire. How much longer was the copper wire than the steel wire at first?

Lesson 17:   Solve *additive compare* word problems modeled with tape diagrams.

©2015 Great Minds. eureka-math.org
G4-M1M2-TE-BK1-1.3.1-1.2016

Name _____ Date _____

Draw a tape diagram to represent each problem. Use numbers to solve, and write your answer as a statement.

A mixture of 2 chemicals measures 1,034 milliliters. It contains some of Chemical A and 755 milliliters of Chemical B. How much less of Chemical A than Chemical B is in the mixture?

EUREKA MATH

Lesson 17: Solve *additive compare* word problems modeled with tape diagrams.

251

Name _____ Date _____

Draw a tape diagram to represent each problem. Use numbers to solve, and write your answer as a statement.

1. Gavin has 1,094 toy building blocks. Avery only has 816 toy building blocks. How many more building blocks does Gavin have?

2. Container B holds 2,391 liters of water. Together, Container A and Container B hold 11,875 liters of water. How many more liters of water does Container A hold than Container B?

Lesson 17: Solve *additive compare* word problems modeled with tape diagrams.

EUREKA
MATH

3. A piece of yellow yarn was 230 inches long. After 90 inches had been cut from it, the piece of yellow yarn was twice as long as a piece of blue yarn. At first, how much longer was the yellow yarn than the blue yarn?

EUREKA MATH

Lesson 17:   Solve *additive compare* word problems modeled with tape diagrams.

©2015 Great Minds. eureka-math.org
G4-M1M2-TE-BK1-1.3.1-1.2016

253

Lesson 18

Objective: Solve multi-step word problems modeled with tape diagrams, and assess the reasonableness of answers using rounding.

Suggested Lesson Structure

- ■ Fluency Practice   (10 minutes)
- ■ Application Problem   (5 minutes)
- ▢ Concept Development   (33 minutes)
- ■ Student Debrief   (12 minutes)
  - **Total Time**   **(60 minutes)**

Fluency Practice (10 minutes)

- Number Patterns **4.OA.5**   (5 minutes)
- Convert Units **4.MD.1**   (5 minutes)

Number Patterns (5 minutes)

Materials: (S) Personal white board

Note: This fluency activity bolsters students' place value understanding and helps them apply these skills to a variety of concepts.

- T: (Project 40,100, 50,100, 60,100, _____.) What is the place value of the digit that's changing?
- S: Ten thousand.
- T: Count with me saying the value of the digit I'm pointing to.
- S: (Point at the ten thousand digit as students count.) 40,000, 50,000, 60,000.
- T: On your personal white board, write what number would come after 60,100.
- S: (Write 70,100.)

Repeat with the following possible sequence: 82,030, 72,030, 62,030, ___; 215,003, 216,003, 217,003, ___; 943,612, 943,512, 943,412, ___; and 372,435, 382,435, 392,435, ___.

Convert Units (5 minutes)

Materials: (S) Personal white board

Note: This fluency activity strengthens understanding of the relationship between kilograms and grams learned in Grade 3, preparing students to use this relationship to solve problems in Module 2, Topic A. Use a number bond to support understanding of the relationship between grams and kilograms.

Lesson 18:   Solve multi-step word problems modeled with tape diagrams, and
assess the reasonableness of answers using rounding.

©2015 Great Minds. eureka-math.org
G4-M1M2-TE-BK1-1.3.1-1.2016

T: Count by 200 grams starting at 0 grams and counting up to 2,000 grams. When you get to 1,000 grams, say "1 kilogram." When you get to 2,000 grams, say "2 kilograms."

S: 0 g, 200 g, 400 g, 600 g, 800 g, 1 kg, 1,200 g, 1,400 g, 1,600 g, 1,800 g, 2 kg.

Repeat the process, this time pulling out the kilogram (e.g., 1 kg 200 g, 1 kg 400 g).

T: (Write 1,300 g = ___ kg ___ g.) On your board, fill in the blanks to make a true number sentence.

S: (Write 1,300 g = 1 kg 300 g.)

Repeat the process for 1,003 g, 1,750 g, 3,450 g, and 7,030 g.

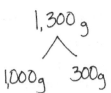

Application Problem (5 minutes)

In all, 30,436 people went skiing in February and January. 16,009 went skiing in February. How many fewer people went skiing in January than in February?

Note: This *comparison subtraction* problem reviews content from Lesson 17.

Concept Development (33 minutes)

Materials: (S) Problem Set

Suggested Delivery of Instruction for Solving Topic F's Word Problems

1. Model the problem.

Have two pairs of students work at the board while the others work independently or in pairs at their seats. Review the following questions before beginning the first problem.

- Can you draw something?
- What can you draw?
- What conclusions can you make from your drawing?

As students work, circulate. Reiterate the questions above.

After two minutes, have the two pairs of students share *only* their labeled diagrams.

For about one minute, have the demonstrating students receive and respond to feedback and questions from their peers.

Lesson 18:   Solve multi-step word problems modeled with tape diagrams, and assess the reasonableness of answers using rounding.   255

©2015 Great Minds. eureka-math.org
G4-M1M2-TE-BK1-1.3.1-1.2016

2. Calculate to solve and write a statement.

Give everyone two minutes to finish work on the problem, sharing their work and thinking with a peer. All should then write their equations and statements for the answer.

3. Assess the solution for reasonableness.

Give students one to two minutes to assess and explain the reasonableness of their solutions.

Note: In Lessons 17–19, the Problem Set comprises the word problems from the lesson and is, therefore, to be used during the lesson itself.

Problem 1: Solve a multi-step word problem requiring addition and subtraction, modeled with a tape diagram, and check the reasonableness of the answer using estimation.

In one year, a factory used 11,650 meters of cotton, 4,950 fewer meters of silk than cotton, and 3,500 fewer meters of wool than silk. How many meters in all were used of the three fabrics?

This problem is a step forward for students as they subtract to find the amount of wool from the amount of silk. Students also might subtract the sum of 4,950 and 3,500 from 11,650 to find the meters of wool and add that to the amount of silk. It is a longer method but makes sense. Circulate and look for other alternate strategies, which can be quickly mentioned or explored more deeply as appropriate. Be advised, however, not to emphasize creativity but rather analysis and efficiency. Ingenious shortcuts might be highlighted.

After students have solved the problem, ask them to check their answers for reasonableness:

 T: How can you know if 21,550 is a reasonable answer? Discuss with your partner.

 S: Well, I can see by looking at the diagram that the amount of wool fits in the part where the amount of silk is unknown, so the answer is a little less than double 12,000. Our answer makes sense.

 S: Another way to think about it is that 11,650 can be rounded to 12 thousands. 12 thousands plus 7 thousands for the silk, since 12 thousands minus 5 thousands is 7 thousands, plus about 4 thousands for the wool. That's 23 thousands.

Lesson 18:   Solve multi-step word problems modeled with tape diagrams, and
                                    assess the reasonableness of answers using rounding.

©2015 Great Minds. eureka-math.org
G4-M1M2-TE-BK1-1.3.1-1.2016

EUREKA
MATH

Problem 2: Solve an additive multi-step word problem using a tape diagram, modeled with a tape diagram, and check the reasonableness of the answer using estimation.

The shop sold 12,789 chocolate and 9,324 cookie dough cones. It sold 1,078 more peanut butter cones than cookie dough cones and 999 more vanilla cones than chocolate cones. What was the total number of ice cream cones sold?

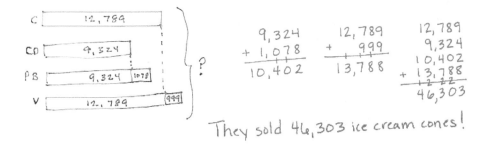

The solution above shows calculating the total number of cones of each flavor and then adding. Students may also add like units before adding the extra parts.

After students have solved the problem, ask them to check their answers for reasonableness.

MP.3

T: How can you know if 46,303 is a reasonable answer? Discuss with your partner.

S: By looking at the tape diagram, I can see we have 2 thirteen thousands units. That's 26 thousands. We have 2 nine thousands units. So, 26 thousands and 18 thousands is 44 thousands. Plus about 2 thousands more. That's 46 thousands. That's close.

S: Another way to see it is that I can kind of see 2 thirteen thousands, and the little extra pieces with the peanut butter make 11 thousands. That is 37 thousands plus 9 thousands from cookie dough is 46 thousands. That's close.

Problem 3: Solve a multi-step word problem requiring addition and subtraction, modeled with a tape diagram, and check the reasonableness of the answer using estimation.

In the first week of June, a restaurant sold 10,345 omelets. In the second week, 1,096 fewer omelets were sold than in the first week. In the third week, 2 thousand more omelets were sold than in the first week. In the fourth week, 2 thousand fewer omelets were sold than in the first week. How many omelets were sold in all in June?

This problem is interesting because 2 thousand more and 2 thousand less mean that there is one more unit of 10,345. We, therefore, simply add in the omelets from the second week to three units of 10,345.

T: How can you know if 40,284 is a reasonable answer? Discuss with your partner.

S: By looking at the tape diagram, it's easy to see it is like 3 ten thousands plus 9 thousands. That's 39 thousands. That is close to our answer.

S: Another way to see it is just rounding one week at a time starting at the first week; 10 thousands plus 9 thousands plus 12 thousands plus 8 thousands. That's 39 thousands.

Problem Set

Please note that in Topic F, the Problem Sets are used in the Concept Developments. As a result, the 10 minutes usually allotted for the completion of the Problem Set are not needed.

Student Debrief (12 minutes)

Lesson Objective: Solve multi-step word problems modeled with tape diagrams, and assess the reasonableness of answers using rounding.

The Student Debrief is intended to invite reflection and active processing of the total lesson experience.

Invite students to review their solutions for the Problem Set. They should check work by comparing answers with a partner before going over answers as a class. Look for misconceptions or misunderstandings that can be addressed in the Student Debrief. Guide students in a conversation to debrief the Problem Set and process the lesson.

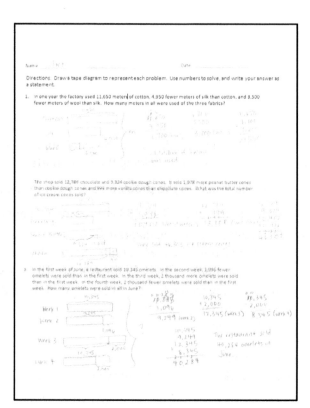

Any combination of the questions below may be used to lead the discussion.

- How are the problems alike? How are they different?
- How was your solution the same and different from those that were demonstrated by your peers?
- Why is there more than one right way to solve, for example, Problem 3?
- Did you see other solutions that surprised you or made you see the problem differently?
- In Problem 1, was the part unknown or the total unknown? What about in Problems 2 and 3?
- Why is it helpful to assess for reasonableness after solving?
- How were the tape diagrams helpful in estimating to test for reasonableness? Why is that?

Lesson 18:   Solve multi-step word problems modeled with tape diagrams, and
                               assess the reasonableness of answers using rounding.

Exit Ticket (3 minutes)

After the Student Debrief, instruct students to complete the Exit Ticket. A review of their work will help with assessing students' understanding of the concepts that were presented in today's lesson and planning more effectively for future lessons. The questions may be read aloud to the students.

Lesson 18:   Solve multi-step word problems modeled with tape diagrams, and
               assess the reasonableness of answers using rounding.

©2015 Great Minds. eureka-math.org
G4-M1M2-TE-BK1-1.3.1-1.2016

259

Name _____   Date _____

Draw a tape diagram to represent each problem. Use numbers to solve, and write your answer as a statement.

1. In one year, the factory used 11,650 meters of cotton, 4,950 fewer meters of silk than cotton, and 3,500 fewer meters of wool than silk. How many meters in all were used of the three fabrics?

2. The shop sold 12,789 chocolate and 9,324 cookie dough cones. It sold 1,078 more peanut butter cones than cookie dough cones and 999 more vanilla cones than chocolate cones. What was the total number of ice cream cones sold?

Lesson 18:   Solve multi-step word problems modeled with tape diagrams, and
                                 assess the reasonableness of answers using rounding.

                  ©2015 Great Minds. eureka-math.org
                  G4-M1M2-TE-BK1-1.3.1-1.2016

EUREKA
MATH™

3. In the first week of June, a restaurant sold 10,345 omelets. In the second week, 1,096 fewer omelets were sold than in the first week. In the third week, 2 thousand more omelets were sold than in the first week. In the fourth week, 2 thousand fewer omelets were sold than in the first week. How many omelets were sold in all in June?

EUREKA
MATH™

Lesson 18:   Solve multi-step word problems modeled with tape diagrams, and
              assess the reasonableness of answers using rounding.

©2015 Great Minds. eureka-math.org
G4-M1M2-TE-BK1-1.3.1-1.2016

261

Name _____   Date _____

Draw a tape diagram to represent the problem. Use numbers to solve, and write your answer as a statement.

Park A covers an area of 4,926 square kilometers. It is 1,845 square kilometers larger than Park B.
Park C is 4,006 square kilometers larger than Park A.

1. What is the area of all three parks?

2. Assess the reasonableness of your answer.

Lesson 18:   Solve multi-step word problems modeled with tape diagrams, and
                           assess the reasonableness of answers using rounding.

                    ©2015 Great Minds. eureka-math.org
                    G4-M1M2-TE-BK1-1.3.1-1.2016

EUREKA MATH™

Name _____ Date _____

Draw a tape diagram to represent each problem. Use numbers to solve, and write your answer as a statement.

1. There were 22,869 children, 49,563 men, and 2,872 more women than men at the fair. How many people were at the fair?

2. Number A is 4,676. Number B is 10,043 greater than A. Number C is 2,610 less than B. What is the total value of numbers A, B, and C?

EUREKA MATH

Lesson 18: Solve multi-step word problems modeled with tape diagrams, and assess the reasonableness of answers using rounding.

©2015 Great Minds. eureka-math.org
G4-M1M2-TE-BK1-1.3.1-1.2016

263

3. A store sold a total of 21,650 balls. It sold 11,795 baseballs. It sold 4,150 fewer basketballs than baseballs. The rest of the balls sold were footballs. How many footballs did the store sell?

Lesson 18: Solve multi-step word problems modeled with tape diagrams, and assess the reasonableness of answers using rounding.

©2015 Great Minds. eureka-math.org
G4-M1M2-TE-BK1-1.3.1-1.2016

EUREKA
MATH™

Lesson 19

Objective: Create and solve multi-step word problems from given tape diagrams and equations.

Suggested Lesson Structure

■ Fluency Practice   (12 minutes)
■ Application Problem   (5 minutes)
□ Concept Development   (30 minutes)
■ Student Debrief   (13 minutes)
   Total Time   **(60 minutes)**

Fluency Practice (12 minutes)

- Rename Units to Subtract **4.NBT.4**   (5 minutes)
- Add Up to the Next Unit **4.NBT.4**   (3 minutes)
- Convert Units **4.MD.1**   (4 minutes)

Rename Units to Subtract (5 minutes)

Note: This fluency activity supports further practice of decomposing a larger unit to make smaller units in order to subtract.

T: (Write 1 ten – 6 ones.) Am I ready to subtract?
S: No.
T: Rename 1 ten as 10 ones. Say the entire number sentence.
S: 10 ones minus 6 ones is 4 ones.

Repeat with 2 tens – 6 ones, 2 tens – 1 ten 6 ones, 1 hundred – 6 tens, 2 hundreds – 4 tens, 3 hundreds – 1 hundred 4 tens, 5 thousands – 3 hundreds, 5 thousands – 3 thousands 3 hundreds, 2 ten thousands – 3 hundreds.

Add Up to the Next Unit (3 minutes)

Note: This fluency activity strengthens students' ability to make the next unit, a skill used when using the arrow way to add or subtract. This activity also anticipates students' use of the arrow way to solve mixed measurement unit addition and subtraction in Module 2.

T: (Write 8.) How many more to make 10?
S: 2.
T: (Write 80.) How many more to make 100?
S: 20.

©2015 Great Minds. eureka-math.org
G4-M1M2-TE-BK1-1.3.1-1.2016

T: (Write 84.) How many more to make 100?

S: 16.

Repeat with the following numbers to make 1000: 200, 250, 450, 475, 600, 680, 700, 720, 800, 805, 855, and 945.

Convert Units (4 minutes)

Note: Reviewing unit conversions that were learned in Grade 3 helps prepare students to solve problems with centimeters and meters in Topic A of Module 2.

Materials: (S) Personal white board

T: (Write 1 m = ___ cm.) How many centimeters are in a meter?

S: 1 m = 100 cm.

Repeat the process for 2 m, 3 m, 8 m, 8 m 50 cm, 7 m 50 cm, and 4 m 25 cm.

T: (Write 100 cm = ___ m.) Say the answer.

S: 100 cm = 1 m.

T: (Write 150 cm = ___ m ___ cm.) Say the answer.

S: 150 cm = 1 m 50 cm. Repeat the process for 250 cm, 350 cm, 950 cm, and 725 cm.

Application Problem (5 minutes)

For Jordan to get to his grandparents' house, he has to travel through Albany and Plattsburgh. From Jordan's house to Albany is 189 miles. From Albany to Plattsburgh is 161 miles. If the total distance of the trip is 508 miles, how far from Plattsburgh do Jordan's grandparents live?

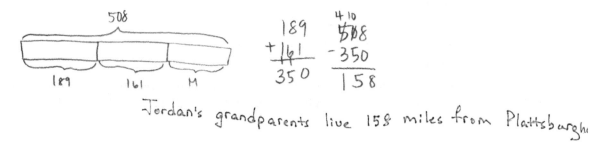

Note: This problem reviews two-step problems from the previous lessons.

Lesson 19:   Create and solve multi-step word problems from given tape diagrams and equations.

©2015 Great Minds. eureka-math.org
G4-M1M2-TE-BK1-1.3.1-1.2016

EUREKA
MATH™

Concept Development (30 minutes)

Materials: (S) Problem Set

Suggested Delivery of Instruction for Lesson 19's Word Problems

1. Draw the labeled tape diagram on the board, and give students the context. Have them write a story problem based on the tape diagram.

Have two pairs of students who you think can be successful with writing a problem work at the board while the others work independently or in pairs at their seats. Review the following questions before beginning the first problem.

- What story makes sense with the diagram?
- What question will I ask in my word problem?

As students work, circulate. Reiterate the questions above.

After two minutes, have the two pairs of students share their stories.

For about one minute, have the demonstrating students receive and respond to feedback and questions from their peers.

2. Calculate to solve and write a statement.

Give everyone two minutes to exchange stories, calculate, and make a statement of the answer.

3. Assess the solution for reasonableness.

Give students one to two minutes to assess and explain the reasonableness of their solutions.

Note: In Lessons 17–19, the Problem Set comprises the word problems from the lesson and is, therefore, to be used during the lesson itself.

Problem 1: Create and solve a simple two-step word problem from the tape diagram below.

Suggested context: people at a football game.

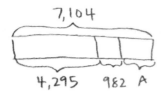

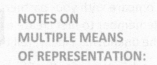

NOTES ON
MULTIPLE MEANS
OF REPRESENTATION:

Students who are English language learners may find it difficult to create their own problems. Work together with a small group of students to explain what the tape diagram is showing. Work with students to write information into the tape diagram. Discuss what is known and unknown. Together, build a question based on the discussion.

Problem 2: Create and solve a two-step addition word problem from the tape diagram below.

Suggested context: cost of two houses.

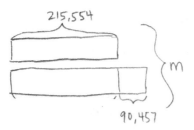

NOTES ON
MULTIPLE MEANS
OF ACTION
AND REPRESENTATION:

Students working below grade level may struggle with the task of creating their own problems. These students may benefit from working together in a partnership with another student. First, encourage them to design a tape diagram showing the known parts, the unknown part, and the whole. Second, encourage them to create a word problem based on the diagram.

Problem 3: Create and solve a three-step word problem involving addition and subtraction from the tape diagram below.

Suggested context: weight in kilograms of three different whales.

MP.2

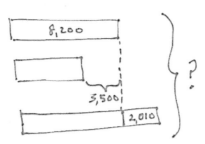

Problem 4: Students use equations to model and solve multi-step word problems.

Display the equation 5,233 + 3,094 + k = 12,946.

 T: Draw a tape diagram that models this equation.

 T: Compare with your partner. Then, create a word problem that uses the numbers from the equation. Remember to first create a context. Then, write a statement about the total and a question about the unknown. Finally, tell the rest of the information.

Students work independently. Students can share problems in partners to solve or select word problems to solve as a class.

Problem Set

Please note that the Problem Set in Topic F comprises the lesson's problems as stated at the introduction of the lesson.

For some classes, it may be appropriate to modify the assignment by specifying which problems they work on first. Some problems do not specify a method for solving. Students should solve these problems using the RDW approach used for Application Problems.

Student Debrief (13 minutes)

Lesson Objective: Create and solve multi-step word problems from given tape diagrams and equations.

The Student Debrief is intended to invite reflection and active processing of the total lesson experience.

Invite students to review their solutions for the Problem Set. They should check work by comparing answers with a partner before going over answers as a class. Look for misconceptions or misunderstandings that can be addressed in the Student Debrief. Guide students in a conversation to debrief the Problem Set and process the lesson.

Any combination of the questions below may be used to lead the discussion.

- How does a tape diagram help when solving a problem?

- What is the hardest part about creating a context for a word problem?

- To write a word problem, what must you know?

- There are many different contexts for Problem 2, but everyone found the same answer. How is that possible?

- What have you learned about yourself as a mathematician over the past module?

- How can you use this new understanding of addition, subtraction, and solving word problems in the future?

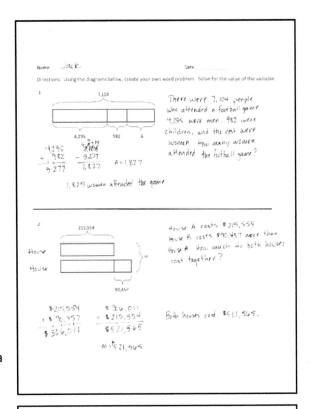

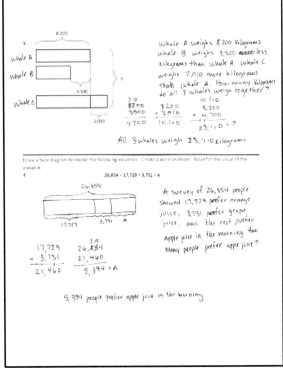

Lesson 19: Create and solve multi-step word problems from given tape diagrams and equations.

©2015 Great Minds. eureka-math.org
G4-M1M2-TE-BK1-1.3.1-1.2016

269

Exit Ticket (3 minutes)

After the Student Debrief, instruct students to complete the Exit Ticket. A review of their work will help with assessing students' understanding of the concepts that were presented in today's lesson and planning more effectively for future lessons. The questions may be read aloud to the students.

Lesson 19: Create and solve multi-step word problems from given tape diagrams and equations.

©2015 Great Minds. eureka-math.org
G4-M1M2-TE-BK1-1.3.1-1.2016

EUREKA MATH™

Name _____ Date _____

Using the diagrams below, create your own word problem. Solve for the value of the variable.

1.

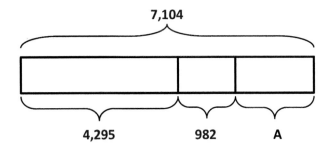

2.

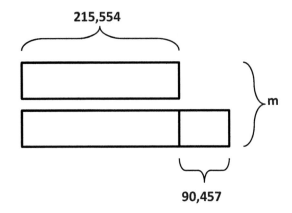

Lesson 19: Create and solve multi-step word problems from given tape diagrams and equations.

©2015 Great Minds. eureka-math.org
G4-M1M2-TE-BK1-1.3.1-1.2016

271

3.

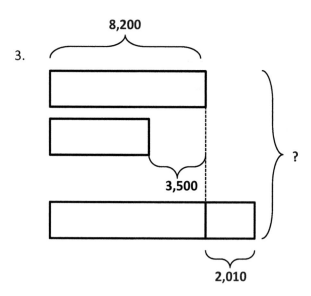

8,200

3,500

?

2,010

---

4. Draw a tape diagram to model the following equation. Create a word problem. Solve for the value of the variable.

$$26,854 = 17,729 + 3,731 + A$$

EUREKA
MATH™

Name _____ Date _____

Using the diagram below, create your own word problem. Solve for the value of the variable.

1.

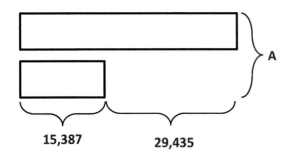

15,387   29,435

2. Using the equation below, draw a tape diagram and create your own word problem. Solve for the value of the variable.

$$248,798 = 113,205 + A + 99,937$$

Lesson 19:   Create and solve multi-step word problems from given tape diagrams
                and equations.

©2015 Great Minds. eureka-math.org
G4-M1M2-TE-BK1-1.3.1-1.2016

273

Name _____   Date _____

Using the diagrams below, create your own word problem. Solve for the value of the variable.

1. At the local botanical gardens, there are _____

    Redwoods and _____ Cypress trees.

    There are a total of _____ Redwood,

    Cypress, and Dogwood trees.

    How many _____

    _____

    _____?

Redwood	Cypress	Dogwood
6,294	3,849	A

12,115

2. There are 65,302 _____

    _____.

    There are 37,436 fewer _____

    _____.

    How many _____

    _____?

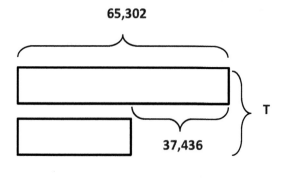

65,302

37,436

T

Lesson 19:   Create and solve multi-step word problems from given tape diagrams and equations.

©2015 Great Minds. eureka-math.org
G4-M1M2-TE-BK1-1.3.1-1.2016

EUREKA
MATH

3. Use the following tape diagram to create a word problem. Solve for the value of the variable.

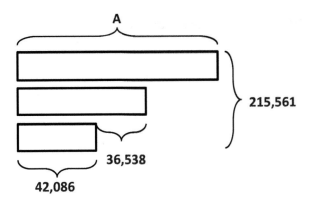

4. Draw a tape diagram to model the following equation. Create a word problem. Solve for the value of the variable.

$$27,894 + A + 6,892 = 40,392$$

Lesson 19:   Create and solve multi-step word problems from given tape diagrams
                  and equations.

©2015 Great Minds. eureka-math.org
G4-M1M2-TE-BK1-1.3.1-1.2016

275

Name _____ Date _____

1. Compare the values of each 7 in the number 771,548. Use a picture, numbers, or words to explain.

2. Compare using >, <, or =. Write your answer inside the circle.

   a. 234 thousands + 7 ten thousands  241,000

   b. 4 hundred thousands – 2 thousands 200,000

   c. 1 million 4 hundred thousands + 6 hundred thousands

   d. 709 thousands – 1 hundred thousand ◯ 708 thousands

Module 1:   Place Value, Rounding, and Algorithms for Addition and Subtraction

EUREKA
MATH™

3. Norfolk, VA, has a population of 242,628 people. Baltimore, MD, has 376,865 more people than Norfolk. Charleston, SC, has 496,804 less people than Baltimore.

   a. What is the total population of all three cities? Draw a tape diagram to model the word problem. Then, solve the problem.

   b. Round to the nearest hundred thousand to check the reasonableness of your answer for the population of Charleston, SC.

   c. Record each city's population in numbers, in words, and in expanded form.

d. Compare the population of Norfolk and Charleston using >, <, or =.

e. Eddie lives in Fredericksburg, VA, which has a population of 24,286. He says that Norfolk's population is about 10 times as large as Fredericksburg's population. Explain Eddie's thinking.

End-of-Module Assessment Task Standards Addressed	Topics A–F

Use the four operations with whole numbers to solve problems.

4.OA.3   Solve multistep word problems posed with whole numbers and having whole-number answers using the four operations, including problems in which remainders must be interpreted. Represent these problems using equations with a letter standing for the unknown quantity. Assess the reasonableness of answers using mental computation and estimation strategies including rounding.

Generalize place value understanding for multi-digit whole numbers.

4.NBT.1   Recognize that in a multi-digit whole number, a digit in one place represents ten times what it represents in the place to its right. *For example, recognize that 700 ÷ 70 = 10 by applying concepts of place value and division.*

4.NBT.2   Read and write multi-digit whole numbers using base-ten numerals, number names, and expanded form. Compare two multi-digit numbers based on meanings of the digits in each place, using >, =, and < symbols to record the results of comparisons.

4.NBT.3   Use place value understanding to round multi-digit whole numbers to any place.

Use place value understanding and properties of operations to perform multi-digit arithmetic.

4.NBT.4   Fluently add and subtract multi-digit whole numbers using the standard algorithm.

Evaluating Student Learning Outcomes

A Progression Toward Mastery is provided to describe steps that illuminate the gradually increasing understandings that students develop *on their way to proficiency.* In this chart, this progress is presented from left (Step 1) to right (Step 4). The learning goal for students is to achieve Step 4 mastery. These steps are meant to help teachers and students identify and celebrate what the students CAN do now and what they need to work on next.

©2015 Great Minds. eureka-math.org
G4-M1M2-TE-BK1-1.3.1-1.2016

A Progression Toward Mastery

Assessment Task Item and Standards Addressed	STEP 1 Little evidence of reasoning without a correct answer. (1 Point)	STEP 2 Evidence of some reasoning without a correct answer. (2 Points)	STEP 3 Evidence of some reasoning with a correct answer or evidence of solid reasoning with an incorrect answer. (3 Points)	STEP 4 Evidence of solid reasoning with a correct answer. (4 Points)
1 **4.NBT.1**	The student provides limited reasoning about the relationship of the values of the 7s.	The student can reason about the relationship between the values of the 7s but does not show a supporting picture or numbers.	The student is able to reason about the relationship of the 7s, but her reasoning does not fully support her picture or numbers.	The student correctly reasons the 7 in the hundred thousands place is 10 times the value of the 7 in the ten thousands place, using a picture, numbers, or words to explain.
2 **4.NBT.2** **4.NBT.4**	The student correctly answers less than two of the four parts.	The student correctly answers two of the four parts.	The student correctly answers three of the four parts.	The student correctly answers all four parts: a. > b. > c. = d. <
3 **4.NBT.1** **4.NBT.2** **4.NBT.3** **4.NBT.4** **4.OA.3**	The student correctly answers less than two of the five parts.	The student correctly answers two of the five parts.	The student answers four or five of the five parts correctly but with only some reasoning in Parts (b) and (e). OR The student answers three or four of the parts correctly with solid reasoning for all parts.	The student correctly answers all five parts: a. 984,810. b. The population of Baltimore is about 600,000. The population of Charleston is about 500,000 less than Baltimore, or 100,000. Therefore, 122,689 is a reasonable answer. c. Charleston, SC: One hundred twenty-two thousand, six hundred eighty-nine. 100,000 + 20,000 + 2,000 + 600 + 80 + 9.

EUREKA MATH™

A Progression Toward Mastery

				Baltimore, MD: Six hundred nineteen thousand, four hundred ninety-three. 600,000 + 10,000 + 9,000 + 400 + 90 + 3. Norfolk, VA: Two hundred forty-two thousand, six hundred twenty-eight. 200,000 + 40,000 + 2,000 + 600 + 20 + 8.
				d. Norfolk: 242,628 > Charleston, 122,689.
				e. Eddie is correct to think that Norfolk's population is about 10 times that of Fredericksburg's because Norfolk's population is about 240,000, while Fredericksburg's is about 24,000. 240,000 is ten times as many as 24,000.

Name ___Jack_____   Date _____

1. Compare the values of each 7 in the number 771,548. Use a picture, numbers, or words to explain.

The 7 in the hundred thousands place is ten times the value of the 7 in the ten thousands place.

$$10 \times 70,000 = 700,000$$

hundred thousands	ten thousands	thousands	hundreds	tens	ones
7	7	1	5	4	8
7	0	0	0	0	0
	7	0	0	0	0
		1	0	0	0
			5	0	0
				4	0
					8

2. Compare using >, <, or =. Write your answer inside the circle.

a. 234 thousands + 7 ten thousands   241,000

$$\begin{array}{r} 234,000 \\ +\ \ 70,000 \\ \hline 304,000 \end{array}$$

b. 4 hundred thousands – 2 thousands   200,000

$$\begin{array}{r} 3\,9\,10 \\ \cancel{400},000 \\ -\ \ \ 2,000 \\ \hline 398,000 \end{array}$$

c. 1 million   4 hundred thousands + 6 hundred thousands

$$\begin{array}{r} 400,000 \\ +\ 600,000 \\ \hline 1,000,000 \end{array}$$

d. 709 thousands – 1 hundred thousand   708 thousands

$$\begin{array}{r} 709,000 \\ -100,000 \\ \hline 609,000 \end{array}$$

Module 1:   Place Value, Rounding, and Algorithms for Addition and Subtraction

©2015 Great Minds. eureka-math.org
G4-M1M2-TE-BK1-1.3.1-1.2016

EUREKA
MATH™

3. Norfolk, VA has a population of 242,628 people. Baltimore, MD has 376,865 more people than Norfolk.
    Charleston, SC has 496,804 less people than Baltimore.

    a. What is the total population of all three cities? Draw a tape diagram to model the word problem.
        Then solve the problem.

Norfolk | 242,628 | 376,865

Baltimore [   ]

Charleston [   ]
                496,804

Baltimore
$$\begin{array}{r} 242,628 \\ + 376,865 \\ \hline 619,493 \end{array}$$

Charleston
$$\begin{array}{r} 619,493 \\ - 496,804 \\ \hline 122,689 \end{array}$$

$$\begin{array}{r} 242,628 \\ 619,493 \\ + 122,689 \\ \hline 984,810 \end{array}$$

The total population of all
three cities is 984,810.

    b. Round to the nearest hundred thousand to check the reasonableness of your answer for the
        population of Charleston, SC.

Baltimore's population rounded to the nearest hundred thousand is 600,000
Charleston's population is about 500,000 less than Baltimore's population
600,000 - 500,000 = 100,000. The answer of 122,689 for the
population of Charleston is reasonable because 122,689 rounded
to the nearest hundred thousand is 100,000.

    c. Record each city's population in numbers, in words, and in expanded form.

Baltimore: 619,493   Six hundred nineteen thousand, four hundred ninety-three
            600,000 + 10,000 + 9,000 + 400 + 90 + 3

Norfolk: 242,628   two hundred forty-two thousand, six hundred twenty-eight
            200,000 + 40,000 + 2,000 + 600 + 20 + 8

Charleston: 122,689   one hundred twenty-two thousand, six hundred eighty-nine
            100,000 + 20,000 + 2,000 + 600 + 80 + 9

    d. Compare the population of Norfolk and Charleston using >, <, or =.

        Norfolk   Charleston
        242,628 > 122,689

    e. Eddie lives in Fredericksburg, VA, which has a population of 24,286. He says that Norfolk's population
        is about 10 times as large as Fredericksburg's population. Explain Eddie's thinking.

Eddie's thinking is correct because Norfolk's population is 242,628
which can be rounded to 240,000. Fredericksburg's population can be
rounded to 24,000. 240 thousands is ten times as large as
24 thousands.

H Th.	T Th.	Th.	H	T	O
2	4	0	0	0	0
2	4	0	0	0	0

Answer Key

Eureka Math
Grade 4
Module 1

Special thanks go to the Gordon A. Cain Center and to the Department of Mathematics at Louisiana State University for their support in the development of *Eureka Math*.

4
GRADE

Mathematics Curriculum

Answer Key

GRADE 4 • MODULE 1

Place Value, Rounding, and Algorithms for Addition and Subtraction

Lesson 1

Sprint

Side A

1.	20	12.	70	23.	10	34.	8
2.	30	13.	80	24.	2	35.	7
3.	40	14.	90	25.	3	36.	9
4.	50	15.	100	26.	10	37.	6
5.	10	16.	8	27.	5	38.	8
6.	2	17.	7	28.	1	39.	110
7.	3	18.	9	29.	2	40.	11
8.	5	19.	6	30.	3	41.	3
9.	1	20.	10	31.	6	42.	12
10.	4	21.	5	32.	7	43.	140
11.	60	22.	1	33.	9	44.	14

Side B

1.	10	12.	60	23.	2	34.	7
2.	20	13.	70	24.	10	35.	8
3.	30	14.	80	25.	3	36.	9
4.	40	15.	90	26.	2	37.	6
5.	50	16.	7	27.	1	38.	7
6.	3	17.	6	28.	10	39.	110
7.	2	18.	8	29.	5	40.	11
8.	4	19.	10	30.	3	41.	120
9.	1	20.	9	31.	3	42.	12
10.	5	21.	1	32.	4	43.	130
11.	100	22.	5	33.	9	44.	13

EUREKA
MATH

Problem Set

1. a. Chart accurately labeled; 30; 30; disks accurately drawn

   b. Chart accurately labeled; 20; 200; disks accurately drawn

   c. Chart accurately labeled; 40; 4,000; disks accurately drawn

2. a. 10

   b. 3; 3

   c. Ten times as many

   d. 2; explanations will vary.

3. 300; explanations will vary.

4. $8,000; explanations will vary.

5. a. 8

   b. 40

   c. 50

   d. 10 times as many

6. 10

Exit Ticket

1. Chart accurately labeled

2. 4 hundreds; 40 hundreds; 4 thousands

3. 4 thousands is 10 times as many as 4 hundreds.

Homework

1. a. Chart accurately labeled; 40; 40; disks accurately drawn

   b. Chart accurately labeled; 20; 200; disks accurately drawn

   c. Chart accurately labeled; 50; 5,000; disks accurately drawn

2. a. 10; 1

   b. 6; 6

   c. 10 times as many

   d. 40; explanations will vary.

3. 600 GB; explanations will vary.

4. $2,000; explanations will vary.

5. a. 12

   b. 90

   c. 70

   d. 10 times as many

6. 10

EUREKA
MATH™

Module 1:   Place Value, Rounding, and Algorithms for Addition and Subtraction

287

©2015 Great Minds. eureka-math.org
G4-M1M2-TE-BK1-1.3.1-1.2016

Lesson 2

Problem Set

1. a. Chart accurately labeled; 20; 2 ten thousands; disks accurately drawn

    b. Chart accurately labeled; 30; 3 hundred thousands; disks accurately drawn

    c. Chart accurately labeled; 40; 4 hundreds; disks accurately drawn

2. 60 tens; 600

    70 hundreds; 7,000

    3 hundreds; 300

    6 thousands; 6,000

    40 thousands; 40,000

3. 4 hundreds 3 tens; 430

    2 thousands 3 hundreds; 2,300

    7 ten thousands 8 thousands; 78,000

    6 hundreds 4 ones; 604

    4 thousands 3 ones; 4,003

4. Explanations will vary; chart proves answer.

5. Explanations will vary; chart proves answer.

6. $24,600

7. 4,590

8. a. 900,000

    b. The population of Planet Ruba is 10 times as many as Planet Zamba.

Exit Ticket

1. a. 406,000

    b. 802

2. $395,800

EUREKA
MATH

Homework

1. a. Chart accurately labeled; 40; 4 ten thousands; disks accurately drawn

    b. Chart accurately labeled; 40; 4 hundreds; disks accurately drawn

2. 30 tens; 300

    50 hundreds; 5,000

    9 thousands; 9,000

    70 thousands; 70,000

3. 2 hundreds 1 tens; 210

    5 thousands 5 hundreds; 5,500

    2 hundreds 7 ones; 207

    4 thousands 8 tens; 4,080

4. a. $9,500

    b. $95

Lesson 3

Sprint

Side A

1.	3	12.	21	23.	30	34.	27
2.	3	13.	21	24.	27	35.	12
3.	6	14.	24	25.	12	36.	9
4.	6	15.	24	26.	24	37.	6
5.	9	16.	27	27.	15	38.	21
6.	12	17.	27	28.	21	39.	24
7.	12	18.	30	29.	18	40.	33
8.	15	19.	30	30.	30	41.	33
9.	15	20.	9	31.	15	42.	36
10.	18	21.	3	32.	18	43.	39
11.	18	22.	6	33.	3	44.	39

Side B

1.	3	12.	21	23.	27	34.	12
2.	3	13.	21	24.	9	35.	27
3.	6	14.	24	25.	24	36.	6
4.	6	15.	24	26.	12	37.	21
5.	9	16.	27	27.	21	38.	9
6.	12	17.	27	28.	15	39.	24
7.	12	18.	30	29.	18	40.	33
8.	15	19.	30	30.	15	41.	33
9.	15	20.	3	31.	30	42.	39
10.	18	21.	30	32.	3	43.	39
11.	18	22.	6	33.	18	44.	36

EUREKA
MATH™

Problem Set

1. a. 1,234
    b. 12,345
    c. 123,456
    d. 1,234,567
    e. 12,345,678,901

2. 100
    1,000
    1,000,000
    12,000

3. a. Disks accurately drawn; 5,100
    b. Disks accurately drawn; 251,000

4. a. Disks or numbers accurately represented;
        30,000; 30
    b. Disks or numbers accurately represented;
        320,000; 320
    c. Disks or numbers accurately represented;
        321,040; 321

5. Disks or numbers prove equivalency.

Exit Ticket

1. a. 9,304
    b. 62,789
    c. 108,953

2. 27,300 accurately written; 27

Homework

1. a. 4,321
    b. 54,321
    c. 224,466
    d. 2,224,466
    e. 10,010,011,001

2. 100
    1,000
    12,000

3. a. Disks accurately drawn; 3,200
    b. Disks accurately drawn; 152,000

4. a. Disks or numbers accurately represented;
        50,000; 50
    b. Disks or numbers accurately represented;
        440,000; 440
    c. Disks or numbers accurately represented;
        273,050; 273

5. Disks or numbers prove equivalent amounts.

Lesson 4

Problem Set

1. a. Units accurately labeled; 90,523 written in chart

    b. Ninety thousand, five hundred twenty-three

    c. 90,000 + 500 + 20 + 3

2. a. Units accurately labeled; 905,203 written in chart

    b. Nine hundred five thousand, two hundred three

    c. 900,000 + 5,000 + 200 + 3

3. 2,480; 2,000 + 400 + 80

    20,482; twenty thousand, four hundred eighty-two

    64,106; 60,000 + 4,000 + 100 + 6

    Six hundred four thousand, sixteen; 600,000 + 4,000 + 10 + 6

    Nine hundred sixty thousand, sixty; 900,000 + 60,000 + 60

4. Both ways of reading 4,400 are acceptable; explanations will vary.

Exit Ticket

1. a. Units accurately labeled

    b. 806,302 written in chart

    c. Eight hundred six thousand, three hundred two

2. 100,000 + 60,000 + 500 + 80 + 2

Module 1:   Place Value, Rounding, and Algorithms for Addition and Subtraction

EUREKA
MATH™

Homework

1. a. Units accurately labeled; 50,679 written in chart

    b. Fifty thousand, six hundred seventy-nine

    c. 50,000 + 600 + 70 + 9

2. a. Units accurately labeled; 506,709 written in chart

    b. Five hundred six thousand, seven hundred nine

    c. 500,000 + 6,000 + 700 + 9

3. 5,370; 5,000 + 300 + 70

    50,372; fifty thousand, three hundred seventy-two

    39,701; 30,000 + 9,000 + 700 + 1

    Three hundred nine thousand, seventeen; 300,000 + 9,000 + 10 + 7

    Seven hundred seventy thousand, seventy; 700,000 + 70,000 + 70

4. Answers and explanations will vary.

Lesson 5

Sprint

Side A

1.	4	12.	28	23.	40	34.	36
2.	4	13.	28	24.	36	35.	16
3.	8	14.	32	25.	16	36.	12
4.	8	15.	32	26.	32	37.	8
5.	12	16.	36	27.	12	38.	28
6.	12	17.	36	28.	28	39.	32
7.	16	18.	40	29.	24	40.	44
8.	20	19.	40	30.	40	41.	44
9.	20	20.	12	31.	20	42.	48
10.	24	21.	4	32.	24	43.	48
11.	24	22.	8	33.	4	44.	52

Side B

1.	4	12.	28	23.	36	34.	16
2.	4	13.	28	24.	12	35.	36
3.	8	14.	32	25.	32	36.	8
4.	8	15.	32	26.	16	37.	28
5.	12	16.	36	27.	28	38.	12
6.	12	17.	36	28.	20	39.	32
7.	16	18.	40	29.	24	40.	44
8.	20	19.	40	30.	20	41.	44
9.	20	20.	4	31.	40	42.	48
10.	24	21.	40	32.	4	43.	48
11.	24	22.	8	33.	24	44.	52

EUREKA MATH™

Problem Set

1. a. Units accurately labeled; disks accurately drawn; >

    b. Units accurately labeled; disks accurately drawn; <

2. a. >

    b. >

    c. =

    d. <

3. 4,240 ft, 4,340 ft, 4,960 ft, 5,344 ft; Slide Mountain

4. 820; 2,008; 2,080; 8,002; 8,200

5. 728,000; 720,800; 708,200; 87,300

6. Proxima Centauri 268,269 AUs, Alpha Centauri 275,725 AUs, Barnard's Star 377,098 AUs, Sirius 542,774 AUs, Epsilon Eridani 665,282 AUs

Exit Ticket

1. 2,398 points, 2,699 points, 2,709 points, 2,976 points; Bonnie

2. a. Answers will vary.

    b. Answers will vary.

Homework

1. a. Units accurately labeled; disks accurately drawn; >

    b. Units accurately labeled; disks accurately drawn; <

2. a. >

    b. <

    c. =

    d. >

3. 1,450 ft, 1,483 ft, 1,670 ft, 1,776 ft; One World Trade Center

4. 750; 5,007; 5,070; 7,505; 7,550

5. 640,020; 426,000; 406,200; 46,600

6. Nevada, Arizona, Montana, California, Texas, Alaska

Lesson 6

Problem Set

1.   a.   Units accurately labeled; disks accurately drawn; 615,472

     b.   Units accurately labeled; disks accurately drawn; 381,036

     c.   Units accurately labeled; disks accurately drawn; 100,000 more

2.   249,867 points; explanations will vary.

3.   a.   50,060

     b.   11,195

     c.   1,000,000

     d.   29,231

     e.   100,000

     f.   1,000

4.   a.   160,010; 180,010; 200,010; explanations will vary.

     b.   998,756; 698,756; 598,756; explanations will vary.

     c.   742,369; 740,369; 739,369; explanations will vary.

     d.   128,910; 108,910; 98,910; explanations will vary.

Exit Ticket

1.   469,235; 470,235; 473,235; explanations will vary.

2.   a.   57,879

     b.   224,560

     c.   446,080

     d.   796,233

3.   209,782; explanations will vary.

EUREKA MATH

©2015 Great Minds. eureka-math.org
G4-M1M2-TE-BK1-1.3.1-1.2016

Homework

1. a. Units accurately labeled; disks accurately drawn; 460,313

    b. Units accurately labeled; disks accurately drawn; 405,040

    c. Units accurately labeled; disks accurately drawn; 100,000 more

2. a. 176,960

    b. 12,097

    c. 839,000

    d. 452,210

    e. 1,000

    f. 100,000

3. a. 146,555; 148,555; 150,555; explanations will vary.

    b. 754,321; 784,321; 794,321; explanations will vary.

    c. 325,876; 525,876; 625,876; explanations will vary.

    d. 264,445; 244,445; 234,445; explanations will vary.

4. $64,098; explanations will vary.

Lesson 7

Problem Set

1. a. 7,000

    b. 9,000

    c. 16,000

    d. 40,000

    e. 399,000

    f. 840,000

2. $5,572 \approx 6,000$; $8,147 \approx 8,000$; $10,996 \approx 11,000$; 25,000 km

3. $12,748 \approx 13,000$; $11,702 \approx 12,000$; Tyler; explanations will vary.

4. $43,499; $42,500

Exit Ticket

1. a. 8,000

    b. 13,000

    c. 324,000

2. Susie; explanations will vary.

Homework

1. a. 6,000

    b. 4,000

    c. 33,000

    d. 79,000

    e. 251,000

    f. 700,000

2. $981 \approx 1,000$; explanations will vary.

3. $5,990 \approx $6,000$; $4,720 \approx $5,000$; Sophia's family; explanations will vary.

4. Incorrect; explanations will vary.

Module 1:   Place Value, Rounding, and Algorithms for Addition and Subtraction

©2015 Great Minds. eureka-math.org
G4-M1M2-TE-BK1-1.3.1-1.2016

Lesson 8

Sprint

Side A

1.	5	12.	45	23.	6,500	34.	685
2.	50	13.	55	24.	650	35.	9,450
3.	500	14.	550	25.	65	36.	3,950
4.	15	15.	5,500	26.	265	37.	2,455
5.	150	16.	250	27.	9,265	38.	7,085
6.	1,500	17.	350	28.	85	39.	3,205
7.	35	18.	750	29.	95	40.	8,635
8.	350	19.	5,750	30.	995	41.	8,195
9.	450	20.	75	31.	9,995	42.	2,515
10.	25	21.	675	32.	445	43.	4,895
11.	35	22.	6,750	33.	8,350	44.	6,665

Side B

1.	15	12.	55	23.	7,500	34.	585
2.	150	13.	65	24.	750	35.	9,550
3.	1,500	14.	650	25.	75	36.	2,950
4.	25	15.	6,500	26.	275	37.	3,455
5.	250	16.	350	27.	9,275	38.	6,085
6.	2,500	17.	450	28.	85	39.	4,205
7.	45	18.	850	29.	95	40.	7,635
8.	450	19.	5,850	30.	995	41.	7,195
9.	550	20.	85	31.	9,995	42.	3,515
10.	35	21.	685	32.	455	43.	5,895
11.	45	22.	6,850	33.	8,450	44.	7,775

EUREKA MATH™ **Module 1:** Place Value, Rounding, and Algorithms for Addition and Subtraction **299**

©2015 Great Minds. eureka-math.org
G4-M1M2-TE-BK1-1.3.1-1.2016

Problem Set

1. a. 50,000; number line accurately models work.

   b. 40,000; number line accurately models work.

   c. 410,000; number line accurately models work.

2. a. 200,000; number line accurately models work.

   b. 400,000; number line accurately models work.

   c. 1,000,000; number line accurately models work.

3. 1,000,000; number line accurately models work.

4. Possible digits are 0, 1, 2, 3, or 4; number line accurately models work.

5. a. 370,000

   b. 400,000

Exit Ticket

1. a. 40,000; number line accurately models work.

   b. 980,000; number line accurately models work.

2. a. 100,000; number line accurately models work.

   b. 1,000,000; number line accurately models work.

3. 800,000

Homework

1. a. 70,000; number line accurately models work.

   b. 50,000; number line accurately models work.

   c. 110,000; number line accurately models work.

2. a. 900,000; number line accurately models work.

   b. 800,000; number line accurately models work.

   c. 600,000; number line accurately models work.

3. 500,000; number line accurately models work.

4. Possible digits are 0, 1, 2, 3, or 4; number line accurately models work.

5. a. 380,000

   b. 400,000

Lesson 9

Problem Set

1. a. 5,000

    b. 5,000

    c. 42,000

    d. 802,000

    e. Explanations will vary.

2. a. 30,000

    b. 30,000

    c. 790,000

    d. 710,000

    e. Explanations and numbers will vary.

3. a. 800,000

    b. 900,000

    c. 800,000

    d. 1,000,000

    e. Explanations and numbers will vary.

4. a. Explanations will vary.

    b. Estimate is not reasonable; explanations will vary.

    c. 30,000

Exit Ticket

1. 766,000; 770,000; 800,000

2. 17,000; 20,000; explanations will vary.

Homework

1. a. 7,000

    b. 3,000

    c. 16,000

    d. 706,000

    e. Explanations will vary.

2. a. 90,000

    b. 90,000

    c. 790,000

    d. 910,000

    e. Explanations and numbers will vary.

3. a. 100,000

    b. 800,000

    c. 600,000

    d. 800,000

    e. Explanations and numbers will vary.

4. a. 849,999; 750,000

    b. 404,999; 395,000

    c. 30,499; 29,500

Lesson 10

Sprint

Side A

1.	20,000	12.	40,000	23.	190,000	34.	160,000
2.	30,000	13.	140,000	24.	90,000	35.	20,000
3.	40,000	14.	40,000	25.	100,000	36.	920,000
4.	540,000	15.	60,000	26.	100,000	37.	40,000
5.	50,000	16.	460,000	27.	100,000	38.	60,000
6.	60,000	17.	20,000	28.	200,000	39.	700,000
7.	70,000	18.	30,000	29.	800,000	40.	240,000
8.	370,000	19.	40,000	30.	30,000	41.	710,000
9.	60,000	20.	240,000	31.	50,000	42.	190,000
10.	710,000	21.	80,000	32.	650,000	43.	780,000
11.	30,000	22.	180,000	33.	60,000	44.	440,000

Side B

1.	10,000	12.	30,000	23.	190,000	34.	150,000
2.	20,000	13.	130,000	24.	90,000	35.	30,000
3.	30,000	14.	30,000	25.	100,000	36.	930,000
4.	530,000	15.	50,000	26.	100,000	37.	30,000
5.	40,000	16.	350,000	27.	100,000	38.	50,000
6.	50,000	17.	30,000	28.	200,000	39.	600,000
7.	60,000	18.	40,000	29.	800,000	40.	140,000
8.	360,000	19.	50,000	30.	20,000	41.	610,000
9.	50,000	20.	250,000	31.	40,000	42.	180,000
10.	610,000	21.	70,000	32.	640,000	43.	890,000
11.	20,000	22.	170,000	33.	50,000	44.	440,000

©2015 Great Minds. eureka-math.org
G4-M1M2-TE-BK1-1.3.1-1.2016

EUREKA
MATH™

Problem Set

1. a. 544,000
    b. 540,000
    c. 500,000
2. a. 2,800
    b. 32,900
    c. 132,900
    d. 6,000
    e. 37,000
    f. 101,000

g. 40,000
h. 50,000
i. 1,000,000
j. 400,000
k. 400,000
l. 900,000

3. No; explanations will vary.
4. Answers and explanations will vary.
5. 70,000; 7,000; $\approx$ 10 trips

Exit Ticket

1. a. 599,000; 600,000; 600,000
    b. Explanations will vary.
2. Answers and explanations will vary.

Homework

1. a. 845,000
    b. 850,000
    c. 800,000
2. a. 800
    b. 12,800
    c. 951,200
    d. 1,000
    e. 65,000
    f. 99,000

g. 60,000
h. 80,000
i. 900,000
j. 900,000
k. 500,000
l. 700,000

3. a. Answers and explanations will vary.
    b. Answers and explanations will vary.
    c. Answers and explanations will vary.

Lesson 11

Problem Set

1.   a.   6,579
       b.   7,579
       c.   7,582
       d.   8,807
       e.   10,807
       f.   17,841
       g.   58,146
       h.   106,538
       i.   901,256
       j.   1,554
       k.   286,026

2.   240,029
3.   4,485
4.   31,318

Exit Ticket

1.   a.   25,914
       b.   4,226
       c.   8,080

2.   54,427

Homework

1.   a.   8,953
       b.   37,649
       c.   870,898
       d.   301,050
       e.   662,831
       f.   380,880
       g.   119,714
       h.   381,848
       i.   1,000,000

2.   a.   15,123 lb
       b.   17,353 lb
       c.   20,020 lb
       d.   5,020 lb

©2015 Great Minds. eureka-math.org
G4-M1M2-TE-BK1-1.3.1-1.2016

Lesson 12

Problem Set

1. a. 330

   b. 337

   c. Explanations will vary.

2. a. 3,000

   b. 2,918

   c. Explanations will vary.

3. a. 44,000

   b. 44,020

   c. Explanations will vary.

4. a. 53,443

   b. 54,000; explanations will vary.

Exit Ticket

   $31,771; explanations will vary.

Homework

1. a. 24,000

   b. 23,613

   c. Explanations will vary.

2. a. 157,593

   b. 157,000; explanations will vary.

3. a. 30,238

   b. Explanations will vary.

Lesson 13

Problem Set

1. a. 4,023
   b. 4,023
   c. 2,208
   d. 4,190
   e. 6,030
   f. 2,523
   g. 9,010
   h. 227,110
   i. 98,220

2. 12,009
3. 471 y
4. 52,411 lb
5. 109,014 mi

Exit Ticket

1. a. 6,011
   b. 13,920
   c. 6,511
2. 7,050

Homework

1. a. 2,090
   b. 408,110
   c. 330,011
   d. 30,011
   e. 890,130
   f. 106,010
   g. 1,511
   h. 371,631

2. 24,717
3. 1,922
4. $312,571
5. a. 390,211
   b. 204,110

Module 1:   Place Value, Rounding, and Algorithms for Addition and Subtraction

EUREKA MATH™

Lesson 14

Problem Set

1. a. 1,090
   b. 990
   c. 47,984
   d. 988
   e. 93,189
   f. 92,979
   g. 2,889
   h. 49,979
   i. 92,943

2. 57,600 s
3. 284,700
4. 1,816
5. $10,909

Exit Ticket

1. 13,589
2. 29,464
3. 356

Homework

1. a. 50,497
   b. 275,497
   c. 345,897
   d. 158,497
   e. 90,517
   f. 858,919
   g. 857,011
   h. 87,897
   i. 258,989

2. 212,181 lb
3. 92,944
4. 361,200 lb

Lesson 15

Problem Set

1. a. 9,980
    b. 91,680
    c. 197,859
    d. 167,574
    e. 408,000
    f. 407,500
    g. 8,089
    h. 7,431

2. 3,679 mi
3. 227,367 gal
4. $929

Exit Ticket

1. 176,035
2. 84,369

Homework

1. a. 8,818
    b. 53,776
    c. 179,667
    d. 127,780
    e. 55,061
    f. 197,750
    g. 720,511
    h. 755,000
    i. 523,836

2. 7,919 mi
3. 598,909
4. $674,700
5. 18,647 g

EUREKA MATH

Lesson 16

Sprint

Side A

1.	200	12.	140	23.	102	34.	260
2.	300	13.	190	24.	103	35.	375
3.	400	14.	195	25.	104	36.	633
4.	900	15.	185	26.	107	37.	809
5.	100	16.	184	27.	207	38.	470
6.	700	17.	173	28.	307	39.	735
7.	500	18.	162	29.	807	40.	417
8.	800	19.	262	30.	804	41.	604
9.	600	20.	762	31.	409	42.	1,004
10.	120	21.	527	32.	608	43.	1,040
11.	130	22.	387	33.	903	44.	1,184

Side B

1.	100	12.	130	23.	101	34.	250
2.	200	13.	170	24.	102	35.	385
3.	300	14.	175	25.	103	36.	631
4.	700	15.	165	26.	109	37.	607
5.	500	16.	164	27.	209	38.	460
6.	900	17.	153	28.	309	39.	725
7.	400	18.	142	29.	709	40.	413
8.	800	19.	242	30.	704	41.	602
9.	600	20.	842	31.	408	42.	1,003
10.	110	21.	529	32.	603	43.	1,030
11.	120	22.	389	33.	905	44.	1,148

Problem Set

1. a. 19,000 lb

    b. 19,190 lb

    c. Explanations will vary.

2. a. 500,000 gal

    b. 597,420 gal

    c. Explanations will vary.

3. a. 53,000 mi

    b. 53,558 mi

    c. Explanations will vary.

4. 10,994; explanations will vary.

5. 78,497 lb; explanations will vary.

Exit Ticket

1. 64,000

2. 63,213

3. Explanations will vary.

Homework

1. a. 40,000

    b. 40,699

    c. Explanations will vary.

2. a. 700,000

    b. 601,801

    c. Explanations will vary.

3. 19,999; explanations will vary.

EUREKA
MATH

Lesson 17

Problem Set

1. $13,838

2. 290,694

3. 1,125 kg

4. 150 m

Exit Ticket

476 mL

Homework

1. 278

2. 7,093 L

3. 160 in

Lesson 18

Problem Set

1. 21,550 m
2. 46,303
3. 40,284

Exit Ticket

1. 16,939 sq km
2. Answers will vary.

Homework

1. 124,867
2. 31,504
3. 2,210

Module 1:   Place Value, Rounding, and Algorithms for Addition and Subtraction

EUREKA
MATH™

Lesson 19

Problem Set

1. Word problems will vary; 1,827
2. Word problems will vary; 521,565
3. Word problems will vary; 23,110
4. Tape diagram models the equation; word problems will vary; 5,394

Exit Ticket

1. Word problems will vary; 60,209
2. Tape diagram models the equation; word problems will vary; 35,656

Homework

1. Word problems will vary; 1,972
2. Word problems will vary; 93,168
3. Word problems will vary; 94,851
4. Tape diagram models the equation; word problems will vary; 5,606

Teacher Edition

Eureka Math
Grade 4
Module 2

Special thanks go to the Gordon A. Cain Center and to the Department of Mathematics at Louisiana State University for their support in the development of *Eureka Math*.

For a free *Eureka Math* Teacher
Resource Pack, Parent Tip
Sheets, and more please
visit www.Eureka.tools

Printed in the U.S.A.
This book may be purchased from the publisher at eureka-math.org
10 9 8 7 6 5 4 3 2
ISBN 978-1-63255-371-3

Mathematics Curriculum

Table of Contents

GRADE 4 • MODULE 2

Unit Conversions and Problem Solving with Metric Measurement

Grade 4 • Module 2

Unit Conversions and Problem Solving with Metric Measurement

OVERVIEW

The idea of a mixed unit shows up in varied contexts. For instance, students have become accustomed to thinking of 250 as the mixed units of 2 hundreds 5 tens. Mixed units are also used in the context of 2 hr 5 min, $2.50, 2 km 5 m, 2' 5", and $2\frac{5}{8}$ (hours and minutes, dollars and cents, kilometers and meters, feet and inches, ones and eighths). While the context and the units may vary greatly, there are many common threads present in any mixed unit calculation. Consider the connections and similarities between the following equalities:

2 thousands	437 ones	=	2,437 ones
2 kilometers	437 meters	=	2,437 meters
2 kilograms	437 grams	=	2,437 grams
2 liters	437 milliliters	=	2,437 milliliters

In order to explore the process of working with mixed units, Module 2 focuses on length, mass, and capacity in the metric system[1] where place value serves as a natural guide for moving between larger and smaller units.

In Topic A, students review place value concepts while building fluency with decomposing, or converting from larger to smaller units (**4.MD.1**). They learn the relative sizes of measurement units, building off prior knowledge of grams and kilograms from Grade 3 (**3.MD.2**) and meters and centimeters from Grade 2 (**2.MD.3**). Conversions between the units are recorded in a two-column table. Single-step problems involving addition and subtraction of metric units provide an opportunity to practice mental math calculations as well as the addition and subtraction algorithms established in Module 1. Students reason by choosing to convert between mixed and single units before or after the computation (**4.MD.2**). Connecting their familiarity with both metric units and place value, the module moves swiftly through each unit of conversion, spending only one day on each type. This initial understanding of unit conversions allows for further application and practice, such as multiplying and dividing metric units, throughout subsequent modules.

In Topic B, students continue to build off their measurement work from previous grade levels. They solidify their understanding of the relationship between metric units and the place value chart and apply unit conversions to solve and reason about multi-step word problems (**4.MD.2**). Applying the skills learned in Module 1, students discover and explore the relationship between place value and conversions. The beauty of both the place value and measurement systems is the efficiency and precision permitted by the use of different size units to express a given quantity. As students solve word problems by adding and subtracting

---

[1]Pounds, ounces, time, and money are covered in Module 7.

metric units, their ability to reason in parts and wholes is taken to the next level. This is important preparation for multi-digit operations and for manipulating fractional units in future modules. Tape diagrams and number lines serve as models throughout the module to support the application of the standard algorithm to word problems.

Notes on Pacing for Differentiation

Although composed of just five lessons, Module 2 has great importance in the Grade 4 sequence of modules. Module 2, along with Module 1, is paramount in setting the foundation for developing fluency with the manipulation of place value units, a skill upon which Module 3 greatly depends. Teachers who have taught Module 2 prior to Module 3 have reportedly moved through Module 3 more efficiently than colleagues who have omitted it. Module 2 also sets the foundation for work with fractions and mixed numbers in Module 5. Therefore, it is not recommended to omit any lessons from Module 2.

To help with the pacing of Module 3's Topic A, consider replacing the Convert Units fluencies in Module 2, Lessons 1–3, with area and perimeter fluencies. Also, consider incorporating Problem 1 from Module 3, Lesson 1, into the fluency component of Module 2, Lessons 4 and 5.

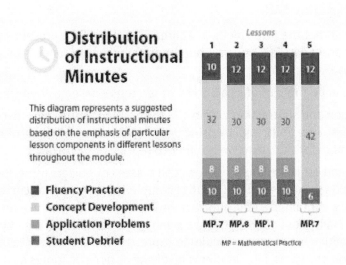

Distribution of Instructional Minutes

This diagram represents a suggested distribution of instructional minutes based on the emphasis of particular lesson components in different lessons throughout the module.

■ Fluency Practice
Concept Development
■ Application Problems
■ Student Debrief

MP = Mathematical Practice

Focus Grade Level Standards

Solve problems involving measurement and conversion of measurements from a larger unit to a smaller unit.[2]

4.MD.1[3] Know relative sizes of measurement units within one system of units including km, m, cm; kg, g; lb, oz.; l, ml; hr, min, sec. Within a single system of measurement, express measurements in a larger unit in terms of a smaller unit. Record measurement equivalents in a two-column table. *For example, know that 1 ft is 12 times as long as 1 in. Express the length of a 4 ft snake as 48 in. Generate a conversion table for feet and inches listing the number pairs (1, 12), (2, 24), (3, 36), …*

4.MD.2[4] Use the four operations to solve word problems involving distances, intervals of time, liquid volumes, masses of objects, and money, including problems involving simple fractions or decimals, and problems that require expressing measurements given in a larger unit in terms of a smaller unit. Represent measurement quantities using diagrams such as number line diagrams that feature a measurement scale.

Foundational Standards

2.NBT.1 Understand that the three digits of a three-digit number represent amounts of hundreds, tens, and ones; e.g., 706 equals 7 hundreds, 0 tens, and 6 ones. Understand the following as a special case:

    a.   100 can be thought of as a bundle of ten tens—called a "hundred."

2.MD.5 Use addition and subtraction within 100 to solve word problems involving lengths that are given in the same units, e.g., by using drawings (such as drawings of rulers) and equations with a symbol for the unknown number to represent the problem.

3.MD.2 Measure and estimate liquid volumes and masses of objects using standard units of grams (g), kilograms (kg), and liters (L). (Excludes compound units such as cm^3 and finding the geometric volume of a container.) Add, subtract, multiply, or divide to solve one-step word problems involving masses or volumes that are given in the same units, e.g., by using drawings (such as a beaker with a measurement scale) to represent the problem. (Excludes multiplicative comparison problems, i.e., problems involving notions of "times as much.")

4.OA.3 Solve multistep word problems posed with whole numbers and having whole-number answers using the four operations, including problems in which remainders must be interpreted. Represent these problems using equations with a letter standing for the unknown quantity. Assess the reasonableness of answers using mental computation and estimation strategies including rounding.

4.NBT.4 Fluently add and subtract multi-digit whole numbers using the standard algorithm.

---

[2]4.MD.3 is addressed in Module 3.

[3]Pounds, ounces, and time are addressed in Module 7. This is a non-tested standard, but expressing metric measurements of length, mass, and capacity from larger to smaller units strengthens the upcoming modules.

[4]Time and money are addressed in Module 7. This is a non-tested standard, but the contexts of operating on distance, volume, and mass strengthen the upcoming modules.

Focus Standards for Mathematical Practice

MP.1   **Make sense of problems and persevere in solving them.** Students use place value knowledge to convert larger units to smaller units before adding and subtracting. They fluently add and subtract metric units of length, weight, and capacity using the standard algorithm. Tape diagrams and number lines help students conceptualize a problem before it is solved and are used to assess the reasonableness of an answer.

MP.7   **Look for and make use of structure.** Students use knowledge of place value and mixed units to find patterns when converting from a larger unit to a smaller unit. They recognize that 1 thousand equals 1,000 ones and relate that to 1 kilometer equals 1,000 meters. Using this pattern, they might extend thinking to convert smaller to larger units when making a conversion chart.

MP.8   **Look for and express regularity in repeated reasoning.** Students find that metric unit conversions share a relationship on the place value chart. For example, 1,000 ones equals 1 thousand, 1,000 g equals 1 kg, 1,000 mL equals 1 L, and 1,000 m equals 1 km. Knowing and using these conversions and similarities allows for quick and easy conversion and calculation.

Overview of Module Topics and Lesson Objectives

Standards		Topics and Objectives	Days
4.MD.1 4.MD.2	A	**Metric Unit Conversions** Lesson 1: Express metric length measurements in terms of a smaller unit; model and solve addition and subtraction word problems involving metric length. Lesson 2: Express metric mass measurements in terms of a smaller unit; model and solve addition and subtraction word problems involving metric mass. Lesson 3: Express metric capacity measurements in terms of a smaller unit; model and solve addition and subtraction word problems involving metric capacity.	3
4.MD.1 4.MD.2	B	**Application of Metric Unit Conversions** Lesson 4: Know and relate metric units to place value units in order to express measurements in different units. Lesson 5: Use addition and subtraction to solve multi-step word problems involving length, mass, and capacity.	2
		End-of-Module Assessment: Topics A–B (assessment ½ day, return ½ day, remediation or further applications 1 day)	2
Total Number of Instructional Days			**7**

Terminology

New or Recently Introduced Terms

- Convert (express a measurement in a different unit; rename units)
- Kilometer (km, a unit of measure for length)
- Mass (the measure of the amount of matter in an object)
- Milliliter (mL, a unit of measure for liquid volume)
- Mixed units (e.g., 3 m 43 cm)

Familiar Terms and Symbols[5]

- =, <, > (equal to, less than, greater than)
- Algorithm (a step-by-step procedure to solve a particular type of problem)
- Capacity (the maximum amount that something can contain)
- Distance (the length of the line segment joining two points)
- Equivalent (equal)
- Kilogram (kg), gram (g) (units of measure for mass)
- Larger or smaller unit (used in a comparison of units)
- Length (the measurement of something from end to end)
- Liter (L) (unit of measure for liquid volume)
- Measurement (dimensions, quantity, or capacity as determined by comparison with a standard)
- Meter (m), centimeter (cm) (units of measure for length)
- Mixed units (e.g., 2 tens 4 ones, 2 kilometers 34 meters)
- Simplifying strategy (a mental math or recorded method for making a problem easier to solve)
- Table (used to represent data)
- Times as much as (e.g., 1 hundred is 10 times as much as 1 ten)
- Weight (the measurement of how heavy something is)

Suggested Tools and Representations

- Balance scale, weights (masses)
- Centimeter ruler, meter stick
- Liter containers with millimeter scale
- Number line
- Tape diagram
- Two-column table

---

[5]These are terms and symbols students have used or seen previously.

Scaffolds[6]

The scaffolds integrated into *A Story of Units* give alternatives for how students access information as well as express and demonstrate their learning. Strategically placed margin notes are provided within each lesson elaborating on the use of specific scaffolds at applicable times. They address many needs presented by English language learners, students with disabilities, students performing above grade level, and students performing below grade level. Many of the suggestions are organized by Universal Design for Learning (UDL) principles and are applicable to more than one population. To read more about the approach to differentiated instruction in *A Story of Units,* please refer to "How to Implement *A Story of Units.*"

Assessment Summary

Type	Administered	Format	Standards Addressed
End-of-Module Assessment Task	After Topic B	Constructed response with rubric	4.MD.1 4.MD.2

---

[6]Students with disabilities may require Braille, large print, audio, or special digital files. Please visit the website www.p12.nysed.gov/specialed/aim for specific information on how to obtain student materials that satisfy the National Instructional Materials Accessibility Standard (NIMAS) format.

Mathematics Curriculum

Topic A

Metric Unit Conversions

4.MD.1, 4.MD.2

Focus Standards:	4.MD.1[1]	Know relative sizes of measurement units within one system of units including km, m, cm; kg, g; lb, oz.; l, ml; hr, min, sec. Within a single system of measurement, express measurements in a larger unit in terms of a smaller unit. Record measurement equivalents in a two-column table. *For example, know that 1 ft is 12 times as long as 1 in. Express the length of a 4 ft snake as 48 in. Generate a conversion table for feet and inches listing the number pairs (1, 12), (2, 24), (3, 36), …*
	4.MD.2[2]	Use the four operations to solve word problems involving distances, intervals of time, liquid volumes, masses of objects, and money, including problems involving simple fractions or decimals, and problems that require expressing measurements given in a larger unit in terms of a smaller unit. Represent measurement quantities using diagrams such as number line diagrams that feature a measurement scale.
Instructional Days:	3	
Coherence -Links from:	G2–M2	Addition and Subtraction of Length Units
	G3–M2	Place Value and Problem Solving with Units of Measure
-Links to:	G5–M1	Place Value and Decimal Fractions
	G5–M2	Multi-Digit Whole Number and Decimal Fraction Operations

In order to explore the process of working with mixed units, Module 2 focuses on length, mass, and capacity in the metric system,[3] where place value serves as a natural guide for moving between larger and smaller units. In Topic A, students review place value concepts while building fluency with decomposing, or converting from larger to smaller units (**4.MD.1**). They learn the relative sizes of measurement units, building off prior knowledge of grams and kilograms from Grade 3 (**3.MD.2**) and meters and centimeters from Grade 2 (**2.MD.3**). Conversions between the units are recorded in a two-column table, beginning in Lesson 1. Recording the unit conversions in a table allows students to notice patterns when converting from a smaller unit to a larger unit (e.g., 200 centimeters is the same as 2 meters because 1 meter is equal to 100 centimeters). Single-step problems involving addition and subtraction of metric units provide an

---

[1]Pounds, ounces, and time are addressed in Module 7. This is a non-tested standard, but expressing metric measurements of length, mass, and capacity from larger to smaller units strengthens the upcoming modules.

[2]Time and money are addressed in Module 7. This is a non-tested standard, but the context of operating on distance, volume, and mass strengthens the upcoming modules. This module only focuses on addition and subtraction. Multiplication and division are addressed in future modules.

[3]Pounds, ounces, time, and money are covered in Module 7.

opportunity to practice simplifying strategies (e.g., mental math strategies) as well as the addition and subtraction algorithm established in Module 1 (**4.NBT.4**). Students practice reasoning by choosing to convert mixed units to a single unit before or after the computation (**4.MD.2**).

$$2 \text{ km } 608 \text{ m } + 3 \text{ km } 412 \text{ m}$$

Algorithms

$$
\begin{array}{r}
2 \text{ km } 608 \text{ m} \\
+ \ 3 \text{ km } 412 \text{ m} \\
\hline
5 \text{ km } 1020 \text{ m}
\end{array}
$$

$\overset{\wedge}{1 \text{ km } 20 \text{ m}}$

$6 \text{ km } 20 \text{ m} = 6{,}020 \text{ m}$

OR

$$
\begin{array}{r}
2{,}608 \text{ m} \\
+ \ 3{,}412 \text{ m} \\
\hline
6{,}020 \text{ m} = 6 \text{ km } 20 \text{ m}
\end{array}
$$

Simplifying Strategies

$2 \text{ km } + 3 \text{ km } = 5 \text{ km}$

$608 \text{ m } + 412 \text{ m } = 600 \text{ m} + 420 \text{ m}$

$\overset{\wedge}{600 \quad 8} \qquad = 1{,}020 \text{ m}$

$5 \text{ km } + 1 \text{ km } 20 \text{ m } = 6 \text{ km } 20 \text{ m}$

OR

$2{,}608 \text{ m } + 3{,}412 \text{ m}$

$2{,}000 \quad 600 \qquad 8 \qquad 3{,}000 \quad 400 \qquad 12$

$5{,}000 \text{ m} + 1{,}000 \text{ m} + 20 \text{ m} = 6{,}020 \text{ m}$

Word problems provide a context in which to apply the conversions and include the addition and subtraction of mixed units. Connecting students' familiarity with both metric units and place value, the module moves swiftly through each unit of conversion, spending only one day on each type of measurement. This initial understanding of unit conversions allows for further application and practice, such as when multiplying and dividing metric units, throughout subsequent modules.

A Teaching Sequence Toward Mastery of Metric Unit Conversions
Objective 1: Express metric length measurements in terms of a smaller unit; model and solve addition and subtraction word problems involving metric length. (Lesson 1)
Objective 2: Express metric mass measurements in terms of a smaller unit; model and solve addition and subtraction word problems involving metric mass. (Lesson 2)
Objective 3: Express metric capacity measurements in terms of a smaller unit; model and solve addition and subtraction word problems involving metric capacity. (Lesson 3)

Lesson 1

Objective: Express metric length measurements in terms of a smaller unit; model and solve addition and subtraction word problems involving metric length.

Suggested Lesson Structure

■ Fluency Practice   (10 minutes)

■ Application Problem   (8 minutes)

☐ Concept Development   (32 minutes)

■ Student Debrief   (10 minutes)

   Total Time   **(60 minutes)**

A NOTE ON STANDARDS ALIGNMENT:

In this lesson and the entire module, students convert metric length units in the context of addition and subtraction problems involving mixed units. This lesson builds on the content of **2.MD.5** and **3.MD.2**.

On some occasions, students work beyond the **4.MD.1** and **4.MD.2** standards by converting from a smaller unit to a larger unit. They do this by creating a connection between units of measures related to place value.

If students are not ready for the conversions up, have them work in small groups to further develop the number sense necessary for understanding these conversions, and always accept answers in the smaller unit.

Fluency Practice (10 minutes)

▪ Convert Units **4.MD.1**   (2 minutes)

▪ Meter and Centimeter Number Bonds **4.MD.1**   (8 minutes)

Convert Units (2 minutes)

Note: Isolated review builds fluency with conversion so that students can use this skill as a tool for solving word problems.

    T: (Write 100 cm = _____ m.) 100 centimeters is the same as how many meters?

    S: 1 meter.

Repeat the process with the following possible sequence:
200 cm, 300 cm, 800 cm, and 500 cm.

    T: (Write 1 m = _____ cm.) How many centimeters are in 1 meter?

    S: 100 centimeters.

Repeat the process with the following possible sequence: 2 m, 3 m, 7 m, 4 m, and 9 m.

EUREKA MATH™

Meter and Centimeter Number Bonds (8 minutes)

Materials: (S) Personal white board

Note: This fluency activity prepares students to add and subtract meters and centimeters later in the lesson.

T: (Project a number bond with 150 cm written as the whole and 1 m as one of the parts.) How many centimeters are in 1 meter?

S: 100 centimeters.

T: (Beneath 1 m, write 100 cm.) On your personal white boards, write a number bond filling in the unknown part.

S: (Write a number bond with a whole of 150 cm and parts of 1 m and 50 cm.)

Repeat the process with wholes of 180 cm, 120 cm, 125 cm, 105 cm, and 107 cm.

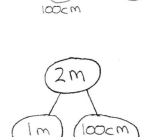

T: (Project a number bond with 2 m written as the whole, 1 m as one of the parts, and ____ cm as the other part.) Fill in the unknown part.

S: (Write a number bond with 2 m as the whole, 1 m as one of the parts, and 100 cm as the other part.)

T: Show a number bond with a whole of 3 meters and pull out 100 centimeters. Name the other part in meters.

S: (Draw a number bond with 3 m as the whole, 100 cm as one of the parts, and 2 m as the other part.)

Repeat the process with the following possible sequence: 5 meters, 8 meters, 9 meters, and 10 meters.

Application Problem (8 minutes)

Martha, George, and Elizabeth sprint a combined distance of 10,000 meters. Martha sprints 3,206 meters. George sprints 2,094 meters. How far does Elizabeth sprint? Solve using an algorithm or a simplifying strategy.

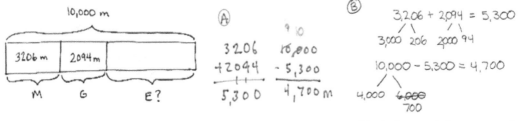

Note: This Application Problem builds on Grade 4 Module 1 Lesson 19. Note that Solution A models the standard algorithm, whereas Solution B records a simplifying strategy using number bonds. A number bond demonstrates part—whole relationships and is a way to record completing a whole or taking part from a whole. This Application Problem leads to the Concept Development of this lesson because the problem involves the metric unit of a meter.

Lesson 1:   Express metric length measurements in terms of a smaller unit;
              model and solve addition and subtraction word problems involving
              metric length.   11

©2015 Great Minds. eureka-math.org
G4-M1M2-TE-BK1-1.3.1-1.2016

Concept Development (32 minutes)

Materials: (T) Staples, ruler, meter stick, teacher-made poster with metric units (shown below)
(S) Personal white board

Problem 1: Understand 1 centimeter, 1 meter, and 1 kilometer in terms of concrete objects.

Begin with a five-minute discussion about the length of a centimeter, meter, and kilometer.

- Use familiar, concrete examples such as a staple, the height of a countertop, and the distance to a local landmark that you know to be about 1 **kilometer**.

- Have students measure the size of concrete examples that are given using centimeters or meters.

- Display a chart such as the one shown below.

- Add other examples to the chart, such as the width of a fingernail, the width of a door, the distance of two and a half laps around a running track, the length of a base ten cube, the height of a stack of five pennies, the outstretched arms of a child, and the distance around a soccer field four times. Show a meter stick to reference the exact size of a centimeter and a meter.

Metric Units of Length		
Centimeter	meter	kilometer
• length of staple	• height of countertop	• distance from the school to the train station

NOTES ON MULTIPLE MEANS OF REPRESENTATION:

English language learners may benefit from further discussion of concrete items that are about the same length as a centimeter, meter, or kilometer. Write examples on index cards of items that are a centimeter, a meter, or a kilometer in length. Have students place them in the appropriate columns of a chart. Provide students with blank index cards so they can create their own cards to add to the chart.

NOTES ON MULTIPLE MEANS OF ENGAGEMENT:

Ask students where they have heard the prefix *kilo-* before. As they learned in Grade 3, 1 kilogram equals 1,000 grams, so 1 kilometer equals 1,000 meters. Ask how many bytes are in 1 kilobyte.

Lesson 1: Express metric length measurements in terms of a smaller unit; model and solve addition and subtraction word problems involving metric length.

EUREKA MATH

Problem 2: Compare the sizes and note relationships between meters and kilometers as conversion equivalencies.

Use a two-column table, as pictured to the right, to support the following sequence.

	Distance	
km		m
1		1,000
2		2,000
3		3,000
7		7,000
70		70,000

T: 1 km = 1,000 m. How many meters are in 2 km? 3 km? 7 km? 70 km?

S: 2,000 m, 3,000 m, 7,000 m, 70,000 m.

T: Write 2,000 m = _____ km on your personal white board. If 1,000 m equals 1 km, 2,000 m equals how many kilometers?

MP.7

S: 2 kilometers.

Repeat for 8,000 m, 10,000 m, and 9,000 m.

T: Compare kilometers and meters.

S: A kilometer is a longer distance because we need 1,000 meters to equal 1 kilometer. → 1 kilometer is 1,000 times as much as 1 meter.

T: (Display 1 km 500 m = _____ m.) Let's **convert**, or rename, 1 km 500 m to meters. 1 kilometer is equal to how many meters?

S: 1,000 meters.

T: 1,000 meters plus 500 meters is 1,500 meters. (Fill in the blank.)

T: (Display 1 km 300 m = ___ m.) 1 kilometer 300 meters is equal to how many meters?

S: 1,300 meters.

Repeat with 5 km 30 m. (Anticipate the incorrect answer of 530 m.)

T: 2,500 meters is equal to how many kilometers? How do you know?

S: 2 km 500 m. We made two groups of 1,000 meters, so we have 2 kilometers and 500 meters.

Repeat with 5,005 m.

Problem 3: Add mixed units of length using the algorithm or simplifying strategies.

Display horizontally: 5 km + 2,500 m.

T: Talk for one minute with your partner about how to solve this problem.

S: We can't add different units together. → We can convert the kilometers to meters before adding. 5 kilometers equals 5,000 meters, so 5,000 m + 2,500 m = 7,500 m. → I'm going to rename 7,500 m to 7 km 500 m.

T: Renaming 7,500 m to 7 km 500 m created a **mixed unit**. Mixed units can be helpful when using a simplifying strategy.

T: Are you going to use the algorithm or a simplifying strategy to solve?

S: Simplifying strategy.

T: Why?

Lesson 1:   Express metric length measurements in terms of a smaller unit;
             model and solve addition and subtraction word problems involving
             metric length.   13

S: There is no regrouping. → The units are easy to combine. → It's just like adding place value units.

$$5 \text{ km} + 2,500 \text{ m}$$
$$5 \text{ km} + 2 \text{ km } 500 \text{ m} = 7 \text{ km } 500 \text{ m}$$
$$5,000 \text{ m} + 2500 \text{ m} = 7,500 \text{ m} = 7 \text{ km } 500 \text{ m}$$

T: When we added meters, the answer was 7,500 m. When we added mixed units, the answer was 7 km 500 m. Are these answers equal? Why or why not?

S: It is the same amount because 7 km = 7,000 m and 7,000 m + 500 m = 7,500 m.

T: (Display horizontally: 1 km 734 m + 4 km 396 m.) Simplifying strategy or the algorithm? Discuss with a partner.

S: Simplifying strategy, because 7 hundred plus 3 hundred is 1 thousand. 1 thousand meters equals 1 kilometer. 96 + 34 is easy, since the 4 gets 96 to 100. 6 kilometers, 130 meters. → But there are three renamings, and the sum of the meters is more than a thousand. My head is spinning. → I'm going to try it mentally and then check with the algorithm.

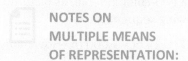

NOTES ON MULTIPLE MEANS OF REPRESENTATION:

Students performing below grade level may struggle with the concept of regrouping in order to add or subtract mixed units. Be sure to relate regrouping back to the work done in the fluency activity and in Problem 1. Explicitly show them the connection between the conversions that they learned to make and how that applies to adding and subtracting with mixed units. Consider the following:

We can't add different units together. If I need to convert 5 kilometers to meters, and I know 1 kilometer is equal to 1,000 meters, then 5 kilometers equals 5,000 meters. Now, I can add 5,000 meters and 2,500 meters.

T: Choose the way you want to do it. You will have two minutes. If you finish before the two minutes are up, try solving it a different way. Let's have two pairs of students work at the board, one pair using the algorithm and one pair recording a simplifying strategy.

After two minutes, review the student work on the board, which hopefully includes strategies such as those below. If not, gently supplement or provide alternative solutions as shown below. Solutions A and B use the algorithm. Solutions C and D are simplifying strategies.

Ⓐ
$$\begin{array}{r} 1 \text{ km} \quad 734 \text{ m} \\ + \; 4 \text{ km} \quad 396 \text{ m} \\ \hline 5 \text{ km } 1130 \text{ m} \end{array}$$

1 km   130 m
6 km 130 m

Ⓑ
$$\begin{array}{r} 1734 \text{ m} \\ + \, 4396 \text{ m} \\ \hline 6130 \text{ m} \end{array}$$

6 km 130 m

Ⓒ
1 km + 4 km = 5 km
734 + 396 = 730 + 400
                    = 1130
730   4
5 km + 1 km 130 m =
                    6 km 130 m

Ⓓ
734 + 396   = 1130
700   34   300   96
5 km + 1 km 130m = 6 km 130 m

Lesson 1:   Express metric length measurements in terms of a smaller unit; model and solve addition and subtraction word problems involving metric length.

©2015 Great Minds. eureka-math.org
G4-M1M2-TE-BK1-1.3.1-1.2016

EUREKA MATH™

Problem 4: Subtract mixed units of length using the algorithm or simplifying strategies.

T: (Display 10 km – 3 km 140 m horizontally.) Simplifying strategy or the algorithm? Discuss with a partner.

S: Oh, for sure, I'm using the algorithm. There are no meters in the number I'm subtracting from. → That's like 10 thousand minus 3 thousand 140. Algorithm for me. → I can do mental math. I'll show you when we solve.

T: Choose the way you want to do it. You will have two minutes. If you finish before the two minutes are up, try solving it a different way. Let's have two pairs of students work at the board, one pair using the algorithm and one pair recording a simplifying strategy.

After two minutes, review the student work on the board, which hopefully includes strategies such as those below. If not, gently supplement or provide alternative solutions as shown below. Solutions A and B use the algorithms. Solutions C and D are simplifying strategies.

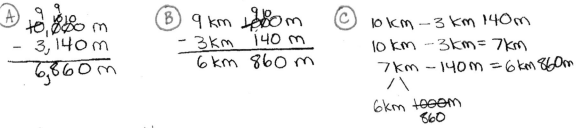

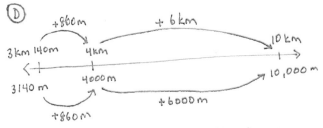

T: Look at Solution A. How did they set up to solve using the algorithm?

S: They converted everything to meters.

T: What did they do in Solution B?

S: They renamed 1 kilometer for 1,000 meters right away.

T: What happened in Solution C?

S: They subtracted the 3 kilometers first.

T: And then?

S: Subtracted the meters from 1 kilometer after renaming 1 kilometer as 1,000 meters.

T: Does anyone have a question for the mental math team?

A NOTE ON STANDARDS ALIGNMENT:

The concept of converting the answer into mixed units reaches beyond the fourth-grade standard. For those students working above grade level, acknowledge the conversion. Students working at or below grade level are not expected to convert their answers.

Lesson 1: Express metric length measurements in terms of a smaller unit; model and solve addition and subtraction word problems involving metric length.

©2015 Great Minds. eureka-math.org
G4-M1M2-TE-BK1-1.3.1-1.2016

15

S: How did you know 1 thousand minus 140 was 860?

S: We just subtracted 1 hundred and then thought of 40 less than 900. We know 6 tens and 4 tens is 1 hundred, so it wasn't too hard.

T: What about Solution D?

S: They used a number line to show a counting up strategy. It's like Solution E. They just represented it in a different way.

T: And Solution E?

S: They counted up from 3 km 140 m to 4 km first and then added 6 more km to get to 10 km.

T: With your partner, take a moment to review the solution strategies on the board. Tell your partner why 6 km 860 m is equal to 6,860 m.

S: The number line team showed 6 km 860 m is equal to 6,860 m by matching kilometers to meters. → You can regroup 6 kilometers as 6,000 meters. → You can regroup 6,000 meters as 6 kilometers. → Both are the same amounts, but they are represented using different units, either mixed or a single unit.

Problem 5: Solve a word problem involving mixed units of length using the algorithm or simplifying strategies.

Sam practiced his long jump in P.E. On his first attempt, he jumped 1 meter 47 centimeters. On his second attempt, he jumped 98 centimeters. How much farther did Sam jump on his first attempt than his second?

T: Take two minutes with your partner to draw a tape diagram to model this problem. (Circulate as students work.)

T: Your diagrams show a comparison between two values. How can you solve for the unknown?

S: Subtract 98 cm from 1 m 47 cm.

T: Will you use the algorithm or a simplifying strategy?

As before, invite two pairs to the board to solve as others work at their desks. Solution A shows the algorithm. Solutions B, C, and D show simplifying strategies.

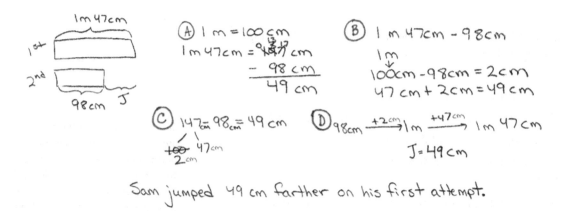

Lesson 1:   Express metric length measurements in terms of a smaller unit; model and solve addition and subtraction word problems involving metric length.

©2015 Great Minds. eureka-math.org
G4-M1M2-TE-BK1-1.3.1-1.2016

Problem Set (10 minutes)

Students should do their personal best to complete the Problem Set within the allotted 10 minutes. Some problems do not specify a method for solving. This is an intentional reduction of scaffolding that invokes MP.5, Use Appropriate Tools Strategically. Students should solve these problems using the RDW approach used for Application Problems.

For some classes, it may be appropriate to modify the assignment by specifying which problems students should work on first. With this option, let the purposeful sequencing of the Problem Set guide the selections so that problems continue to be scaffolded. Balance word problems with other problem types to ensure a range of practice. Consider assigning incomplete problems for homework or at another time during the day.

Student Debrief (10 minutes)

Lesson Objective: Express metric length measurements in terms of a smaller unit; model and solve addition and subtraction word problems involving metric length.

The Student Debrief is intended to invite reflection and active processing of the total lesson experience.

Invite students to review their solutions for the Problem Set. They should check work by comparing answers with a partner before going over answers as a class. Look for misconceptions or misunderstandings that can be addressed in the Debrief. Guide students in a conversation to debrief the Problem Set and process the lesson.

Any combination of the questions below may be used to lead the discussion.

- What pattern did you notice in the equivalences for Problems 1 and 2 of the Problem Set? How did converting 1 **kilometer** to 1,000 meters in Problem 1(a) help you to solve Problem 2(a)?

- How did solving Problem 2 prepare you to solve Problem 3?

- For Problem 3, Parts (c) and (d), explain how you found your answer in terms of the smaller of the two units. What challenges did you face?

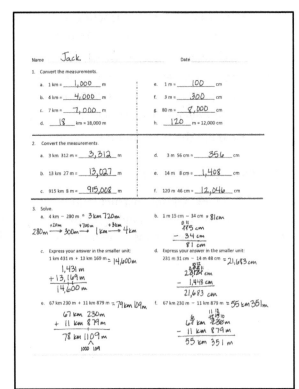

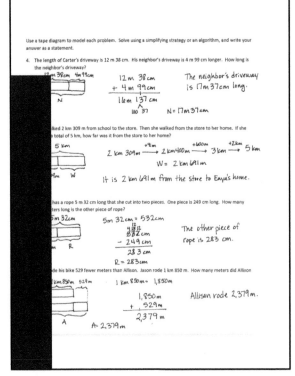

- When adding and subtracting **mixed units** of length, what are two ways that you can solve the problem? Explain to your partner.

- How did solving Problems 1, 2, and 3 help you to solve the rest of the problems on the Problem Set?

- Look at Problem 5 in the Concept Development. How did you draw your tape diagram? Explain to your partner how you solved this problem.

- What new math vocabulary did we use today to communicate precisely?

- How did the Application Problem connect to today's lesson?

Exit Ticket (3 minutes)

After the Student Debrief, instruct students to complete the Exit Ticket. A review of their work will help with assessing students' understanding of the concepts that were presented in today's lesson and planning more effectively for future lessons. The questions may be read aloud to the students.

18   **Lesson 1:**   Express metric length measurements in terms of a smaller unit;
                               model and solve addition and subtraction word problems involving
                               metric length.

©2015 Great Minds. eureka-math.org
G4-M1M2-TE-BK1-1.3.1-1.2016

Name _____   Date _____

1. Convert the measurements.

    a. 1 km = _____ m

    b. 4 km = _____ m

    c. 7 km = _____ m

    d. _____ km = 18,000 m

    e. 1 m = _____ cm

    f. 3 m = _____ cm

    g. 80 m = _____ cm

    h. _____ m = 12,000 cm

2. Convert the measurements.

    a. 3 km 312 m = _____ m

    b. 13 km 27 m = _____ m

    c. 915 km 8 m = _____ m

    d. 3 m 56 cm = _____ cm

    e. 14 m   8 cm = _____ cm

    f. 120 m 46 cm = _____ cm

3. Solve.

    a. 4 km − 280 m

    b. 1 m 15 cm − 34 cm

    c. Express your answer in the smaller unit:
        1 km 431 m + 13 km 169 m

    d. Express your answer in the smaller unit:
        231 m 31 cm − 14 m 48 cm

    e. 67 km 230 m + 11 km 879 m

    f. 67 km 230 m − 11 km 879 m

Lesson 1:   Express metric length measurements in terms of a smaller unit;
            model and solve addition and subtraction word problems involving
            metric length.

19

©2015 Great Minds. eureka-math.org
G4-M1M2-TE-BK1-1.3.1-1.2016

Use a tape diagram to model each problem. Solve using a simplifying strategy or an algorithm, and write your answer as a statement.

4. The length of Carter's driveway is 12 m 38 cm. His neighbor's driveway is 4 m 99 cm longer. How long is his neighbor's driveway?

5. Enya walked 2 km 309 m from school to the store. Then, she walked from the store to her home. If she walked a total of 5 km, how far was it from the store to her home?

6. Rachael has a rope 5 m 32 cm long that she cut into two pieces. One piece is 249 cm long. How many centimeters long is the other piece of rope?

7. Jason rode his bike 529 fewer meters than Allison. Jason rode 1 km 850 m. How many meters did Allison ride?

Lesson 1:   Express metric length measurements in terms of a smaller unit; model and solve addition and subtraction word problems involving metric length.

©2015 Great Minds. eureka-math.org
G4-M1M2-TE-BK1-1.3.1-1.2016

EUREKA
MATH™

Name _____   Date _____

1. Complete the conversion table.

Distance	
71 km	_____ m
_____ km	30,000 m
81 m	_____ cm
_____ m	400 cm

2. 13 km 20 m = _____ m

3. 401 km 101 m − 34 km 153 m = _____

4. Gabe built a toy tower that measured 1 m 78 cm. After building some more, he measured it, and it was 82 cm taller. How tall is his tower now? Draw a tape diagram to model this problem. Use a simplifying strategy or an algorithm to solve, and write your answer as a statement.

 EUREKA MATH™

Lesson 1: Express metric length measurements in terms of a smaller unit; model and solve addition and subtraction word problems involving metric length.

©2015 Great Minds. eureka-math.org
G4-M1M2-TE-BK1-1.3.1-1.2016

21

Name _____   Date _____

1. Find the equivalent measures.

    a.   5 km = _____ m   e.   7 m = _____ cm

    b.   13 km = _____ m   f.   19 m = _____ cm

    c.   _____ km = 17,000 m   g.   _____ m = 2,400 cm

    d.   60 km = _____ m   h.   90 m = _____ cm

2. Find the equivalent measures.

    a.   7 km 123 m = _____ m   d.   7 m 45 cm = _____ cm

    b.   22 km 22 m = _____ m   e.   67 m 7 cm = _____ cm

    c.   875 km 4 m = _____ m   f.   204 m 89 cm = _____ cm

3. Solve.
    a.   2 km 303 m − 556 m   b.   2 m − 54 cm

    c.   Express your answer in the smaller unit: d.   Express your answer in the smaller unit:
         338 km 853 m + 62 km 71 m   800 m 35 cm − 154 m 49 cm

    e.   701 km − 523 km 445 m   f.   231 km 811 m + 485 km 829 m

Lesson 1:   Express metric length measurements in terms of a smaller unit;
                              model and solve addition and subtraction word problems involving
                              metric length.

EUREKA
MATH™

Use a tape diagram to model each problem. Solve using a simplifying strategy or an algorithm, and write your answer as a statement.

4. The length of Celia's garden is 15 m 24 cm. The length of her friend's garden is 2 m 98 cm more than Celia's. What is the length of her friend's garden?

5. Sylvia ran 3 km 290 m in the morning. Then, she ran some more in the evening. If she ran a total of 10 km, how far did Sylvia run in the evening?

6. Jenny's sprinting distance was 356 meters shorter than Tyler's. Tyler sprinted a distance of 1 km 3 m. How many meters did Jenny sprint?

7. The electrician had 7 m 23 cm of electrical wire. He used 551 cm for one wiring project. How many centimeters of wire does he have left?

Lesson 1: Express metric length measurements in terms of a smaller unit; model and solve addition and subtraction word problems involving metric length.

23

©2015 Great Minds. eureka-math.org
G4-M1M2-TE-BK1-1.3.1-1.2016

Lesson 2

Objective: Express metric mass measurements in terms of a smaller unit; model and solve addition and subtraction word problems involving metric mass.

Suggested Lesson Structure

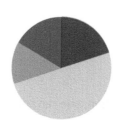

■ Fluency Practice	(12 minutes)
▨ Application Problem	(8 minutes)
▢ Concept Development	(30 minutes)
■ Student Debrief	(10 minutes)
Total Time	**(60 minutes)**

A NOTE ON STANDARDS ALIGNMENT:

In Module 2, students convert metric mass units to add and subtract mixed units. This lesson builds on the content of **2.MD.5** and **3.MD.2**.

Occasionally, students work beyond the **4.MD.1** and **4.MD.2** standards by converting from a smaller unit to a larger unit. They do this by creating a connection between metric units and place value units.

Develop students' basic number sense to make these conversions, and always accept answers in the smaller unit.

Fluency Practice (12 minutes)

- Convert Units **4.MD.1**   (4 minutes)
- Unit Counting **4.MD.1**   (4 minutes)
- Add and Subtract Meters and Centimeters **4.MD.2**   (4 minutes)

Convert Units (4 minutes)

Materials: (S) Personal white board

Note: Isolated review builds fluency with conversion so that students can use this skill as a tool for solving word problems.

> T: (Write 1 m = ___ cm.) 1 meter is how many centimeters?
>
> S: 100 centimeters.

Repeat the process with the following possible sequence: 2 m, 3 m, 9 m, and 6 m.

> T: (Write 1,000 g = ____ kg.) 1,000 grams is the same as how many kilograms?
>
> S: 1 kilogram.

Repeat the process with the following possible sequence: 2,000 g, 3,000 g, 7,000 g, and 5,000 g.

NOTES ON MULTIPLE MEANS OF REPRESENTATION:

Use color to customize the presentation of the Convert Units activity. Enhance learners' perception of the information by consistently displaying meters in one color (e.g., red), while displaying centimeters in a different color (e.g., green). In addition, use color to distinguish the two parts of the number bond.

Lesson 2:   Express metric mass measurements in terms of a smaller unit; model and solve addition and subtraction word problems involving metric mass.

©2015 Great Minds. eureka-math.org
G4-M1M2-TE-BK1-1.3.1-1.2016

EUREKA MATH™

T: (Project a number bond with 2 kg written as the whole, 1 kg as one of the parts, and _____ g as the other part.) Fill in the unknown part.

S: (Write a number bond with 2 kg as the whole, 1 kg as one of the parts, and 1,000 g as the other part.)

T: Write the whole as an addition sentence with mixed units.

S: (Write 1 kg + 1,000 g = 1 kg + 1 kg = 2 kg.)

Repeat the process with the following possible sequence: 3 kg = 2 kg + 1,000 g and 5 kg = 4 kg + 1,000 g.

Unit Counting (4 minutes)

Note: This fluency activity deepens student understanding of the composition and decomposition of unit conversions, laying a foundation for adding and subtracting meters and centimeters. The numbers in bold type indicate the point at which the direction of the counting changes.

Direct students to count by 50 cm in the following sequence, letting them know with gestures when to change direction in counting:

- 50 cm, 100 cm, 150 cm, 200 cm, 250 cm, **300 cm**, 250 cm, 200 cm, 150 cm, 100 cm, 50 cm.
- 50 cm, 1 m, 150 cm, 2 m, 250 cm, **3 m**, 250 cm, 2 m, 150 cm, 1 m, 50 cm.
- 50 cm, 1 m, 1 m 50 cm, 2 m, 2 m 50 cm, **3 m**, 2 m 50 cm, 2 m, 1 m 50 cm, 1 m, 50 cm.

Add and Subtract Meters and Centimeters (4 minutes)

Materials: (S) Personal white board

Note: Reviewing this concept from Lesson 1 helps students work towards mastery of adding and subtracting meters and centimeters.

T: (Write 540 cm + 320 cm = _____.) Say 540 centimeters in meters and centimeters.

S: 5 meters 40 centimeters.

T: (Write 5 m 40 cm below 540 cm.) Say 320 centimeters in meters and centimeters.

S: 3 meters 20 centimeters.

T: (Write 3 m 20 cm below 320 cm.) Add the meters.

S: 5 meters + 3 meters = 8 meters.

T: (Write 5 m 40 cm + 3 m 20 cm = ___.) Add the centimeters.

S: 40 centimeters + 20 centimeters = 60 centimeters.

T: (Write 8 m 60 cm as the sum on the line.) Say the addition sentence in centimeters.

S: 540 centimeters + 320 centimeters = 860 centimeters.

T: (Write 420 cm + 350 cm = _____.) On your personal white board, write 420 cm + 350 cm by representing each number of centimeters as meters and centimeters, and then combining meters and centimeters.

S: (Write 4 m 20 cm + 3 m 50 cm = 7 m 70 cm.)

Repeat the process with the following possible sequence: 650 cm – 140 cm and 780 cm – 210 cm.

Lesson 2:   Express metric mass measurements in terms of a smaller unit; model and solve addition and subtraction word problems involving metric mass.

©2015 Great Minds. eureka-math.org
G4-M1M2-TE-BK1-1.3.1-1.2016

25

Application Problem (8 minutes)

The distance from school to Zoie's house is 3 kilometers 469 meters. Camie's house is 4 kilometers 301 meters farther away from Zoie's. How far is it from Camie's house to school? Solve using an algorithm or a simplifying strategy.

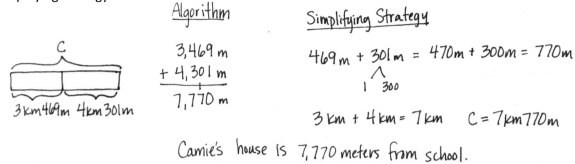

Note: This Application Problem reviews Lesson 1. Students express a metric measurement in a larger unit in terms of a smaller unit and model and solve an addition word problem involving kilometers and meters. Be sure to discuss why 7,770 m and 7 km 770 m are the same.

Concept Development (30 minutes)

Materials: (T) 1-liter water bottle, 1,000 small paper clips, dollar bill, dictionary, balance scale, weights (1 kg and 1 g) (S) Personal white board

Problem 1: Convert kilograms to grams.

Display the words *weight* and *mass*.

- T: (Hold up a 1-liter bottle of water.) This bottle of water weighs 1 kilogram. We can also say that it has a **mass** of 1 kilogram. This is what a scientist would say.
- T: (Hold up the dictionary.) This dictionary weighs about 1 kilogram.
- T: (Hold up the paperclip.) The mass of this small paperclip is about 1 gram. A dollar bill weighs about 1 gram, too.
- T: (Write on the board: 1 kilogram = 1,000 grams.) If the mass of this dictionary is about 1 kilogram, about how many small paperclips will be as heavy as this dictionary?
- S: 1,000 paper clips.

NOTES ON TERMINOLOGY:

Mass is a fundamental measure of the amount of matter in an object. While weight is a measurement that depends upon the force of gravity (one would weigh less on the Moon than one does on Earth), mass does not depend upon the force of gravity. We use both words here, but it is not important for students to recognize the distinction at this time.

Take one minute to balance 1 dictionary and 1,000 small paperclips on a scale. Alternatively, use a 1-kilogram mass weight. Also balance 1 small paperclip and a 1-gram weight.

Lesson 2:   Express metric mass measurements in terms of a smaller unit; model and solve addition and subtraction word problems involving metric mass.

©2015 Great Minds. eureka-math.org
G4-M1M2-TE-BK1-1.3.1-1.2016

EUREKA MATH

T: Let's use a chart to show the relationship between kilograms and grams.

T: (Display a two-column chart, and fill it in together.)

MP.8 We know that 1 kilogram equals 1,000 grams.

T: How many grams is 2 kilograms?

S: 2,000 g.

T: How many kilograms is 3,000 grams?

S: 3 kg.

Continue up to 10 kilograms.

T: Compare kilograms and grams.

S: A kilogram is heavier because we need 1,000 grams to equal 1 kilogram. → 1 kilogram is 1,000 times as much as 1 gram.

T: (Display 1 kg 500 g = _____ g.) Let's convert 1 kg 500 g to grams. 1 kilogram is equal to how many grams?

S: 1,000 grams.

T: 1,000 grams plus 500 grams is 1,500 grams. (Fill in the blank.)

T: (Display 1 kg 300 g = ___ g.) 1 kg 300 g is equal to how many grams?

S: 1,300 grams.

Mass	
kg	g
1	1,000
2	2,000
3	3,000
4	4,000
5	5,000
6	6,000
7	7,000
8	8,000
9	9,000
10	10,000

Repeat with 5 kg 30 g. (Anticipate the incorrect answer of 530 g.)

T: 2,500 grams is equal to how many kilograms?

S: 2 kg 500 g. We made two groups of 1,000 grams, so we have 2 kilograms and 500 grams.

Repeat with 5,005 g.

Problem 2: Add mixed units of mass using the algorithm or a simplifying strategy.

T: (Display 8 kg + 8,200 g horizontally.) Talk for one minute with your partner about how to solve this problem.

S: We can't add different units together. → We can convert the kilograms to grams before adding. We can rename 8 kg to 8,000 g. 8,000 g + 8,200 g = 16,200 g. → We can rename 8,200 g to 8 kg 200 g.

T: Are you going to use the algorithm or a simplifying strategy?

S: A simplifying strategy!

T: Why?

Lesson 2: Express metric mass measurements in terms of a smaller unit; model and solve addition and subtraction word problems involving metric mass.   27

©2015 Great Minds. eureka-math.org
G4-M1M2-TE-BK1-1.3.1-1.2016

S: There is no regrouping. I can add the numbers easily in my head. 8,200 g = 8 kg 200 g.
      8 kg 200 g + 8 kg = 16 kg 200 g.

$$8 \text{ kg} + 8,200 \text{ g}$$
$$8 \text{ kg} + 8 \text{ kg } 200 \text{ g} = 16 \text{ kg } 200 \text{ g}$$
$$8,000 \text{ g} + 8,200 \text{ g} = 16,200 \text{ g} = 16 \text{ kg } 200 \text{ g}$$

T: (Display 25 kg 537 g + 5 kg 723 g horizontally.) A simplifying strategy or the algorithm? Discuss with
      your partner.

S: I think the algorithm because the numbers are too big.
      → There is regrouping and the numbers are not easy
      to combine. → I think I can use a simplifying strategy.

T: Choose the way you want to do it. You will have two
      minutes. If you finish before the two minutes are up,
      try solving it a different way. Let's have two pairs of
      students work at the board, one pair using the
      algorithm, one pair recording a simplifying strategy.

> **NOTES ON
> MULTIPLE MEANS
> OF ENGAGEMENT:**
>
> Vary your demands and provide
> supportive tools (e.g., calculators) to
> students as they meet the challenge of
> regrouping, conversions, and two
> methods of solving. Students working
> below grade level may benefit from
> mastering one method of solving first.
> Or, consider altering the degree of
> difficulty of the computations.

After two minutes, review the student work on the board,
which hopefully includes strategies such as those below. If not,
gently supplement or provide alternative solutions such as the
ones below. Solutions A and B use an algorithm. Solutions C
and D are simplifying strategies.

<table>
<tr><td>Ⓐ

25 kg 537 g
+ 5 kg 723 g
——————
30 kg 1260 g
∧
1 kg 260 g

31 kg 260 g</td><td>Ⓑ

25,537 g
+ 5,723 g
——————
31,260 g</td><td>Ⓒ
25 kg + 5 kg = 30 kg
537 g + 723 g = 530 g + 730 g
∧
530 7   = 1260 g
1 kg 260 g
30 kg + 1 kg + 260 g = 31 kg 260 g</td><td>Ⓓ
537 g + 723 g = 1,200 g + 60 g
∧   ∧
500 37 700 23 = 1,260 g
∧
1,000 g 260 g
25 kg + 5 kg + 1 kg + 260 g = 31 kg 260 g</td></tr>
</table>

Note: Students have been learning numerous simplifying strategies since Grade 1. These are only two of the
strategies they may have learned. Encourage students to compare their strategies as they work through each
problem they solve mentally.

Problem 3: Subtract mixed units of mass using the algorithm or a simplifying strategy.

T: (Display 10 kg – 2 kg 250 g horizontally.) A simplifying strategy or the algorithm? Discuss with a
      partner.

S: There are no grams in the number I'm subtracting from, so I'm going to use the algorithm. → This is
      like 10 thousand minus 2 thousand 250. I'm going to use the algorithm, because there is a lot of
      regrouping. → I think I can do this with a simplifying strategy, because we are subtracting from
      10 kg.

Lesson 2:   Express metric mass measurements in terms of a smaller unit; model
                                and solve addition and subtraction word problems involving metric
                                mass.
                       ©2015 Great Minds. eureka-math.org
                       G4-M1M2-TE-BK1-1.3.1-1.2016

T: Choose the way you want to do it. You will have two minutes. If you finish before two minutes is up, try solving the other way. Let's have two pairs of students work at the board, one pair using the algorithm, one pair recording a simplifying strategy.

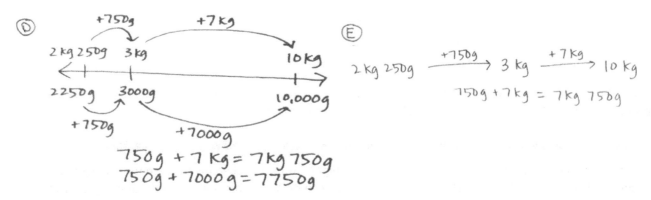

After two minutes, review the student work on the board, which hopefully includes strategies such as those above. If not, gently supplement or provide alternative solutions such as the ones shown above. Solutions A and B use an algorithm. Solutions C, D, and E are simplifying strategies.

T: Look at the first algorithm used by your peers. How did they prepare the problem for subtraction?

S: They renamed 10 kilograms as 9 kilograms and 1,000 grams first.

T: What did they do in their second solution?

S: Converted kilograms to grams.

T: How did our first simplifying strategy pair solve the problem?

S: They subtracted the 2 kilograms first.

T: And then?

S: Subtracted the 250 grams from 1 kilogram.

T: Does anyone have a question for the simplifying strategy math team?

S: How did you know 1 thousand minus 250 was 750?

S: We just subtracted 2 hundred from 1 thousand and then thought of 50 less than 800.

T: How did the next simplifying strategies team solve the problem?

S: They added up from 2 kilograms 250 grams to 3 kilograms first, and then added 7 more kilograms to get to 10 kilograms.

Lesson 2:   Express metric mass measurements in terms of a smaller unit; model and solve addition and subtraction word problems involving metric mass.

©2015 Great Minds. eureka-math.org
G4-M1M2-TE-BK1-1.3.1-1.2016

29

T: What does the number line show?

S: It shows how we can count up from 2 kilograms 250 grams to 10 kilograms to find our answer. It also shows that 7 kilograms 750 grams is equivalent to 7,750 grams.

T: With your partner, take a moment to review the solution strategies on the board.

T: (Display 32 kg 205 g – 5 kg 316 g horizontally.) A simplifying strategy or the algorithm? Discuss with a partner.

S: Those numbers are not easy to subtract. I'm going to use the algorithm. → Definitely the algorithm. There are not enough grams in the first number, so I know we will have to regroup.

T: Choose the way you want to do it and solve.

$$32 \text{ kg } 205g - 5 \text{ kg } 316g$$

Note: Not all problems are easily solved using a simplifying strategy. Encourage students to evaluate the problem carefully to determine the most efficient course for solving problems.

Problem 4: Solve a word problem involving mixed units of mass, modeled with a tape diagram.

A suitcase cannot weigh more than 23 kilograms for a flight. Robert packed his suitcase for his flight, and it weighs 18 kilograms 705 grams. How many more grams can he add to his suitcase without going over the weight limit?

T: Read with me. Take one minute to draw and label a tape diagram. (Allow students time to work.)

T: Tell your partner the known and unknown information.

S: We know how much Robert's suitcase is allowed to weigh and how much it already weighs. We don't know how many more grams it can hold to reach the maximum allowed weight of 23 kilograms.

T: Will you use the algorithm or a simplifying strategy? Label the unknown part on your diagram and make a statement of the solution.

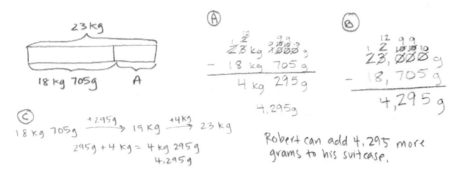

Circulate, reviewing the students' work, which hopefully includes strategies such as those above. If not, gently supplement. Solutions A and B use the algorithm. Solution C is a simplifying strategy.

Lesson 2:   Express metric mass measurements in terms of a smaller unit; model and solve addition and subtraction word problems involving metric mass.

©2015 Great Minds. eureka-math.org
G4-M1M2-TE-BK1-1.3.1-1.2016

Problem Set (10 minutes)

Students should do their personal best to complete the Problem Set within the allotted 10 minutes. For some classes, it may be appropriate to modify the assignment by specifying which problems they work on first. Some problems do not specify a method for solving. Students should solve these problems using the RDW approach used for Application Problems.

Student Debrief (10 minutes)

Lesson Objective: Express metric mass measurements in terms of a smaller unit; model and solve addition and subtraction word problems involving metric mass.

The Student Debrief is intended to invite reflection and active processing of the total lesson experience.

Invite students to review their solutions for the Problem Set. They should check work by comparing answers with a partner before going over answers as a class. Look for misconceptions or misunderstandings that can be addressed in the Debrief. Guide students in a conversation to debrief the Problem Set and process the lesson.

Any combination of the questions below may be used to lead the discussion.

- In our lesson, we solved addition and subtraction problems two different ways but got equivalent answers. Is one answer better than the other? Why or why not?

- What did you do differently in Problem 3 when it asked you to express the answer in the smaller unit versus in mixed units?

- In Problem 6, did it make sense to answer in the smallest unit or mixed units? Why? When might it be better to answer in the smallest unit?

- Explain to your partner how you solved Problem 7. Was there more than one way to solve it?

- How did the Application Problem connect to today's lesson?

- How did today's lesson of weight conversions build on yesterday's lesson of length conversions?

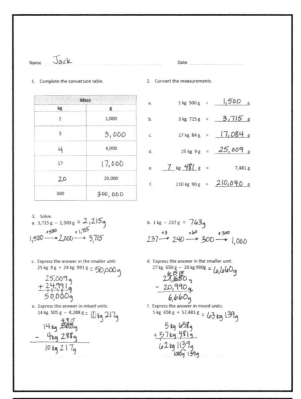

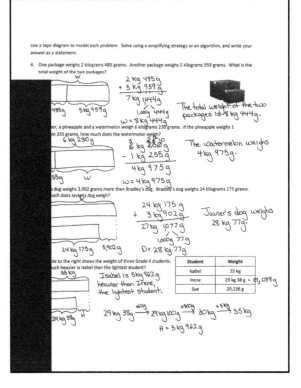

Lesson 2: Express metric mass measurements in terms of a smaller unit; model and solve addition and subtraction word problems involving metric mass.   31

©2015 Great Minds. eureka-math.org
G4-M1M2-TE-BK1-1.3.1-1.2016

- What is **mass**?
- When might we use grams rather than kilograms?

Exit Ticket (3 minutes)

After the Student Debrief, instruct students to complete the Exit Ticket. A review of their work will help with assessing students' understanding of the concepts that were presented in today's lesson and planning more effectively for future lessons. The questions may be read aloud to the students.

Lesson 2:   Express metric mass measurements in terms of a smaller unit; model
and solve addition and subtraction word problems involving metric
mass.

©2015 Great Minds. eureka-math.org
G4-M1M2-TE-BK1-1.3.1-1.2016

Name _____   Date _____

1. Complete the conversion table.

Mass	
kg	**g**
1	1,000
3	
	4,000
17	
	20,000
300	

2. Convert the measurements.

a.   1 kg 500 g   =   _____ g

b.   3 kg 715 g   =   _____ g

c.   17 kg 84 g   =   _____ g

d.   25 kg 9 g   =   _____ g

e.   _____ kg _____ g   =   7,481 g

f.   210 kg 90 g   =   _____ g

3. Solve.

a.   3,715 g − 1,500 g

b. 1 kg − 237 g

c. Express the answer in the smaller unit:
25 kg 9 g + 24 kg 991 g

d. Express the answer in the smaller unit:
27 kg 650 g − 20 kg 990 g

e. Express the answer in mixed units:
14 kg 505 g − 4,288 g

f. Express the answer in mixed units:
5 kg 658 g + 57,481 g

©2015 Great Minds. eureka-math.org
G4-M1M2-TE-BK1-1.3.1-1.2016

Use a tape diagram to model each problem. Solve using a simplifying strategy or an algorithm, and write your answer as a statement.

4. One package weighs 2 kilograms 485 grams. Another package weighs 5 kilograms 959 grams. What is the total weight of the two packages?

5. Together, a pineapple and a watermelon weigh 6 kilograms 230 grams. If the pineapple weighs 1 kilogram 255 grams, how much does the watermelon weigh?

6. Javier's dog weighs 3,902 grams more than Bradley's dog. Bradley's dog weighs 24 kilograms 175 grams. How much does Javier's dog weigh?

7. The table to the right shows the weight of three fish tanks. How much heavier is fish tank A than the lightest fish tank?

Fish Tank	Weight
A	35 kg
B	29 kg 38 g
C	29,238 g

Lesson 2:   Express metric mass measurements in terms of a smaller unit; model and solve addition and subtraction word problems involving metric mass.

© 2015 Great Minds. eureka-math.org
G4-M1M2-TE-BK1-1.3.1-1.2016

EUREKA
MATH

Name _____   Date _____

1. Convert the measurements.

    a.   21 kg 415 g = _____ g

    b.   2 kg 91 g = _____ g

    c.   87 kg 17 g = _____ g

    d.   ____ kg _____ g = 96,020 g

Use a tape diagram to model the following problem. Solve using a simplifying strategy or an algorithm, and write your answer as a statement.

2.   The table to the right shows the weight of three dogs. How much more does the Great Dane weigh than the Chihuahua?

Dog	Weight
Great Dane	59 kg
Golden Retriever	32 kg 48 g
Chihuahua	1,329 g

Lesson 2:   Express metric mass measurements in terms of a smaller unit; model and solve addition and subtraction word problems involving metric mass.

©2015 Great Minds. eureka-math.org
G4-M1M2-TE-BK1-1.3.1-1.2016

35

Name _____   Date _____

1. Complete the conversion table.

Mass	
kg	g
1	1,000
6	
	8,000
15	
	24,000
550	

2. Convert the measurements.

a.   2 kg 700 g   =   _____ g

b.   5 kg 945 g   =   _____ g

c.   29 kg 58 g   =   _____ g

d.   31 kg 3 g   =   _____ g

e.   66,597 g   =   _____ kg _____ g

f.   270 kg 41 g   =   _____ g

3. Solve.
   a. 370 g + 80 g   b. 5 kg − 730 g

   c. Express the answer in the smaller unit: d. Express the answer in the smaller unit:
      27 kg 547 g + 694 g   16 kg + 2,800 g

   e. Express the answer in mixed units: f. Express the answer in mixed units:
      4 kg 229 g − 355 g   70 kg 101 g − 17 kg 862 g

Lesson 2:   Express metric mass measurements in terms of a smaller unit; model
                              and solve addition and subtraction word problems involving metric
                              mass.

EUREKA
MATH

Use a tape diagram to model each problem. Solve using a simplifying strategy or an algorithm, and write your answer as a statement.

4. One suitcase weighs 23 kilograms 696 grams. Another suitcase weighs 25 kilograms 528 grams. What is the total weight of the two suitcases?

5. A bag of potatoes and a bag of onions combined weigh 11 kilograms 15 grams. If the bag of potatoes weighs 7 kilograms 300 grams, how much does the bag of onions weigh?

6. The table to the right shows the weight of three dogs. What is the difference in weight between the heaviest and lightest dog?

Dog	Weight
Lassie	21 kg 249 g
Riley	23 kg 128 g
Fido	21,268 g

Lesson 2:   Express metric mass measurements in terms of a smaller unit; model and solve addition and subtraction word problems involving metric mass.   37

©2015 Great Minds. eureka-math.org
G4-M1M2-TE-BK1-1.3.1-1.2016

Lesson 3

Objective: Express metric capacity measurements in terms of a smaller unit; model and solve addition and subtraction word problems involving metric capacity.

Suggested Lesson Structure

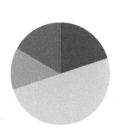

■ Fluency Practice   (12 minutes)
■ Application Problem   (8 minutes)
□ Concept Development   (30 minutes)
■ Student Debrief   (10 minutes)

Total Time   **(60 minutes)**

> **NOTES ON STANDARDS ALIGNMENT:**
>
> In Module 2, students convert metric capacity units to add and subtract mixed units. This lesson builds on the content of **2.MD.5** and **3.MD.2**.
>
> Occasionally, students work beyond the **4.MD.1** and **4.MD.2** standards by converting from a smaller unit to a larger unit. They do this by connecting metric units to place value units.
>
> Develop students' basic number sense to make these conversions, and always accept answers in the smaller unit.

Fluency Practice (12 minutes)

- Convert Units **4.MD.1**   (3 minutes)
- Unit Counting **4.MD.1**   (5 minutes)
- Add and Subtract Meters and Centimeters **4.MD.2**   (4 minutes)

Convert Units (3 minutes)

Materials: (S) Personal white board

Note: Isolated review builds fluency with conversion so that students can use this skill as a tool for solving word problems.

T: (Write 1 m = _____ cm.) 1 meter is how many centimeters?
S: 100 centimeters.

Repeat the process with the following possible sequence: 2 m, 4 m, 4 m 50 cm, 8 m 50 cm, 8 m 5 cm, and 6 m 35 cm.

T: (Write 1,000 m = _____ km.) 1,000 meters is the same as how many kilometers?
S: 1 kilometer.

Repeat the process with the following possible sequence: 2,000 m, 3,000 m, 6,000 m, and 9,000 m.

T: (Project a number bond with 2 kilometers written as the whole, 1 kilometer as one of the parts, and _____ m as the other part.) Fill in the unknown part.
S: (Write a number bond with 2 kilometers as the whole, 1 kilometer as one of the parts, and 1,000 m as the other part.)

Lesson 3:   Express metric capacity measurements in terms of a smaller unit; model and solve addition and subtraction word problems involving metric capacity.

T: Write the whole as an addition sentence with mixed units.

S: (Write 1 km + 1,000 m = 2 km.)

Repeat the process with the following possible sequence: 2 km + 1,000 m = 3 km and 1,000 m + 7 km = 8 km.

Unit Counting (5 minutes)

Note: This fluency activity deepens student understanding of the composition and decomposition of units, laying a foundation for adding and subtracting grams and kilograms. The numbers in bold type indicate the point at which the direction of the counting changes.

Direct students to count by grams in the following sequence, letting them know with gestures when to change direction in counting:

- 500 g, 1,000 g, 1,500 g, 2,000 g, 2,500 g, **3,000 g**, 2,500 g, 2,000 g, 1,500 g, 1,000 g, 500 g
- 500 g, 1 kg, 1,500 g, 2 kg, 2,500 g, **3 kg**, 2,500 g, 2 kg, 1,500 g, 1 kg, 500 g
- 500 g, 1 kg, 1 kg 500 g, 2 kg, 2 kg 500 g, **3 kg**, 2 kg 500 g, 2 kg, 1 kg 500 g, 1 kg, 500 g
- 200 g, 400 g, 600 g, 800 g, 1 kg, 1 kg 200 g, 1 kg 400 g, 1 kg 600 g, 1 kg 800 g, 2 **kg**
- 600 g, 1,200 g, 1,800 g, 2,400 g, **3 kg**, 2,400 g, 1,800 g, 1,200 g, 600 g
- 600 g, 1 kg 200 g, 1 kg 800 g, 2 kg 400 g, **3 kg**, 2 kg 400 g, 1 kg 800 g, 1 kg 200 g, 600 g

Add and Subtract Meters and Centimeters (4 minutes)

Materials: (S) Personal white board

Note: Reviewing this concept from Lesson 1 helps students work towards mastery of adding and subtracting meters and centimeters.

T: Write 560 cm + 230 cm = ____. Below it, write ____ m ____ cm + ____ m ____ cm = ____ m ____ cm on your personal white boards. Now, complete the two addition sentences.

S: (Write 560 cm + 230 cm = 790 cm. Below it, write 5 m 60 cm + 2 m 30 cm = 7 m 90 cm.)

Repeat the process with the following possible sequence: 650 cm − 230 cm and 470 cm + 520 cm.

Lesson 3:   Express metric capacity measurements in terms of a smaller unit; model and solve addition and subtraction word problems involving metric capacity.

©2015 Great Minds. eureka-math.org
G4-M1M2-TE-BK1-1.3.1-1.2016

39

Application Problem (8 minutes)

A liter of water weighs 1 kilogram. The Lee family took 3 liters of water with them on a hike. At the end of the hike, they had 290 grams of water left. How much water did they drink? Draw a tape diagram, and solve using an algorithm or a simplifying strategy.

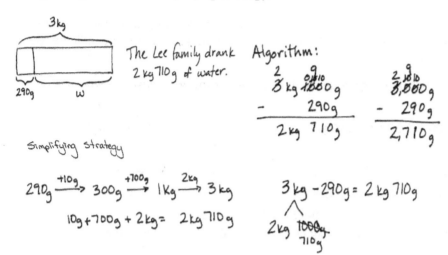

NOTES ON MULTIPLE MEANS OF ACTION AND EXPRESSION:

Scaffold constructed responses with sentence frames, such as, "The Lee family drank _____ of water." Or, have students dictate their responses to a partner. Provide sheets with pre-formatted tape diagrams that can be slipped inside personal white boards, or use virtual manipulatives as an alternative.

Note: This Application Problem reviews working with grams and kilograms from Lesson 2 while connecting to today's work with liters. Students can express kilograms in terms of grams and subtract to solve a measurement word problem involving a tape diagram. Students may also recall that 1 milliliter of water weighs 1 gram and use this fact to report their answer in liters and milliliters.

Concept Development (30 minutes)

Materials: (T) 3-liter beaker, bucket of water (S) 3-liter graduated beaker (marked with liters and milliliters), bucket of water, personal white board

Note: For Problem 1, students should work in groups of three students each.

Problem 1: Compare the sizes and note the relationship between 1 liter and 1 milliliter.

T: Point to the mark on your beaker that says 1 liter.

T: Pour water into your beaker until you reach that amount. Now, how many **milliliters** are in your beaker?

S: 1,000 mL.

T: How do you know?

S: 1 liter is the same as 1,000 milliliters. The beaker shows both measurements on the scale.

T: (Write 1 L = 1,000 mL on the board.)

Lesson 3:   Express metric capacity measurements in terms of a smaller unit; model and solve addition and subtraction word problems involving metric capacity.

©2015 Great Minds. eureka-math.org
G4-M1M2-TE-BK1-1.3.1-1.2016

T: With your partner, locate 1,500 mL and pour in more water to measure 1,500 mL. Now, how many liters do you have?

S: Less than 2 but more than 1 liter. → 1 liter 500 milliliters.

T: Yes, just like we named mixed units of kilograms and grams in the last lesson, we can use mixed units of liters and milliliters by using both sides of the scale on the beaker.

T: (Write 1 L 500 mL = 1,500 mL on the board.)

T: Pour water to measure 2 liters. How many milliliters are equal to 2 liters?

S: 2,000 milliliters.

T: Pour more water to measure 2,200 mL. Discuss the capacity of the beaker.

S: The beaker is not at capacity. There are only 2 L 200 mL of water in the beaker. → The beaker has a capacity of 3 liters but is only filled to 2 L 200 mL. → If we pour 800 mL more water into the beaker, it will reach capacity.

Activity: Prepare several beakers with different amounts of water, for example, 1 liter, 1,400 milliliters, 1,750 milliliters, 2 liters, and 2,300 milliliters. Have students circulate to each beaker, recording the amount of water as mixed units of liters and milliliters and as milliliters. Compare answers as a class and record findings on the board to show equivalency between mixed units of liters and milliliters, and milliliters.

Problem 2: Add mixed units of capacity using the algorithm or a simplifying strategy.

T: (Display 32 L 420 mL + 13 L 585 mL horizontally.) Will you use a simplifying strategy or an algorithm?

S: A simplifying strategy, because 420 milliliters decomposes to 15 milliliters, 5 milliliters, and 400 milliliters. 585 milliliters plus 15 milliliters makes 600 milliliters. 600 milliliters and 400 milliliters make 1 liter. Then, I add 5 milliliters to 1 liter. When I add that to 45 liters, I get 46 liters 5 milliliters. → There are some renamings, so I'll use an algorithm. → I will solve it mentally, and then check my work with the algorithm.

T: Choose the way you want to do it. I will give you two minutes. If you finish before the two minutes are up, try solving a different way. Let's have two pairs of students work at the board, one pair using the algorithm, one pair recording a simplifying strategy.

After two minutes, review the student work on the board, which hopefully includes strategies such as those below. If not, gently supplement or provide alternative solutions such as the ones shown below. Solutions A and B use the algorithms. Solution C is a simplifying strategy.

A
$$32,420 \text{ mL}$$
$$+ \ 13,585 \text{ mL}$$
$$46,005 \text{ mL}$$
$$46 \text{ L } 5 \text{ mL}$$

B
$$32 \text{ L } 420 \text{ mL}$$
$$+ \ 13 \text{ L } 585 \text{ mL}$$
$$45 \text{ L } 1005 \text{ mL}$$
$$1 \text{ L } 5 \text{ mL}$$
$$46 \text{ L } 5 \text{ mL}$$

C
$$32 \text{ L } + 13 \text{ L} = 45 \text{ L}$$
$$420 \text{ mL} + 585 \text{ mL} = 405 \text{ mL} + 600 \text{ mL}$$
$$405 \quad 15 \qquad\qquad = 1,005 \text{ mL}$$
$$45 \text{ L} + 1 \text{ L} + 5 \text{ mL} = 46 \text{ L } 5 \text{ mL}$$

Lesson 3:   Express metric capacity measurements in terms of a smaller unit; model and solve addition and subtraction word problems involving metric capacity.

41

©2015 Great Minds. eureka-math.org
G4-M1M2-TE-BK1-1.3.1-1.2016

T: What strategies can we use to solve?

S: We can convert to milliliters before adding. 32 L 420 mL = 32,420 mL. 13 L 585 mL = 13,585 mL. The sum is 46,005 mL.

S: I know that 1,000 mL = 1 L, so 46,005 mL is equivalent to 46 L 5 mL.

S: We can also add the mixed units. 32 L + 13 L = 45 L. 420 mL + 585 mL = 1,005 mL. 1,005 mL is the same as 1 L 5 mL. When I add 45 L and 1 L 5 mL, I get a sum of 46 L 5 mL.

S: We can also count up. 32 L 420 mL + 580 mL = 33 L. → 33 L + 13 L = 46 L. → 46 L + 5 mL = 46 L 5 mL.

Problem 3: Subtract mixed units of capacity using the algorithm or a simplifying strategy.

T: (Display 12 L 215 mL − 8 L 600 mL horizontally.) A simplifying strategy or the algorithm? Discuss with a partner.

S: Oh, for sure, I'm using the algorithm. We have to rename a liter. → A simplifying strategy. I can count on from 8 liters 600 milliliters. → I can do mental math. I'll show you when we solve.

T: Choose the way you want to do it. I will give you two minutes. If you finish before the two minutes are up, try solving a different way. Let's have two pairs of students work at the board, one pair using the algorithm, one pair recording a simplifying strategy.

After two minutes, review the student work on the board, which hopefully includes strategies such as those above. If not, gently supplement or provide alternative solutions such as the ones shown above. Solutions A and B use the algorithms. Solutions C, D, and E are simplifying strategies.

Express metric capacity measurements in terms of a smaller unit; model and solve addition and subtraction word problems involving metric capacity.

EUREKA
MATH™

T: Look at the first problem. How did they set it up?

S: They regrouped 12 liters 215 milliliters as 11 liters 1,215 milliliters.

T: How is the second problem set up?

S: They converted to milliliters before solving, and then wrote their answer as a mixed unit.

T: Does anyone have a question about any of the simplifying strategies?

S: Why did you convert 4 liters to 4,000 milliliters and combine that with 215 milliliters?

S: I couldn't subtract 600 from 215, so I converted to milliliters to regroup.

T: How did counting on work?

S: You could add to regroup and make a liter and then add enough liters and milliliters to reach the total.

T: Take a moment to review the solution strategies on the board. Compare the counting up strategies, the number line, and the arrow way.

Problem 4: Solve a word problem involving mixed units of capacity.

Jennifer is making 2,170 milliliters of her favorite drink that combines iced tea and lemonade. If she puts in 1 liter 300 milliliters of iced tea, how much lemonade does she need?

T: Read with me. Take two minutes to draw and label a tape diagram. (Allow time for students to work.)

T: Tell your partner the known and unknown information.

S: We know how much iced tea she puts in and how much of her favorite drink she is making. We don't know how much lemonade she needs.

MP.1

T: Work with your partner to solve. Will you use a simplifying strategy or an algorithm?

S: A simplifying strategy. I know that 300 milliliters + 700 milliliters is 1,000 milliliters. That brings us to 2 liters. Then, all I need to do is add 170 milliliters more. 700 mL + 170 mL = 870 mL.

T: Label the unknown part on your tape diagram, and make a statement of the solution.

S: Jennifer needs 870 milliliters of lemonade.

> NOTES ON
> MULTIPLE MEANS
> OF ACTION AND
> EXPRESSION:
>
> Help learners develop plans and strategies to solve word problems. Provide a problem-solving checklist that students can use to monitor their steps as they solve.

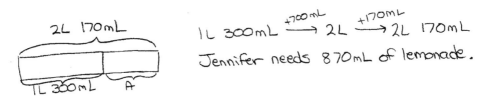

T: With your partner, check your answer by using the subtraction algorithm.

Lesson 3:   Express metric capacity measurements in terms of a smaller unit; model and solve addition and subtraction word problems involving metric capacity.

©2015 Great Minds. eureka-math.org
G4-M1M2-TE-BK1-1.3.1-1.2016

43

Problem Set (10 minutes)

Students should do their personal best to complete the Problem Set within the allotted 10 minutes. For some classes, it may be appropriate to modify the assignment by specifying which problems they work on first. Some problems do not specify a method for solving. Students should solve these problems using the RDW approach used for Application Problems.

Student Debrief (10 minutes)

Lesson Objective: Express metric capacity measurements in terms of a smaller unit; model and solve addition and subtraction word problems involving metric capacity.

The Student Debrief is intended to invite reflection and active processing of the total lesson experience.

Invite students to review their solutions for the Problem Set. They should check work by comparing answers with a partner before going over answers as a class. Look for misconceptions or misunderstandings that can be addressed in the Debrief. Guide students in a conversation to debrief the Problem Set and process the lesson. Any combination of the questions below may be used to lead the discussion.

- In Problem 4(a), what was your strategy for ordering the drinks?

- Discuss why you chose to solve Problem 5 mixed units or converting all units to millili

- Which strategy do you prefer for adding and subtracting mixed units? Why is one way preferable to the other for you?

- What new terms to describe capacity did you learn today?

- What patterns have you noticed about the vocabulary used to measure length, mass, and capacity?

- How did the Application Problem connect to today's lesson?

- Describe the relationship between liters and **milliliters**.

- How did today's lesson relate to the lessons on mass and length?

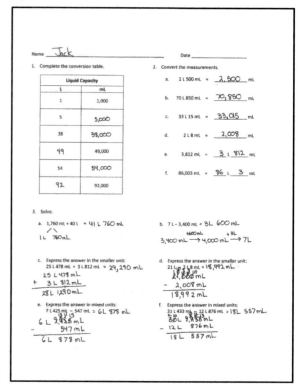

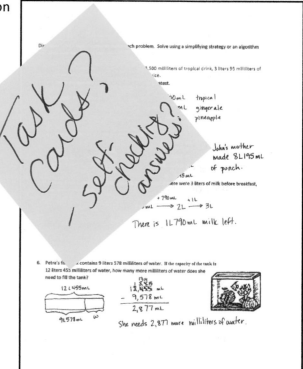

Lesson 3:   Express metric capacity measurements in terms of a smaller unit; model and solve addition and subtraction word problems involving metric capacity.

Exit Ticket (3 minutes)

After the Student Debrief, instruct students to complete the Exit Ticket. A review of their work will help with assessing students' understanding of the concepts that were presented in today's lesson and planning more effectively for future lessons. The questions may be read aloud to the students.

Lesson 3:   Express metric capacity measurements in terms of a smaller unit;
model and solve addition and subtraction word problems involving
metric capacity.

©2015 Great Minds. eureka-math.org
G4-M1M2-TE-BK1-1.3.1-1.2016

45

Name _____   Date _____

1. Complete the conversion table.

Liquid Capacity	
L	mL
1	1,000
5	
38	
	49,000
54	
	92,000

2. Convert the measurements.

a. 2 L 500 mL = _____ mL

b. 70 L 850 mL = _____ mL

c. 33 L 15 mL = _____ mL

d. 2 L 8 mL = _____ mL

e. 3,812 mL = _____ L _____ mL

f. 86,003 mL = _____ L _____ mL

3. Solve.

a. 1,760 mL + 40 L

b. 7 L − 3,400 mL

c. Express the answer in the smaller unit:
25 L 478 mL + 3 L 812 mL

d. Express the answer in the smaller unit:
21 L − 2 L 8 mL

e. Express the answer in mixed units:
7 L 425 mL − 547 mL

f. Express the answer in mixed units:
31 L 433 mL − 12 L 876 mL

Lesson 3: Express metric capacity measurements in terms of a smaller unit; model and solve addition and subtraction word problems involving metric capacity.

EUREKA
MATH

Use a tape diagram to model each problem. Solve using a simplifying strategy or an algorithm, and write your answer as a statement.

4. To make fruit punch, John's mother combined 3,500 milliliters of tropical drink, 3 liters 95 milliliters of ginger ale, and 1 liter 600 milliliters of pineapple juice.

   a. Order the quantity of each drink from least to greatest.

   b. How much punch did John's mother make?

5. A family drank 1 liter 210 milliliters of milk at breakfast. If there were 3 liters of milk before breakfast, how much milk is left?

6. Petra's fish tank contains 9 liters 578 milliliters of water. If the capacity of the tank is 12 liters 455 milliliters of water, how many more milliliters of water does she need to fill the tank?

Lesson 3:   Express metric capacity measurements in terms of a smaller unit; model and solve addition and subtraction word problems involving metric capacity.

©2015 Great Minds. eureka-math.org
G4-M1M2-TE-BK1-1.3.1-1.2016

47

Name _____   Date _____

1. Convert the measurements.

   a. 6 L 127 mL = _____ mL

   b. 706 L 220 mL = _____ mL

   c. 12 L 9 mL = _____ mL

   d. _____ L _____ mL = 906,010 mL

2. Solve.

   81 L 603 mL − 22 L 489 mL

Use a tape diagram to model the following problem. Solve using a simplifying strategy or an algorithm, and write your answer as a statement.

3. The Smith's hot tub has a capacity of 1,458 liters. Mrs. Smith put 487 liters 750 milliliters of water in the tub. How much water needs to be added to fill the hot tub completely?

Lesson 3: Express metric capacity measurements in terms of a smaller unit; model and solve addition and subtraction word problems involving metric capacity.

©2015 Great Minds. eureka-math.org
G4-M1M2-TE-BK1-1.3.1-1.2016

EUREKA
MATH™

Name _____   Date _____

1. Complete the conversion table.

Liquid Capacity	
L	**mL**
1	1,000
8	
27	
	39,000
68	
	102,000

2. Convert the measurements.

a.   5 L 850 mL   =   _____ mL

b.   29 L 303 mL   =   _____ mL

c.   37 L 37 mL   =   _____ mL

d.   17 L 2 mL   =   _____ mL

e.   13,674 mL   =   _____ L _____ mL

f.   275,005 mL   =   _____ L _____ mL

3. Solve.

a.   545 mL + 48 mL

b.   8 L − 5,740 mL

c.   Express the answer in the smaller unit:
   27 L 576 mL + 784 mL

d.   Express the answer in the smaller unit:
   27 L + 3,100 mL

e.   Express the answer in mixed units:
   9 L 213 mL − 638 mL

f.   Express the answer in mixed units:
   41 L 724 mL − 28 L 945 mL

Lesson 3:   Express metric capacity measurements in terms of a smaller unit; model and solve addition and subtraction word problems involving metric capacity.

©2015 Great Minds. eureka-math.org
G4-M1M2-TE-BK1-1.3.1-1.2016

49

Use a tape diagram to model each problem. Solve using a simplifying strategy or an algorithm, and write your answer as a statement.

4. Sammy's bucket holds 2,530 milliliters of water. Marie's bucket holds 2 liters 30 milliliters of water. Katie's bucket holds 2 liters 350 milliliters of water. Whose bucket holds the least amount of water?

5. At football practice, the water jug was filled with 18 liters 530 milliliters of water. At the end of practice, there were 795 milliliters left. How much water did the team drink?

6. 27,545 milliliters of gas were added to a car's empty gas tank. If the gas tank's capacity is 56 liters 202 milliliters, how much gas is needed to fill the tank?

Lesson 3:   Express metric capacity measurements in terms of a smaller unit; model and solve addition and subtraction word problems involving metric capacity.

©2015 Great Minds. eureka-math.org
G4-M1M2-TE-BK1-1.3.1-1.2016

EUREKA
MATH™

Mathematics Curriculum

4
GRADE

Topic B
Application of Metric Unit Conversions

4.MD.1, 4.MD.2

Focus Standards:	4.MD.1[1]	Know relative sizes of measurement units within one system of units including km, m, cm; kg, g; lb, oz.; l, ml; hr, min, sec. Within a single system of measurement, express measurements in a larger unit in terms of a smaller unit. Record measurement equivalents in a two-column table. *For example, know that 1 ft is 12 times as long as 1 in. Express the length of a 4 ft snake as 48 in. Generate a conversion table for feet and inches listing the number pairs (1, 12), (2, 24), (3, 36), …*
	4.MD.2[2]	Use the four operations to solve word problems involving distances, intervals of time, liquid volumes, masses of objects, and money, including problems involving simple fractions or decimals, and problems that require expressing measurements given in a larger unit in terms of a smaller unit. Represent measurement quantities using diagrams such as number line diagrams that feature a measurement scale.
Instructional Days:	2	
Coherence -Links from:	G2–M2	Addition and Subtraction of Length Units
	G3–M2	Place Value and Problem Solving with Units of Measure
-Links to:	G5–M1	Place Value and Decimal Fractions
	G5–M2	Multi-Digit Whole Number and Decimal Fraction Operations

In Topic B, students continue to build off their measurement work from previous grade levels. They solidify their understanding of the relationship between metric units and the place value chart and apply unit conversions to solve and reason about multi-step word problems (**4.MD.2**). Applying the skills learned in Module 1, students discover and explore the relationship between place value and conversions. The beauty of both the place value and measurement systems is the efficiency and precision permitted by the use of different size units to express a given quantity.

---

[1]Pounds, ounces, and time are addressed in Module 7. This is a non-tested standard, but expressing metric measurements of length, mass, and capacity from larger to smaller units strengthens the upcoming modules.

[2]Time and money are addressed in Module 7. This is a non-tested standard, but the context of operating on distance, volume, and mass strengthens the upcoming modules.

Lesson 4 connects metric measurement conversions and place value by comparing mixed units of measure and verifying statements such as *1 kilometer is 1,000 times as much as 1 meter*. In Lesson 5, as students solve two- and three-step word problems by adding and subtracting metric units, their ability to reason in parts and wholes is taken to the next level. This is important preparation for multi-digit operations and manipulating fractional units in future modules.

Throughout Topic B, tape diagrams and number lines serve as models to support application of the standard algorithm to word problems. Students solve problems by converting between units and using simplifying strategies or algorithms (**4.MD.1**).

A Teaching Sequence Toward Mastery of Application of Metric Unit Conversions
Objective 1: Know and relate metric units to place value units in order to express measurements in different units.   (Lesson 4)
Objective 2: Use addition and subtraction to solve multi-step word problems involving length, mass, and capacity.   (Lesson 5)

EUREKA MATH

Lesson 4

Objective: Know and relate metric units to place value units in order to express measurements in different units.

Suggested Lesson Structure

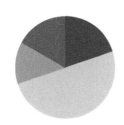

■ Fluency Practice   (12 minutes)
▨ Application Problem   (8 minutes)
▧ Concept Development   (30 minutes)
■ Student Debrief   (10 minutes)
  Total Time   **(60 minutes)**

Fluency Practice (12 minutes)

- Perimeter and Area **4.MD.3**   (4 minutes)
- Add Meters and Centimeters **4.MD.2**   (2 minutes)
- Convert Units **4.MD.1**   (2 minutes)
- Unit Counting **4.MD.1**   (4 minutes)

Perimeter and Area (4 minutes)

Note: This fluency activity prepares students for G4–M3–Lesson 1's Concept Development.

NOTES ON STANDARDS ALIGNMENT:

In Module 2, students convert metric length, mass, and capacity units to add and subtract mixed units. This lesson builds on the content of **2.MD.5** and **3.MD.2**.

Occasionally, students work beyond the **4.MD.1** and **4.MD.2** standards by converting from a smaller unit to a larger unit. They do this by connecting metric units to place value units.

Develop students' basic number sense to make these conversions, and always accept answers in the smaller unit.

T: (Project grid paper with a rectangle of 5 units by 3 units shaded.) What's the length of the longest side?

S: 5 units.

T: (Write *5 units*. Point to the opposite side.) What's the length of the opposite side?

S: 5 units.

T: (Write *5 units*.) What's the sum of the rectangle's two longest sides?

S: 10 units.

T: What's the length of the shortest side?

S: 3 units.

T: (Write *3 units*. Point to the unknown side.) What's the length of the unknown side?

S: 3 units.

T: (Write *3 units*.) What's the sum of the rectangle's two shortest sides?

Lesson 4:   Know and relate metric units to place value units in order to express measurements in different units.

©2015 Great Minds. eureka-math.org
G4-M1M2-TE-BK1-1.3.1-1.2016

53

S: 6 units.

T: What is the sum of the four sides of the rectangle?

S: 16 units.

T: How many square units are in one row?

S: 5 square units.

T: How many rows of 5 square units are there?

S: 3 rows.

T: Let's find how many square units there are in the rectangle, counting by fives.

S: 5, 10, 15.

T: How many square units in all?

S: 15 square units.

Repeat the process for 4 × 3 and 6 × 4 rectangles.

Add Meters and Centimeters (2 minutes)

Materials: (S) Add Meters and Centimeters Pattern Sheet

Note: This work with mixed units of meters and centimeters supports students in understanding mixed units of all kinds: liters and milliliters, kilometers and meters, kilograms and grams, and whole numbers and fractional units.

T: (Distribute Add Meters and Centimeters Pattern Sheet.) Do as many problems as you can in two minutes. If you finish early, skip-count by 400 milliliters on the back. Stop when you get to 4,000 milliliters. Then, go back through each multiple, and convert multiples of 1,000 milliliters to whole liters.

Convert Units (2 minutes)

Materials: (S) Personal white board

Note: Isolated review builds fluency with conversion so that students can use this skill as a tool for solving word problems.

T: (Write 1 m 20 cm = _____ cm.) 1 m 20 cm is how many centimeters?

S: 120 centimeters.

Repeat the process for the following possible sequence: 1 m 80 cm, 1 m 8 cm, and 2m 4 cm.

T: (Write 1,500 g = ___ kg ___ g.) On your personal white boards, fill in the equation.

S: (Write 1,500 g = 1 kg 500 g.)

Repeat the process for the following possible sequence: 1,300 g, 1,030 g, and 1,005 g.

T: (Write 1 liter 700 mL = ___ mL.) On your boards, fill in the equation.

S: (Write 1 liter 700 mL = 1,700 mL.)

Repeat the process for the following possible sequence: 1 liter 70 mL, 1 liter 7 mL, and 1 liter 80 mL.

Lesson 4:   Know and relate metric units to place value units in order to express
                              measurements in different units.

©2015 Great Minds. eureka-math.org
G4-M1M2-TE-BK1-1.3.1-1.2016

Unit Counting (4 minutes)

Note: This fluency activity deepens student understanding of the composition and decomposition of unit conversions, laying a foundation for adding and subtracting liters and milliliters. The numbers in bold type indicate the point at which the direction of the counting changes.

Direct students to count by liters in the following sequence:

- 500 mL, 1,000 mL, 1,500 mL, 2,000 mL, 2,500 mL, **3,000 mL**, 2,500 mL, 2,000 mL, 1,500 mL, 1,000 mL, 500 mL

- 500 mL, 1 liter, 1,500 mL, 2 liters, 2,500 mL, **3 liters**, 2,500 mL, 2 liters, 1,500 mL, 1 liter, 500 mL

- 500 mL, 1 liter, 1 liter 500 mL, 2 liters, 2 liters 500 mL, **3 liters**, 2 liters 500 mL, 2 liters, 1 liter 500 mL, 1 liter, 500 mL

- 200 mL, 400 mL, 600 mL, 800 mL, 1 liter, 1 liter 200 mL, 1 liter 400 mL, 1 liter 600 mL, 1 liter 800 mL, 2 liters

- 400 mL, 800 mL, 1,200 mL, 1,600 mL, **2,000 mL**, 1,600 mL, 1,200 mL, 800 mL, 400 mL

- 400 mL, 800 mL, 1 liter 200 mL, 1 liter 600 mL, **2 liters**, 1 liter 600 mL, 1 liter 200 mL, 800 mL, 400 mL

Application Problem (8 minutes)

Adam poured 1 liter 460 milliliters of water into a beaker. Over three days, some of the water evaporated. On the fourth day, 979 milliliters of water remained in the beaker. How much water evaporated?

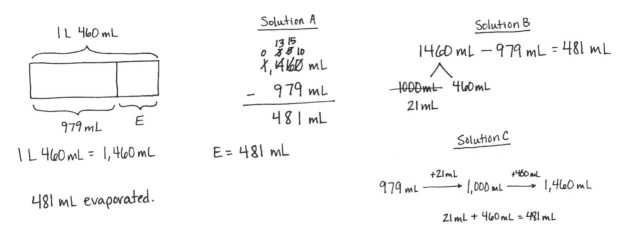

Note: This application problem builds on Lesson 3. Students might express measurements of liters in terms of milliliters and then subtract to solve the measurement word problem using either the more traditional algorithm (Solution A) or a simplifying strategy (Solutions B and C) based on place value decomposition, as pictured above.

EUREKA
MATH™

Lesson 4:   Know and relate metric units to place value units in order to express
measurements in different units.

©2015 Great Minds. eureka-math.org
G4-M1M2-TE-BK1-1.3.1-1.2016

55

Concept Development (30 minutes)

Materials: (T) Unlabeled hundred thousands place value chart (Template) (S) Unlabeled hundred thousands place value chart (Template), personal white board

Problem 1: Note patterns of *times as much as* among units of length, mass, capacity, and place value.

- T: Turn and tell your neighbor the units for mass, length, and capacity that we have learned so far.
- S: Gram, kilogram, centimeter, meter, kilometer, milliliter, and liter.
- T   What relationship have you discovered between milliliters and liters?
- S   1 liter is 1,000 milliliters. → 1 liter is 1,000 times as much as 1 milliliter.
- T: (Write 1 L = 1,000 × 1 mL.) What do you notice about the relationship between grams and kilograms? Meters and kilometers? Write your answers as equations.

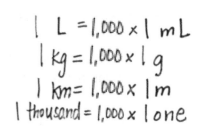

- S: 1 kilogram is 1,000 times as much as 1 gram. (Write 1 kg = 1,000 × 1 g.) 1 kilometer is 1,000 times as much as 1 meter. (Write 1 km = 1,000 × 1 m.)
- T: I wonder if other units have similar relationships. What other units have we discussed in fourth grade so far?
- S: Ones, tens, hundreds, thousands, ten thousands, hundred thousands, and millions.
- T: What do you notice about the units of place value? Are the relationships similar to those of metric units?

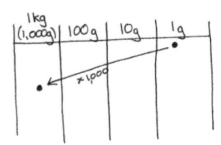

- S: Yes. 1 kilogram is 1,000 times as much as 1 gram, like 1 thousand is 1,000 times as much as 1 one. → And 1 hundred thousand is 1,000 times as much as 1 hundred. → That's true, and 1 ten thousand is 1,000 times as much as 1 ten.
- T: What unit is 100 times as much as 1 centimeter? Write your answer as an equation.
- S: (Write 1 meter = 100 × 1 centimeter.)
- T: Can you think of a place value unit relationship that is similar?

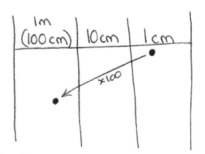

- S: 1 hundred is 100 times as much as 1 one. 1 hundred thousand is 100 times as much as 1 thousand. 1 ten thousand is 100 times as much as 1 hundred.

Problem 2: Relate units of length, mass, and capacity to units of place value.

- T: (Write 1 m = 100 cm.) 1 meter is equal to 100 centimeters. What unit is 100 ones?
- S: 1 hundred equals 100 ones.
- T: I notice 1 kilogram is 1,000 grams and 1 liter is 1,000 milliliters. Did you discover two place value units with a similar relationship?

Lesson 4:   Know and relate metric units to place value units in order to express
               measurements in different units.

©2015 Great Minds. eureka-math.org
G4-M1M2-TE-BK1-1.3.1-1.2016

S: 1 thousand equals 1,000 ones.

T: You can rename 1,200 milliliters as 1 liter 200 milliliters. How could you break 1,200 into place value units?

S: 1,200 is 1 thousand 200 ones.

Repeat renaming for 15,450 milliliters, 15,450 kilograms, and 15,450 ones, as well as 895 cm and 895 ones.

1 L (1,000 mL)	100 mL	10 mL	1 mL
•	••		
1	2	0	0

Problem 3: Compare metric units using place value knowledge and a number line.

T: (Write 724,706 mL __ 72 L 760 mL.) Which is more? Tell your partner how you can use place value knowledge to compare.

100 L (100,000 mL)	10 L (10,000 mL)	1 L (1,000 mL)	100 mL	10 mL	1 mL
	7	2,	7	6	0
7	2	4,	7	0	6

724,706 mL ____ 72 L 760 mL

↓

724 L 706 mL

724 > 72

S: I saw that 724,706 milliliters is 724 liters, and 724 is greater than 72. → I saw that 72 liters is 72,000 milliliters, and 724 thousand is greater than 72 thousand.

T: Draw a number line from 0 kilometers to 2 kilometers. 1 kilometer is how many meters?

0 km
0 m
(0 cm)

1 km
1000 m
(100,000 cm)

2 km
2000 m
(200,000 cm)

S: 1,000 meters.

T: 2 kilometers is equal to how many meters?

S: 2,000 meters.

T: Discuss with your partner how many centimeters are equal to 1 kilometer.

S: 1 meter is 100 centimeters. 1 kilometer is 1 thousand meters. → So, 1 thousand times 1 hundred is 100 thousand. → 2 meters is 200 centimeters, so 10 meters is 1,000 centimeters. 100 meters is ten of those, 10,000 centimeters. Ten of those is 100,000 centimeters.

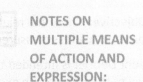

NOTES ON MULTIPLE MEANS OF ACTION AND EXPRESSION:

Reduce the small motor demands of plotting points on a number line by enlarging the number line and offering alternatives to marking with a pencil, such as placing stickers or blocks.

Lesson 4:   Know and relate metric units to place value units in order to express measurements in different units.

©2015 Great Minds. eureka-math.org
G4-M1M2-TE-BK1-1.3.1-1.2016

57

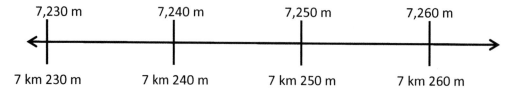

Display a number line as pictured above.

T: (Write 7,256 m, 7 km 246 m, and 725,900 cm.) Work with your partner to place these measurements on a number line. Explain how you know where they are to be placed.

S: I know that 100 centimeters equals 1 meter. In the number 725,900, there are 7,259 hundreds. That means that 725,900 cm equals 7,259 m. Now, I am able to place 725,900 cm on the number line.

S: 7,256 m is between 7,250 m and 7,260 m. It is less than 7,259 m. 7 km 246 m is between 7 km 240 m (7,240 m) and 7 km 250 m (7,250 m).

S: Since all the measurements have 7 kilometers, I can compare meters. 256 is more than 246, and 259 is more than 256.

S: 7 km 246 m is less than 7,256 m, which is less than 725,900 cm.

T: Order the measurements from least to greatest.

Problem Set (10 minutes)

Students should do their personal best to complete the Problem Set within the allotted 10 minutes. For some classes, it may be appropriate to modify the assignment by specifying which problems they work on first. Some problems do not specify a method for solving. Students should solve these problems using the RDW approach used for Application Problems.

Student Debrief (10 minutes)

Lesson Objective: Know and relate metric units to place value units in order to express measurements in different units.

The Student Debrief is intended to invite reflection and active processing of the total lesson experience.

Invite students to review their solutions for the Problem Set. They should check work by comparing answers with a partner before going over answers as a class. Look for misconceptions or misunderstandings that can be addressed in the Debrief. Guide students in a conversation to debrief the Problem Set and process the lesson.

NOTES ON
MULTIPLE MEANS
OF REPRESENTATION:

Clarify math vocabulary during the Debrief using pictures, gestures, and students' first languages. Give students multiple opportunities to articulate their math thinking. Offer English language learners the option of expressing themselves in the language most comfortable to them. Some students may feel more confident responding in writing. Turn-and-talk may also be an effective alternative.

Lesson 4:   Know and relate metric units to place value units in order to express
                             measurements in different units.

©2015 Great Minds. eureka-math.org
G4-M1M2-TE-BK1-1.3.1-1.2016

Any combination of the questions below may be used to lead the discussion.

- What patterns did you notice as you solved Problem 2?

- Explain to your partner how to find the number of centimeters in 1 kilometer. Did you relate each unit to meters? Place value?

- Do you find the number line helpful when comparing measures? Why or why not?

- How are metric units and place value units similar? Different? Do money units relate to place value units similarly? Time units?

- How did finding the amount of water that evaporated from Adam's beaker (in the Application Problem) connect to place value?

- How did the previous lessons on conversions prepare you for today's lesson?

Exit Ticket (3 minutes)

After the Student Debrief, instruct students to complete the Exit Ticket. A review of their work will help with assessing students' understanding of the concepts that were presented in today's lesson and planning more effectively for future lessons. The questions may be read aloud to the students.

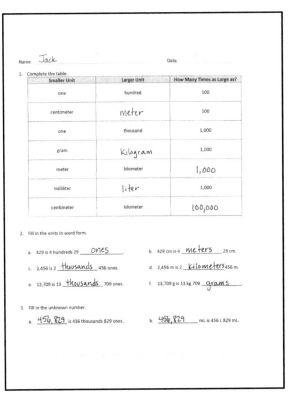

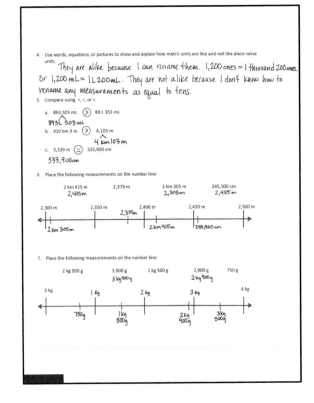

EUREKA MATH™

Lesson 4: Know and relate metric units to place value units in order to express measurements in different units.

59

©2015 Great Minds. eureka-math.org
G4-M1M2-TE-BK1-1.3.1-1.2016

Correct _____

Write in meters and centimeters.

1	3 m + 1 m =	m	cm	23	3 m 10 cm + 1 m 1 cm =	m	cm
2	4 m + 2 m =	m	cm	24	3 m 10 cm + 2 m 2 cm =	m	cm
3	2 m + 3 m =	m	cm	25	3 m 10 cm + 3 m 3 cm =	m	cm
4	5 m + 4 m =	m	cm	26	3 m 20 cm + 3 m 3 cm =	m	cm
5	2 m + 2 m =	m	cm	27	6 m 30 cm + 2 m 20 cm =	m	cm
6	3 m + 3 m =	m	cm	28	8 m 30 cm + 2 m 20 cm =	m	cm
7	4 m + 4 m =	m	cm	29	6 m 50 cm + 2 m 25 cm =	m	cm
8	5 m + 5 m =	m	cm	30	6 m 25 cm + 2 m 25 cm =	m	cm
9	5 m 7 cm + 1 m =	m	cm	31	4 m 70 cm + 1 m 10 cm =	m	cm
10	6 m 7 cm + 1 m =	m	cm	32	4 m 80 cm + 1 m 10 cm =	m	cm
11	7 m 7 cm + 1 m =	m	cm	33	4 m 90 cm + 1 m 10 cm =	m	cm
12	9 m 7 cm + 1 m =	m	cm	34	4 m 90 cm + 1 m 20 cm =	m	cm
13	9 m 7 cm + 1 cm =	m	cm	35	4 m 90 cm + 1 m 60 cm =	m	cm
14	5 m 7 cm + 1 cm =	m	cm	36	5 m 75 cm + 2 m 25 cm =	m	cm
15	3 m 7 cm + 1 cm =	m	cm	37	5 m 75 cm + 2 m 50 cm =	m	cm
16	3 m 7 cm + 3 cm =	m	cm	38	4 m 90 cm + 3 m 50 cm =	m	cm
17	6 m 70 cm + 10 cm =	m	cm	39	5 m 95 cm + 3 m 25 cm =	m	cm
18	6 m 80 cm + 10 cm =	m	cm	40	4 m 85 cm + 3 m 25 cm =	m	cm
19	6 m 90 cm + 10 cm =	m	cm	41	5 m 85 cm + 3 m 45 cm =	m	cm
20	6 m 90 cm + 20 cm =	m	cm	42	4 m 87 cm + 3 m 76 cm =	m	cm
21	6 m 90 cm + 30 cm =	m	cm	43	6 m 36 cm + 4 m 67 cm =	m	cm
22	6 m 90 cm + 60 cm =	m	cm	44	9 m 74 cm + 8 m 48 cm =	m	cm

Lesson 4: Know and relate metric units to place value units in order to express measurements in different units.

EUREKA MATH™

Name _____   Date _____

1. Complete the table.

Smaller Unit	Larger Unit	How Many Times as Large as?
one	hundred	100
centimeter		100
one	thousand	1,000
gram		1,000
meter	kilometer	
milliliter		1,000
centimeter	kilometer	

2. Fill in the units in word form.

a. 429 is 4 hundreds 29 _____.

b. 429 cm is 4 _____ 29 cm.

c. 2,456 is 2 _____ 456 ones.

d. 2,456 m is 2 _____ 456 m.

e. 13,709 is 13 _____ 709 ones.

f. 13,709 g is 13 kg 709 _____.

3. Fill in the unknown number.

a. _____ is 456 thousands 829 ones.

b. _____ mL is 456 L 829 mL.

Lesson 4:   Know and relate metric units to place value units in order to express
measurements in different units.

©2015 Great Minds. eureka-math.org
G4-M1M2-TE-BK1-1.3.1-1.2016

61

4. Use words, equations, or pictures to show and explain how metric units are like and unlike place value units.

5. Compare using >, <, or =.

    a. 893,503 mL 89 L 353 mL

    b. 410 km 3 m ◯ 4,103 m

    c. 5,339 m ◯ 533,900 cm

6. Place the following measurements on the number line:

    2 km 415 m   2,379 m   2 km 305 m   245,500 cm

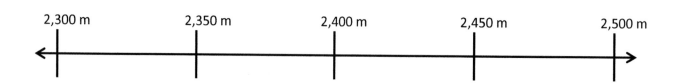

7. Place the following measurements on the number line: ⎨

    2 kg 900 g   3,500 g   1 kg 500 g   2,900 g   750 g

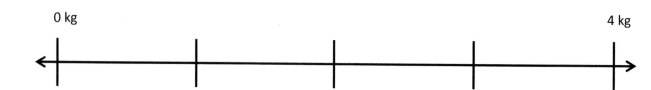

Lesson 4: Know and relate metric units to place value units in order to express measurements in different units.

EUREKA
MATH

Name _____   Date _____

1. Fill in the unknown unit in word form.

    a. 8,135 is 8 _____ 135 ones.   b. 8,135 kg is 8 _____ 135 g.

2. _____ mL is equal to 342 L 645 mL.

3. Compare using >, <, or =.

    a. 23 km 40 m   ( )   2,340 m

    b. 13,798 mL   ( )   137 L 980 mL

    c. 5,607 m   ( )   560,701 cm

4. Place the following measurements on the number line:

    33 kg 100 g   31,900 g   32,350 g   30 kg 500 g

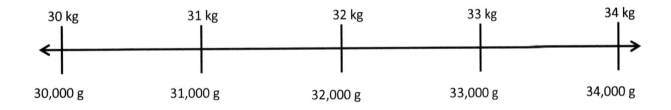

EUREKA
MATH™   Lesson 4:   Know and relate metric units to place value units in order to express
                             measurements in different units.
               ©2015 Great Minds. eureka-math.org
               G4-M1M2-TE-BK1-1.3.1-1.2016

Name _____   Date _____

1. Complete the table.

Smaller Unit	Larger Unit	How Many Times as Large as?
centimeter	meter	100
	hundred	100
meter	kilometer	
gram		1,000
one		1,000
milliliter		1,000
one	hundred thousand	

2. Fill in the unknown unit in word form.

a. 135 is 1 _____ 35 ones.

b. 135 cm is 1 _____ 35 cm.

c. 1,215 is 1 _____ 215 ones.

d. 1,215 m is 1 _____ 215 m.

e. 12,350 is 12 _____ 350 ones.

f. 12,350 g is 12 kg 350 _____.

3. Write the unknown number.

a. _____ is 125 thousands 312 ones.

b. _____ mL is 125 L 312 mL.

Lesson 4:   Know and relate metric units to place value units in order to express
measurements in different units.

©2015 Great Minds. eureka-math.org
G4-M1M2-TE-BK1-1.3.1-1.2016

EUREKA MATH™

4. Fill in each with >, <, or =.

   a. 890,353 mL ◯ 89 L 353 mL

   b. 2 km 13 m ◯ 2,103 m

5. Brandon's backpack weighs 3,140 grams. Brandon weighs 22 kilograms 610 grams more than his backpack. If Brandon stands on a scale wearing his backpack, what will the weight read?

6. Place the following measurements on the number line:

   3 km 275 m   3,500 m   3 km 5 m   394,000 cm

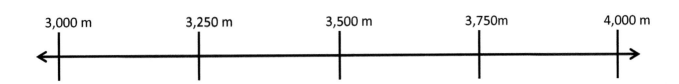

7. Place the following measurements on the number line:

   1 kg 379 g   3,079 g   2 kg 79 g   3,579 g   579 g

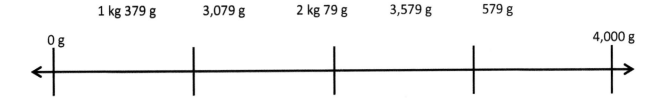

EUREKA
MATH™

Lesson 4: Know and relate metric units to place value units in order to express measurements in different units.

©2015 Great Minds. eureka-math.org
G4-M1M2-TE-BK1-1.3.1-1.2016

65

unlabeled hundred thousands place value chart

Lesson 4: Know and relate metric units to place value units in order to express measurements in different units.

EUREKA
MATH™

Lesson 5

Objective: Use addition and subtraction to solve multi-step word problems involving length, mass, and capacity.

Suggested Lesson Structure

■ Fluency Practice	(12 minutes)
▢ Concept Development	(42 minutes)
■ Student Debrief	(6 minutes)
Total Time	**(60 minutes)**

Fluency Practice (12 minutes)

- Sprint: Convert to Kilograms and Grams **4.MD.1** (8 minutes)
- Convert Units **4.MD.1** (2 minutes)
- Unit Counting **4.MD.1** (2 minutes)

Sprint: Convert to Kilograms and Grams (8 minutes)

Materials: (S) Convert to Kilograms and Grams Sprint

Note: This Sprint helps students automatize their gram and kilogram conversions when applying them in word problems.

Convert Units (2 minutes)

Materials: (S) Personal white board

Note: Isolated review builds fluency with conversion so that students can use this skill as a tool for solving word problems.

   T: (Write 1 L 400 mL = ___ mL.) Fill in the equation.
   S: (Write 1 L 400 mL = 1,400 mL.)

Repeat the process for 1 L 40 mL, 1 L 4 mL, and 1 L 90 mL.

NOTES ON
STANDARDS
ALIGNMENT:

In Module 2, students convert metric length, mass, and capacity units to add and subtract mixed units. This lesson builds on the content of **2.MD.5** and **3.MD.2**.

Occasionally, students work beyond the **4.MD.1** and **4.MD.2** standards by converting from a smaller unit to a larger unit. They do this by connecting metric units to place value units.

Develop students' basic number sense to make these conversions, and always accept answers in the smaller unit.

NOTES ON
MULTIPLE MEANS
OF ENGAGEMENT:

Some of the objectives of the Sprint are to generate excitement about math, to cultivate self-determination and perseverance, and to offer joyful experiences of success in math. The first weeks of school are an appropriate time to involve students in the design of their Sprint experience. Guide students through a discussion to make optimal decisions about tools and supports that can be used, the sequence or timing for completion, and the type of reward and recognition for success and improvement.

Lesson 5: Use addition and subtraction to solve multi-step word problems involving length, mass, and capacity.

©2015 Great Minds. eureka-math.org
G4-M1M2-TE-BK1-1.3.1-1.2016

67

Unit Counting (2 minutes)

Note: This fluency activity deepens student understanding of the composition and decomposition of unit conversions and works toward their mastery of adding and subtracting meters and centimeters. The numbers in bold type indicate the point at which the direction of the counting changes.

Direct students to count by centimeters using the following sequence:

- 800 cm, 1,600 cm, 2,400 cm, 3,200 cm, **4,000 cm**, 3,200 cm, 2,400 cm, 1,600 cm, 800 cm
- 800 cm, 1,600 cm, 2,400 cm, 3,200 cm, **4 m**, 3,200 cm, 2,400 cm, 1,600 cm, 800 cm
- 800 cm, 1 m 600 cm, 2 m 400 cm, 3 m 200 cm, **4 m**, 3 m 200 cm, 2 m 400 cm, 1 m 600 cm, 800 cm

Concept Development (42 minutes)

Materials: (S) Problem Set

Note: In this lesson, the Problem Set is comprised of the word problems from the lesson and used during the lesson itself for Problems 1–4. Problems 5 and 6 should be completed independently at the conclusion of the Concept Development. The lesson concludes with the Debrief.

1. Model the problem.

Have two pairs of students (choose as models those students who are likely to successfully solve the problem) work at the board while the others work independently or in pairs at their seats. Review the following questions before beginning the first problem.

- Can you draw something?
- What can you draw?
- What conclusions can you make from your drawing?

As students work, circulate. Reiterate the questions above.

After two minutes, have the two pairs of students share *only* their labeled diagrams.

For about one minute, have the demonstrating students receive and respond to feedback and questions from their peers.

2. Calculate to solve and write a statement.

Give everyone two minutes to finish work on the problem, sharing their work and thinking with a peer. All should then write their equations and statements for the answer.

3. Assess the solution for reasonableness.

Give students one to two minutes to assess and explain the reasonableness of their solutions.

Lesson 5:   Use addition and subtraction to solve multi-step word problems
involving length, mass, and capacity.

Problem 1: Solve a two-step problem involving grams.

The potatoes Beth bought weighed 3 kilograms 420 grams. Her onions weighed 1,050 grams less than the potatoes. How much did the potatoes and onions weigh together?

Solution 1

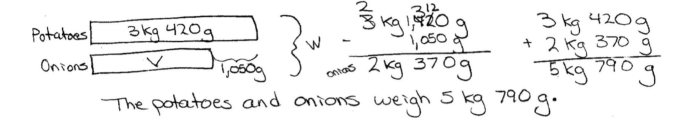

The potatoes and onions weigh 5 kg 790 g.

Solution 2

$$3420 - 1050 = 2370$$

2320 1100
         50

$$2370 + 3420 = 5790$$

2000 370   3000 420

The potatoes and onions weighed 5 kg 790g.

The structure of this problem and what it demands of the students is similar to that found within Module 1. Therefore, students are familiar with the process of a two-step problem. The main differences within this problem are that the focus is on mass and students are computing with mixed units. Lessons 1–4 have prepared the students for mixed unit calculations and conversions. Answering in mixed units or as a single unit of grams should be accepted. Watch for students using alternate strategies as well.

Lesson 5: Use addition and subtraction to solve multi-step word problems involving length, mass, and capacity.

69

©2015 Great Minds. eureka-math.org
G4-M1M2-TE-BK1-1.3.1-1.2016

Problem 2: Solve a two-step problem involving meters.

Adele let out 18 meters 46 centimeters of string to fly her kite. She then let out 13 meters 78 centimeters more before reeling back in 590 centimeters. How long was her string after reeling it in?

Solution 1

Let Out [18 m 46 cm | 13 m 78cm]
reeled In [h   ] 590 cm

$$18\,m\ 46\,cm$$
$$+\ 13\,m\ 78\,cm$$
$$31\,m\ 124\,cm$$
$$1m\ \ 24cm = 32m\ 24\,cm$$
$$32\,m\ 24\,cm = 3{,}224\ cm$$

$$3{,}224\ cm$$
$$-\quad 590\ cm$$
$$2{,}634\ cm$$

The string was 26m 34 cm
after reeling it in.

2,634 cm
 /   \
26m   34 cm

Solution 2

$$18\,m\ 46\,cm\ +\ 13\,m\ 78\,cm$$
$$=\ 31\,m\ 46\,cm\ +\ 78\,cm$$

30 16   70 8

$$=\ 31\,m\ \ 124\,cm$$
$$=\ 32\,m\ \ 24\,cm$$

$$32\,m\ 24\,cm - 590\,cm$$
$$3224\,cm - 590\ cm$$

2224   1000
        410

$$2224 + 410\ =\ 2634$$

The string was 26m 34cm.

This two-step problem requires regrouping from meters to centimeters. As in the previous problem, students use what they have learned so far in Grade 4 to help solve this problem. Students might regroup across mixed units or change to similar units. In the second solution, the student adds the meters first, then the centimeters, and finally subtracts 590 centimeters from the total.

Lesson 5:   Use addition and subtraction to solve multi-step word problems
                          involving length, mass, and capacity.

EUREKA
MATH™

Problem 3

Solve a three-step problem involving liters.

Shyan's barrel contained 6 liters 775 milliliters of paint. She poured in 1 liter 118 milliliters more. The first day, Shyan used 2 liters 125 milliliters of the paint. After the second day, there were 1,769 milliliters of paint remaining in the barrel. How much paint did Shyan use on the second day?

Solution 1

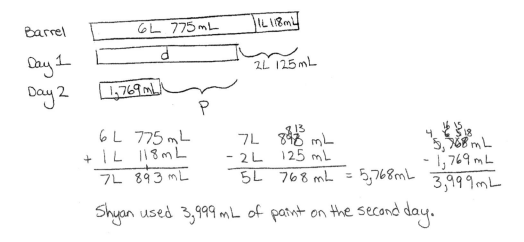

Shyan used 3,999 mL of paint on the second day.

Solution 2

6775 − 2,125 = 4650
4650 + 1118 = 5768
5768 − 1769 = 3999

3768   2000
         231

Shyan used 3 L 999 mL on the second day.

This is a three-step problem involving regrouping across units. Students are familiar with multi-step problems from Module 1 and extend their practice with them by solving with mixed units or converting to milliliters prior to solving. In the second solution, the student sees that it is easy to subtract 2,125 from 6,775 first, then adds the amount Adele poured in, and finally finishes the problem in the same way as shown in Solution 1, by subtracting the part left in the barrel.

Lesson 5:   Use addition and subtraction to solve multi-step word problems involving length, mass, and capacity.

©2015 Great Minds. eureka-math.org
G4-M1M2-TE-BK1-1.3.1-1.2016

71

Problem 4: Solve a three-step problem involving grams.

On Thursday, the pizzeria used 2 kilograms 180 grams less flour than they used on Friday. On Friday, they used 12 kilograms 240 grams. On Saturday, they used 1,888 grams more than on Friday. What was the total amount of flour used over the three days?

Solution 1

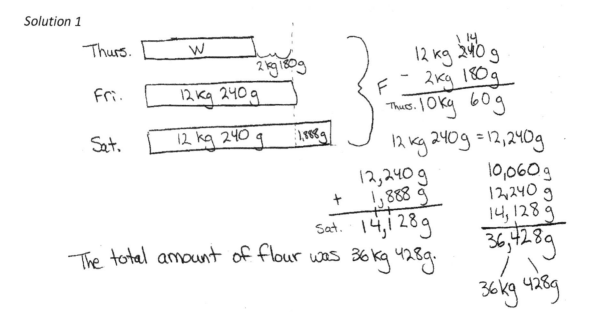

Solution 2

3 units of 12 kg 240 g = 36 kg 720 g

2 kg 180 g − 1 kg 888 = 292 g

1 kg 1000 g

36 kg 720 g − 292 g = 36 kg 428 g

420 300 g

The bakery used 36 kg 428 g.

This three-step problem increases the complexity in that students might calculate, as in the first solution, for the three addends to complete the third step for determining how much flour was used over the three days. In the second solution strategy, the student, because of the tape diagram, notices 3 units of Friday minus the difference between the two small chunks. The answer will be a little less than three Fridays' worth of flour.

Lesson 5: Use addition and subtraction to solve multi-step word problems involving length, mass, and capacity.

EUREKA MATH

Problem Set (10 minutes)

Please note that Problems 1 through 4 of the Problem Set for this lesson are comprised of the lesson's problems as stated at the introduction of the lesson. Problems 5 and 6 may be completed individually during this part of the lesson.

For some classes, it may be appropriate to modify the assignment by specifying which problems they work on first. Some problems do not specify a method for solving. Students should solve these problems using the RDW approach used for Application Problems.

Student Debrief (6 minutes)

Lesson Objective: Use addition and subtraction to solve multi-step word problems involving length, mass, and capacity.

The Student Debrief is intended to invite reflection and active processing of the total lesson experience.

Invite students to review their solutions for the Problem Set. They should check work by comparing answers with a partner before going over answers as a class. Look for misconceptions or misunderstandings that can be addressed in the Debrief. Guide students in a conversation to debrief the Problem Set and process the lesson.

Any combination of the questions below may be used to lead the discussion.

- How was the work completed to solve Problem 5 in the Problem Set different than that of the other problems?

- Did you find yourself using similar strategies to add and to subtract the mixed unit problems? Explain.

- How can drawing different models to represent a problem lead you to a correct answer?

- How was drawing a model helpful in organizing your thoughts to solve Problem 6?

- Describe a mixed unit. What other mixed units can you name?

- How can converting to a smaller unit be useful when solving problems? When is it not useful?

NOTES ON
MULTIPLE MEANS
OF ENGAGEMENT:

Sustain engagement during this challenging lesson by guiding and rewarding responsible collaboration among students. Teach students to independently ask themselves, "Can I draw something? What can I draw? What conclusions can I make from my drawing?" Empower students to self-monitor their math work with a rubric for problem solving. Students working below or above grade level may want to omit drawing. Emphasize the value of modeling. Ask, "How did the picture help you solve? What happened when you did not draw the picture? Why?"

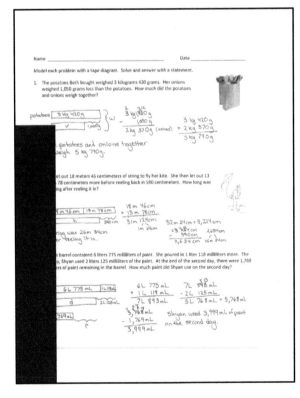

Lesson 5:   Use addition and subtraction to solve multi-step word problems
involving length, mass, and capacity.

73

©2015 Great Minds. eureka-math.org
G4-M1M2-TE-BK1-1.3.1-1.2016

- How is regrouping a mixed unit of measurement similar to regrouping a whole number when adding or subtracting?
- How is converting mixed units of measurement useful in everyday situations?

Exit Ticket (3 minutes)

After the Student Debrief, instruct students to complete the Exit Ticket. A review of their work will help with assessing students' understanding of the concepts that were presented in today's lesson and planning more effectively for future lessons. The questions may be read aloud to the students.

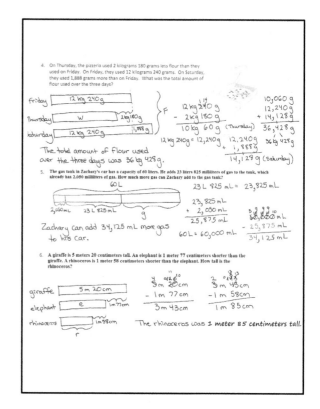

Lesson 5:   Use addition and subtraction to solve multi-step word problems involving length, mass, and capacity.

EUREKA MATH™

A

Number Correct: _____

Convert to Kilograms and Grams

1.	2,000 g =	kg	g	23.	3,800 g =	kg	g
2.	3,000 g =	kg	g	24.	4,770 g =	kg	g
3.	4,000 g =	kg	g	25.	4,807 g =	kg	g
4.	9,000 g =	kg	g	26.	5,065 g =	kg	g
5.	6,000 g =	kg	g	27.	5,040 g =	kg	g
6.	1,000 g =	kg	g	28.	6,007 g =	kg	g
7.	8,000 g =	kg	g	29.	2,003 g =	kg	g
8.	5,000 g =	kg	g	30.	1,090 g =	kg	g
9.	7,000 g =	kg	g	31.	1,055 g =	kg	g
10.	6,100 g =	kg	g	32.	9,404 g =	kg	g
11.	6,110 g =	kg	g	33.	9,330 g =	kg	g
12.	6,101 g =	kg	g	34.	3,400 g =	kg	g
13.	6,010 g =	kg	g	35.	4,000 g + 2,000 g =	kg	g
14.	6,011 g =	kg	g	36.	5,000 g + 3,000 g =	kg	g
15.	6,001 g =	kg	g	37.	4,000 g + 4,000 g =	kg	g
16.	8,002 g =	kg	g	38.	8 × 7,000 g =	kg	g
17.	8,020 g =	kg	g	39.	49,000 g ÷ 7 =	kg	g
18.	8,200 g =	kg	g	40.	16,000 g × 5 =	kg	g
19.	8,022 g =	kg	g	41.	63,000 g ÷ 7 =	kg	g
20.	8,220 g =	kg	g	42.	17 × 4,000 g =	kg	g
21.	8,222 g =	kg	g	43.	13,000 g × 5 =	kg	g
22.	7,256 g =	kg	g	44.	84,000 g ÷ 7 =	kg	g

EUREKA MATH™

Lesson 5: Use addition and subtraction to solve multi-step word problems involving length, mass, and capacity.

B

Number Correct: _____

Improvement: _____

Convert to Kilograms and Grams

1.	1,000 g =	kg	g	23.	2,700 g =	kg	g
2.	2,000 g =	kg	g	24.	3,660 g =	kg	g
3.	3,000 g =	kg	g	25.	3,706 g =	kg	g
4.	8,000 g =	kg	g	26.	4,095 g =	kg	g
5.	6,000 g =	kg	g	27.	4,030 g =	kg	g
6.	9,000 g =	kg	g	28.	5,006 g =	kg	g
7.	4,000 g =	kg	g	29.	3,004 g =	kg	g
8.	7,000 g =	kg	g	30.	2,010 g =	kg	g
9.	5,000 g =	kg	g	31.	2,075 g =	kg	g
10.	5,100 g =	kg	g	32.	1,504 g =	kg	g
11.	5,110 g =	kg	g	33.	1,440 g =	kg	g
12.	5,101 g =	kg	g	34.	4,500 g =	kg	g
13.	5,010 g =	kg	g	35.	3,000 g + 2,000 g =	kg	g
14.	5,011 g =	kg	g	36.	4,000 g + 3,000 g =	kg	g
15.	5,001 g =	kg	g	37.	5,000 g + 4,000 g =	kg	g
16.	7,002 g =	kg	g	38.	9 × 8,000 g =	kg	g
17.	7,020 g =	kg	g	39.	64,000 g ÷ 8 =	kg	g
18.	7,200 g =	kg	g	40.	17,000 g × 5 =	kg	g
19.	7,022 g =	kg	g	41.	54,000 g ÷ 6 =	kg	g
20.	7,220 g =	kg	g	42.	18,000 g × 4 =	kg	g
21.	7,222 g =	kg	g	43.	14 × 5,000 g =	kg	g
22.	4,378 g =	kg	g	44.	96,000 g ÷ 8 =	kg	g

Lesson 5: Use addition and subtraction to solve multi-step word problems involving length, mass, and capacity.

EUREKA MATH™

Name _____ Date _____

Model each problem with a tape diagram. Solve and answer with a statement.

1. The potatoes Beth bought weighed 3 kilograms 420 grams. Her onions weighed 1,050 grams less than the potatoes. How much did the potatoes and onions weigh together?

2. Adele let out 18 meters 46 centimeters of string to fly her kite. She then let out 13 meters 78 centimeters more before reeling back in 590 centimeters. How long was her string after reeling it in?

3. Shyan's barrel contained 6 liters 775 milliliters of paint. She poured in 1 liter 118 milliliters more. The first day, Shyan used 2 liters 125 milliliters of the paint. At the end of the second day, there were 1,769 milliliters of paint remaining in the barrel. How much paint did Shyan use on the second day?

Lesson 5:   Use addition and subtraction to solve multi-step word problems
involving length, mass, and capacity.

©2015 Great Minds. eureka-math.org
G4-M1M2-TE-BK1-1.3.1-1.2016

77

4. On Thursday, the pizzeria used 2 kilograms 180 grams less flour than they used on Friday. On Friday, they used 12 kilograms 240 grams. On Saturday, they used 1,888 grams more than on Friday. What was the total amount of flour used over the three days?

5. The gas tank in Zachary's car has a capacity of 60 liters. He adds 23 liters 825 milliliters of gas to the tank, which already has 2,050 milliliters of gas. How much more gas can Zachary add to the gas tank?

6. A giraffe is 5 meters 20 centimeters tall. An elephant is 1 meter 77 centimeters shorter than the giraffe. A rhinoceros is 1 meter 58 centimeters shorter than the elephant. How tall is the rhinoceros?

Lesson 5: Use addition and subtraction to solve multi-step word problems involving length, mass, and capacity.

©2015 Great Minds. eureka-math.org
G4-M1M2-TE-BK1-1.3.1-1.2016

EUREKA
MATH™

Name _____ Date _____

Model each problem with a tape diagram. Solve and answer with a statement.

1. Jeff places a pineapple with a mass of 890 grams on a balance scale.
    He balances the scale by placing two oranges, an apple, and a lemon
    on the other side. Each orange weighs 280 grams. The lemon weighs
    195 grams less than each orange. What is the mass of the apple?

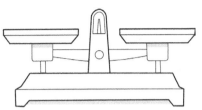

2. Brian is 1 meter 87 centimeters tall. Bonnie is 58 centimeters shorter than Brian. Betina is
    26 centimeters taller than Bonnie. How tall is Betina?

Lesson 5:   Use addition and subtraction to solve multi-step word problems
            involving length, mass, and capacity.

79

©2015 Great Minds. eureka-math.org
G4-M1M2-TE-BK1-1.3.1-1.2016

Name _____ Date _____

Model each problem with a tape diagram. Solve and answer with a statement.

1. The capacity of Jose's vase is 2,419 milliliters of water. He poured 1 liter 299 milliliters of water into the empty vase. Then, he added 398 milliliters. How much more water will the vase hold?

2. Eric biked 1 kilometer 125 meters on Monday. On Tuesday, he biked 375 meters less than on Monday. How far did he bike both days?

3. Kristen's package weighs 37 kilograms 95 grams. Anne's package weighs 4,650 grams less than Kristen's. Mary's package weighs 2,905 grams less than Anne's. How much does Mary's package weigh?

Lesson 5:   Use addition and subtraction to solve multi-step word problems involving length, mass, and capacity.

EUREKA MATH

4. A Springer Spaniel weighs 20 kilograms 490 grams. A Cocker Spaniel weighs 7,590 grams less than a Springer Spaniel. A Newfoundland weighs 52 kilograms 656 grams more than a Cocker Spaniel. What is the difference, in grams, between the weights of the Newfoundland and the Springer Spaniel?

5. Marsha has three rugs. The first rug is 2 meters 87 centimeters long. The second rug has a length 98 centimeters less than the first. The third rug is 111 centimeters longer than the second rug. What is the difference in centimeters between the length of the first rug and the third rug?

6. One barrel held 60 liters 868 milliliters of sap. A second barrel held 20,089 milliliters more sap than the first. A third barrel held 40 liters 82 milliliters less sap than the second. If the sap from the three barrels was poured into a larger container, how much sap would there be in all?

Lesson 5: Use addition and subtraction to solve multi-step word problems involving length, mass, and capacity.

©2015 Great Minds. eureka-math.org
G4-M1M2-TE-BK1-1.3.1-1.2016

81

Name _____ Date _____

1. Complete the conversion charts.

Length	
3 km	_____ m
9 km	_____ m
6 km 435 m	_____ m
12 km 12 m	_____ m

Mass	
3 kg	_____ g
20 kg 300 g	_____ g
1 kg 74 g	_____ g
403 kg 4 g	_____ g

Capacity	
4 L	_____ mL
48 L 808 mL	_____ mL
2 L 20 mL	_____ mL
639 L 6 mL	_____ mL

2. A student completed the problem below. Check his work. Explain how you know if each solution is correct or incorrect.

Convert the following measurements:

a. 24 km = __24,000__ m

b. 16 L = __16,000__ mL

c. 38 kg = __3,800__ g

3. Find the sum or difference.
   a. 493 km 43 m + 17 km 57 m

   b. 25 kg 32 g – 23 kg 83 g

   c. 100 L 99 mL + 2,999 mL

Module 2: Unit Conversions and Problem Solving with Metric Measurement

EUREKA MATH™

©2015 Great Minds. eureka-math.org
G4-M1M2-TE-BK1-1.3.1-1.2016

4. Billy is training for a half marathon. For the problems below, use tape diagrams, numbers, and words to explain each answer.

   a. Each day, Billy runs on the treadmill for 5 kilometers and runs on the outdoor track for 6,000 meters. In all, how many meters does Billy run each day?

   b. Since Billy has started training, he has also been drinking more water. On Saturday, he drank 2 liters 755 milliliters of water. On Sunday, he drank some more. If Billy drank a total of 4 liters 255 milliliters of water on Saturday and Sunday, how many milliliters of water did Billy drink on Sunday?

   c. Since he began exercising so much for his half marathon, Billy has been losing weight. In his first week of training, he lost 2 kilograms 530 grams. In the following two weeks of training, he lost 1 kilogram 855 grams each week. Billy now weighs 61 kilograms 760 grams. What was Billy's weight, in grams, before he started training? Explain your thinking.

End-of-Module Assessment Task   Topics A–B
Standards Addressed

Solve problems involving measurement and conversion of measurements from a larger unit to a smaller unit.

4.MD.1[1]   Know relative sizes of measurement units within one system of units including km, m, cm; kg, g; lb, oz.; l, ml; hr, min, sec. Within a single system of measurement, express measurements in a larger unit in terms of a smaller unit. Record measurement equivalents in a two-column table. *For example, know that 1 ft is 12 times as long as 1 in. Express the length of a 4 ft snake as 48 in. Generate a conversion table for feet and inches listing the number pairs (1, 12), (2, 24), (3, 36), …*

4.MD.2[2]   Use the four operations to solve word problems involving distances, intervals of time, liquid volumes, masses of objects, and money, including problems involving simple fractions or decimals, and problems that require expressing measurements given in a larger unit in terms of a smaller unit. Represent measurement quantities using diagrams such as number line diagrams that feature a measurement scale.

Evaluating Student Learning Outcomes

A Progression Toward Mastery is provided to describe steps that illuminate the gradually increasing understandings that students develop *on their way to proficiency.* In this chart, this progress is presented from left (Step 1) to right (Step 4). The learning goal for students is to achieve Step 4 mastery. These steps are meant to help teachers and students identify and celebrate what the students CAN do now and what they need to work on next.

---

[1] Pounds, ounces, and time are assessed in Module 7.

[2] Time, money, and numbers as fractions or decimals are assessed in Module 7.

A Progression Toward Mastery

Assessment Task Item	STEP 1 Little evidence of reasoning without a correct answer. (1 Point)	STEP 2 Evidence of some reasoning without a correct answer. (2 Points)	STEP 3 Evidence of some reasoning with a correct answer or evidence of solid reasoning with an incorrect answer. (3 Points)	STEP 4 Evidence of solid reasoning with a correct answer. (4 Points)
1 4.MD.1	Student correctly completes fewer than six of the twelve conversions.	Student correctly identifies six to nine of the twelve conversions.	Student correctly identifies ten or eleven of the twelve conversions.	Student correctly completes the conversion chart: ■ 3,000, 9,000, 6,435, 12,012 ■ 3,000, 20,300, 1,074, 403,004 ■ 4,000, 48,808, 2,020, 639,006
2 4.MD.1	Student correctly identifies fewer than two conversions with no evidence of reasoning.	Student correctly identifies two of the conversions with little evidence of reasoning.	Student correctly identifies that Parts (a) and (b) are correct and Part (c) is incorrect but does not provide clear reasoning.	Student correctly reasons that Parts (a) and (b) are correct because 1,000 m equals 1 km and 1,000 mL equals 1 L, and Part (c) is incorrect because 1,000 g equals 1 kg, so 38 kg should equal 38,000 g.
3 4.MD.1 4.MD.2	Student correctly answers fewer than two parts, with multiple computation or conversion errors.	Student correctly answers one of the three parts and makes fewer than two computational or conversion errors on the other parts.	Student correctly answers two of the three parts.	Student correctly answers: a. 510 km 100 m or 510,100 m b. 1 kg 949 g or 1,949 g c. 103 L 98 mL or 103,098 mL

A Progression Toward Mastery

4 4.MD.1 4.MD.2	Student correctly answers fewer than two of the three parts.	Student correctly answers two of the three parts but shows little evidence of reasoning in Part (c).	Student answers three parts correctly but does not show solid reasoning of understanding metric conversions in Part (c).	Student correctly answers all three parts: a. 11,000 meters b. 1,500 milliliters c. 68,000 grams; Explains or shows computation of all measurements and the conversion to grams.

Module 2:   Unit Conversions and Problem Solving with Metric Measurement

EUREKA MATH™

Name __Jack_____   Date _____

1. Complete the following conversion charts:

Length	
3 km	3,000 m
9 km	9,000 m
6 km 435 m	6,435 m
12 km 12 m	12,012 m

Mass	
3 kg	3,000 g
20 kg 300 g	20,300 g
1 kg 74 g	1,074 g
403 kg 4 g	403,004 g

Capacity	
4 L	4,000 mL
48 L 808 mL	48,808 mL
2 L 20 mL	2,020 mL
639 L 6 mL	639,006 mL

2. A student completed the problem below. Check his work. Explain how you know if each solution is correct or incorrect.

Convert the following measurements:

~~a.~~ 24 km = __24,000__ m

~~b.~~ 16 L = __16,000__ mL

Ⓒ 38 kg = __3,800__ g

1 km = 1,000 m
24 km = 24,000 m

1 L = 1,000 mL
16 L = 16,000 mL

1 kg = 1,000 g
38 kg = 38,000 g

Problems a and b are correct because there are 1,000 meters, mL, or grams in 1 km, L, or kg.

Problem C is wrong. 38 kg is really 38,000 g.

3. Find the sum or difference.

a. 493 km 43 m + 17 km 57 m

```
  493 km  43 m
+  17 km  57 m
  510 km 100 m
```

b. 25 kg 32 g − 23 kg 83 g

```
      12
  4 9 2 12
  2̶5̶,̶0̶3̶2̶ g
- 23,083 g
   1,949 g
```

c. 100 L 99mL + 2,999 mL

```
  100,099 mL
+   2,999 mL
  103,098 mL
```

4. Billy is training for a half-marathon. For the problems below, use tape diagrams, numbers, and words to explain each answer.

a. Each day Billy runs on the treadmill for 5 kilometers and runs on the outdoor track for 6,000 meters. In all, how many meters does Billy run each day?

R

| 5 km | 6,000 m |

5 km = 5,000 m

5,000 m + 6,000 m = 11,000 m

R = 11,000 m

Billy runs 11,000 meters each day.

b. Since Billy has started training, he has also been drinking more water. On Saturday, he drank 2 liters 755 milliliters of water. On Sunday, he drank some more. If Billy drank a total of 4 liters 255 milliliters of water on Saturday and Sunday, how many milliliters of water did Billy drink on Sunday?

4 L 255 mL

| 2 L 755 mL | W |

4 L 255 mL = 4,255 mL
2 L 755 mL = 2,755 mL

$$\begin{array}{r} \overset{3}{\cancel{4}},\overset{12}{2}55 \\ -\ 2,755 \\ \hline 1,500 \end{array}$$

W = 1,500 mL

Billy drank 1,500 mL of water on Sunday.

c. Since exercising so much for his half-marathon, Billy has been losing weight. In his first week of training, he lost 2 kilograms 530 grams. In the following two weeks of training, he lost 1 kilogram 855 grams each week. Billy now weighs 61 kilograms 760 grams. What was Billy's weight, in grams, before he started training? Explain your thinking.

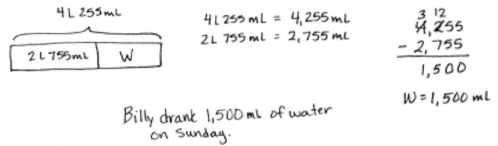

$$\begin{array}{r} 2,530\,g \\ 1,855\,g \\ +\ 1,855\,g \\ \hline 6,240\,g \end{array}$$

$$\begin{array}{r} 61,760\,g \\ +\ 6,240\,g \\ \hline 68,000\,g \end{array}$$

W = 68,000 g

Billy's weight before training was 68,000 grams.

If he lost his weight, he had to weigh more before, so I added all the weight he lost to how much he weighs now for my answer.

EUREKA MATH™

Eureka Math
Grade 4
Module 2

Special thanks go to the Gordon A. Cain Center and to the Department of Mathematics at Louisiana State University for their support in the development of *Eureka Math*.

For a free *Eureka Math* Teacher
Resource Pack, Parent Tip
Sheets, and more please
visit www.Eureka.tools

Answer Key

GRADE 4 • MODULE 2

Unit Conversions and Problem Solving With Metric Measurement

Lesson 1

Problem Set

1. a. 1,000
    b. 4,000
    c. 7,000
    d. 18
    e. 100
    f. 300
    g. 8,000
    h. 120

2. a. 3,312
    b. 13,027
    c. 915,008
    d. 356
    e. 1,408
    f. 12,046

3. a. 3,720 m or 3 km 720 m
    b. 81 cm
    c. 14,600 m
    d. 21,683 cm
    e. 79,109 m or 79 km 109 m
    f. 55,351 m or 55 km 351 m

4. 1,737 cm or 17 m 37 cm

5. 2,691 m or 2 km 691 m

6. 283 cm or 2 m 83 cm

7. 2,379 m or 2 km 379 m

Exit Ticket

1. 71,000; 30; 8,100; 4

2. 13,020

3. 366,948 m or 366 km 948 m

4. 260 cm or 2 m 60 cm

EUREKA
MATH™

Homework

1. a. 5,000

    b. 13,000

    c. 17

    d. 60,000

    e. 700

    f. 1,900

    g. 24

    h. 9,000

2. a. 7,123

    b. 22,022

    c. 875,004

    d. 745

    e. 6,707

    f. 20,489

3. a. 1,747 m or 1 km 747 m

    b. 146 cm or 1 m 46 cm

    c. 400,924 m

    d. 64,586 cm

    e. 177,555 m or 177 km 555 m

    f. 717,640 m or 717 km 640 m

4. 1,822 cm or 18 m 22 cm

5. 6,710 m or 6 km 710 m

6. 647 m

7. 172 cm

©2015 Great Minds. eureka-math.org
G4-M1M2-TE-BK1-1.3.1-1.2016

Lesson 2

Problem Set

1. 3,000; 4; 17,000; 20; 300,000

2. a. 1,500

    b. 3,715

    c. 17,084

    d. 25,009

    e. 7; 481

    f. 210,090

3. a. 2,215 g or 2 kg 215 g

    b. 763 g

    c. 50,000 g

    d. 6,660 g

    e. 10 kg 217 g

    f. 63 kg 139 g

4. 8,444 g or 8 kg 444 g

5. 4,975 g or 4 kg 975 g

6. 28,077 g or 28 kg 77 g

7. 5,962 g or 5 kg 962 g

Exit Ticket

1. a. 21,415

    b. 2,091

    c. 87,017

    d. 96; 20

2. 57 kg 671 g or 57,671 g

EUREKA
MATH™

Homework

1. 6,000; 8; 15,000; 24; 550,000

2. a. 2,700

    b. 5,945

    c. 29,058

    d. 31,003

    e. 66; 597

    f. 270,041

3. a. 450 g

    b. 4,270 g or 4 kg 270 g

    c. 28,241 g

    d. 18,800 g

    e. 3 kg 874 g

    f. 52 kg 239 g

4. 49,224 g or 49 kg 224 g

5. 3,715 g or 3 kg 715 g

6. 1,879 g or 1 kg 879 g

©2015 Great Minds. eureka-math.org
G4-M1M2-TE-BK1-1.3.1-1.2016

Lesson 3

Problem Set

1. 5,000; 38,000; 49; 54,000; 92

2. a. 2,500

   b. 70,850

   c. 33,015

   d. 2,008

   e. 3; 812

   f. 86; 3

3. a. 41,760 L or 41 L 760 mL

   b. 3,600 mL or 3 L 600 mL

   c. 29,290 mL

   d. 18,992 mL

   e. 6 L 878 mL

   f. 18 L 557 mL

4. a. Pineapple, ginger ale, tropical

   b. 8,195 mL or 8 L 195 mL

5. 1,790 mL or 1 L 790 mL

6. 2,877 mL

Exit Ticket

1. a. 6,127

   b. 706,220

   c. 12,009

   d. 906; 10

2. 59,114 mL or 59 L 114 mL

3. 970,250 mL or 970 L 250 mL

EUREKA
MATH™

Homework

1. 8,000; 27,000; 39; 68,000; 102

2. a. 5,850

    b. 29,303

    c. 37,037

    d. 17,002

    e. 13; 674

    f. 275; 5

3. a. 593 mL

    b. 2,260 mL or 2 L 260 mL

    c. 28,360 mL

    d. 30,100 mL

    e. 8 L 575 mL

    f. 12 L 779 mL

4. Marie's bucket

5. 17,735 mL or 17 L 735 mL

6. 28,657 mL or 28 L 657 mL

Lesson 4

Pattern Sheet

1.	4, 0	12.	10, 7	23.	4, 11	34.	6, 10
2.	6, 0	13.	9, 8	24.	5, 12	35.	6, 50
3.	5, 0	14.	5, 8	25.	6, 13	36.	8, 0
4.	9, 0	15.	3, 8	26.	6, 23	37.	8, 25
5.	4, 0	16.	3, 10	27.	8, 50	38.	8, 40
6.	6, 0	17.	6, 80	28.	10, 50	39.	9, 20
7.	8, 0	18.	6, 90	29.	8, 75	40.	8, 10
8.	10, 0	19.	7, 0	30.	8, 50	41.	9, 30
9.	6, 7	20.	7, 10	31.	5, 80	42.	8, 63
10.	7, 7	21.	7, 20	32.	5, 90	43.	11, 3
11.	8, 7	22.	7, 50	33.	6, 0	44.	18, 22

Problem Set

1. Meter; kilogram; 1,000; liter; 100,000

2. a. Ones
   b. Meters
   c. Thousands
   d. Kilometers
   e. Thousands
   f. Grams

3. a. 456,829
   b. 456,829

4. Explanations will vary.

5. a. >
   b. >
   c. =

6. Measurements plotted accurately on the number line

7. Measurements plotted accurately on the number line

Exit Ticket

1. a. Thousands

   b. Kilograms

2. 342,645

3. a. >

   b. <

   c. <

4. Measurements plotted accurately on the number line

Homework

1. One; 1,000; kilogram; thousand; liter; 100,000

2. a. Hundred

   b. Meter

   c. Thousand

   d. Kilometer

   e. Thousands

   f. Grams

3. a. 125,312

   b. 125,312

4. a. >

   b. <

5. 28,890 g or 28 kg 890 g

6. Measurements plotted accurately on the number line

7. Measurements plotted accurately on the number line

Lesson 5

Sprint

Side A

1.	2, 0	12.	6, 101	23.	3, 800	34.	3, 400
2.	3, 0	13.	6, 10	24.	4, 770	35.	6, 0
3.	4, 0	14.	6, 11	25.	4, 807	36.	8, 0
4.	9, 0	15.	6, 1	26.	5, 65	37.	8, 0
5.	6, 0	16.	8, 2	27.	5, 40	38.	56, 0
6.	1, 0	17.	8, 20	28.	6, 7	39.	7, 0
7.	8, 0	18.	8, 200	29.	2, 3	40.	80, 0
8.	5, 0	19.	8, 22	30.	1, 90	41.	9, 0
9.	7, 0	20.	8, 220	31.	1, 55	42.	68, 0
10.	6, 100	21.	8, 222	32.	9, 404	43.	65, 0
11.	6, 110	22.	7, 256	33.	9, 330	44.	12, 0

Side B

1.	1, 0	12.	5, 101	23.	2, 700	34.	4, 500
2.	2, 0	13.	5, 10	24.	3, 660	35.	5, 0
3.	3, 0	14.	5, 11	25.	3, 706	36.	7, 0
4.	8, 0	15.	5, 1	26.	4, 95	37.	9, 0
5.	6, 0	16.	7, 2	27.	4, 30	38.	72, 0
6.	9, 0	17.	7, 20	28.	5, 6	39.	8, 0
7.	4, 0	18.	7, 200	29.	3, 4	40.	85, 0
8.	7, 0	19.	7, 22	30.	2, 10	41.	9, 0
9.	5, 0	20.	7, 220	31.	2, 75	42.	72, 0
10.	5, 100	21.	7, 222	32.	1, 504	43.	70, 0
11.	5, 110	22.	4, 378	33.	1, 440	44.	12, 0

Module 2:   Unit Conversions and Problem Solving With Metric Measurement

EUREKA
MATH™

Problem Set

1. 5,790 g or 5 kg 790 g

2. 2,634 cm or 26 m 34 cm

3. 3,999 mL or 3 L 999 mL

4. 36,428 g or 36 kg 428 g

5. 34,125 mL or 34 L 125 mL

6. 185 cm or 1 m 85 cm

Exit Ticket

1. 245 g

2. 155 cm or 1 m 55 cm

Homework

1. 722 mL

2. 1,875 m or 1 km 875 m

3. 29,540 g or 29 kg 540 g

4. 45,066 g

5. 13 cm

6. 182,700 mL or 182 L 700 mL